The
First Golden Age
of Rocketry

The First Golden Age of Rocketry

FRANK H. WINTER

Smithsonian Institution Press

Washington and London

This book was edited by Dianne Hardy
and designed by Lisa Buck Vann.

Library of Congress Cataloging-in-
Publication Data
Winter, Frank H.
First golden age of rocketry: Congreve
and Hale rockets of the nineteenth
century/by Frank H. Winter.
p. cm.
Includes bibliographical references.
ISBN 0-87474-987-5
1. Rocketry—History—19th century.
I. Title.
TL781.W56 1990
621.43′56′09034—dc20 89—600279 CIP
British Library Cataloguing in Publica-
tion is available

97 96 95 94 93 92 91 90 5 4 3 2 1

Cover: Congreve Rocket Practice, Woolwich, 1841, detail. (S.I. 86—12075)

All illustrations are available through
the Smithsonian Institution and may be
located by using the negative numbers
designated in the captions.

♾ The paper used in this publication
meets the minimum requirements of the
American National Standard for Per-
manence of Paper for Printed Library
Materials Z39.48–1984

Manufactured in the United States of
America

Contents

Acknowledgments

It is impossible to adequately thank all the many individuals in the archives, libraries, and museums worldwide who have contributed toward this book.

Foremost, I wish to thank the personnel of the National Air and Space Museum, Smithsonian Institution, who have always afforded me their complete support in my research. I would particularly like to express my appreciation to the staffs of the Space History Department, the Library, and the Photo Lab. Special mention must be made of Dr. Allan Needell of the Space History Department, who has consistently placed great faith in the project and helped to nurture it.

I am also very grateful to Mitchell R. Sharpe, Frederick I. Ordway III, Edward Peck, and Dr. Loren Morey, who reviewed the manuscript. Messrs. Sharpe and Ordway, well known authorities on the history of the rocket and spaceflight, merit very special thanks for exchanging information with me over the years. Others deserving special thanks are Dr. Å. Ingemar Skoog of Sweden (now of West Germany), Dr. Victor Sokol'skii of the U.S.S.R., Dr.

Mieczyslaw Subotowitz of Poland, and István G. Nagy of Hungary.

I am indebted to many in England, particularly Major Richard Bartelot (since retired) and his staff at the Royal Artillery Institution Library at Woolwich, and John Bensusan-Butt, Colchester Borough Librarian, for significant biographical material on William Hale. During the course of my research I also had the great honor of meeting Hale's great-great-grandaughter, Mrs. Lynn Schechter, then of New Rochelle, New York, with whom I exchanged documents concerning her elusive ancestor.

Also in the United States, my friend George S. James provided me with invaluable insights. To Dr. Robert P. Multhauf, formerly Senior Historian of the American Museum of History, I owe a special debt of gratitude. Tom Crouch and Gregory P. Kennedy, both formerly of the National Air and Space Museum; Richard P. Hallion, now a USAF Historian; and Lee Saegesser of the NASA History Office have all helped me in many ways.

During years of preliminary research, I have consulted almost all of the national libraries of the countries mentioned in this book, in addition to the National Archives, Washington, D.C.; various patent offices worldwide; the Public Record Office, London; Woolwich Public Library, Woolwich, England; Service Historique, Ministère des Armées, Paris; Artillery Museum of the Red Army, Leningrad; Kriegsarchiv, Vienna; Heeresgeschichte Museum, Vienna; Haerens Bibliotek, Copenhagen; Krigsarkivet, Stockholm; Kungl. Armémuseum, Stockholm; Het Nederlands Leger-en Wapenmuseum, Leiden, the Netherlands; Koninklije Landmacht Hoofdwartier, Sectie Krigseschiedenis en Ceremonieel, The Hague; National Archives of India, New Delhi; Associazioni Nazionale dei Granatieri di Sardegna, Rome; Museo Storico Nazionale di Artiglieria, Turin, Italy; Musée Royal de l'Armée et d'Histoire Militaire, Brussels; Deutches Museum, Munich; Zentralbibliothek der Bundesweher, Dusseldorf; Deutsche Bücherei, Leipzig; Servicio Histórico Militar, Madrid; Wojskowy Instytut Historyczny, Warsaw; and the Genikon Epiteleion Stratoy, Dieythynsis Stratoy (Army General Staff, Historical Division), Athens.

Among the numerous special libraries consulted are Det Kongelige Danske Videnskabernes Selskab, Copenhagen; Bibliothek der Technology Hochschule, Hannover; Nederlandsch Historisch Sheepvaart, Amsterdam; Society of the Society of Geneologists, London; Library of the Society of California Pioneers, San Francisco; and the New Bedford Whaling Museum Library, New Bedford, Mass.

The museums I have visited in my search for nineteenth-century rockets and related documents include the Rotunda, Woolwich, England; the Science

Museum, London; Musée de l'Arméc, Paris; Tojhusmuseet, Copenhagen; Museo del Erjecito, Madrid; Museo da Artilharia, Lisbon; K.E. Tsiolkovsky State Museum of Cosmonautics, Kaluga, U.S.S.R.; Muzeum Wojska Polskiego, Warsaw; West Point Museum, West Point, New York; Museum of the Confederacy, Richmond; Fort Ward Museum, Alexandria, Virginia; Mariner's Museum, Newport News, Virginia; and the New Bedford Whaling Museum, New Bedford, Mass.

Finally, I wish to thank my wife Fe Dulce R. Winter for her infinite patience. It is to her and our two children, Ronald Roy Winter and Elaine Roxane Winter, that I dedicate this book.

Preface

The rocket is one thousand years old. Of that millenium, little more than half a century of the history of rocketry has been adequately documented. This is not surprising considering that the shorter span represents our own dynamic technological age, in which rockets have revolutionized warfare, orbited thousands of artificial satellites around Earth, boosted the first unmanned probes to the planets, transported six manned expeditions to the Moon, and paved the way for permanent space stations. As complex and varied as they are, all modern rockets have a common ancestor—the modest gunpowder rocket—that had its peak of development in the nineteenth century. The purpose of this book is to help balance the historical record by focusing on that epoch as the first great age of rocketry.

Prior to the nineteenth century, in most places outside India the rocket was limited in size and use to small pasteboard fireworks. Antiquated oral traditions and empiricism guided the rocket-making process. Beginning in the early 1800s, the Englishman William Congreve initiated the modern process of research and development in rocketry. In a sense, the rocket came of age with the Congreve era. Congreve created the world's first rocket weapons system, consisting of standard calibers of war rockets, from 3- to 300-pounders, with which to challenge Napoleon's invasion plans for England. He introduced the mass production of rockets, improved their accuracy, was the first to plot firing angles for optimum ranges, and worked out rocket tactics. In addition, he devised new ignition techniques, more powerful warhead compositions, land and sea launchers, transport vehicles, and rocket-firing vessels. A Congreve rocket ship fought at the bombardment of Fort McHenry, giving rise to the line—"And the rockets' red glare" in the American national anthem. For land forces, Congreve established "rocket brigades," designed their accoutrements, and wrote operating manuals.

Other nations emulated Britain and established their own rocket systems. This international interest led to the publication of more than two dozen books on the subject in a half dozen countries, a large number of articles, and the issuance of numerous patents. Nonmilitary applications also appeared, such as the lifesaving rocket. The first mathematical rocket ballistic studies were made with dynamotors and ballistic pendulums, and suggestions were advanced for rocket propulsion for air- and spacecraft.

In the 1840s, another Englishman, William Hale, introduced major improvements in war rockets that were also widely adopted. His improvements, which were further refined by his son William, Jr., reflected Industrial Revolution advances in steam power and metallurgy.

Congreve-Hale rockets appeared in a turbulent age, which opened with the Napoleonic wars and was followed by various struggles for national independence, exemplified by the *Risorgimento* ("Resurgence") in Italy. The period was also marked by conflicts connected with British colonial expansion. The rocket played a part in many of these conflicts, both great and small.

Outside Congreve's system of rocket tactics, there is no evidence that the weapon changed fundamental military strategy, but in many instances rockets gave an edge to the element of surprise. Indeed, their primary tactical value was psychological—to demoralize the enemy. The writhing, hissing projectiles, usually flying at threateningly low levels, terrified untrained troops, native warriors, and cavalry horses. One outstanding example was the routing of raw American militia at Bladensburg, Maryland, in 1814 by means of Congreve rockets, leading to the British army's destruction of the U.S. capital at Washington. During the first half of the nineteenth century, incendiary carcass rockets easily inflicted havoc against wooden ships. The examples presented here show how rockets were used internationally in a wide variety of military situations, both on land and sea. Not surprisingly, Congreve and Hale rocket specimens still survive and embellish many a military museum.

Despite notable successes, however, the gunpowder rocket had serious inherent drawbacks that inevitably led to its decline as a viable weapon as the 1900s approached. Its most glaring fault was its unpredictability—sometimes rockets "fizzled" or embarked on wild flights. This was due to the nonuniform, largely manual method of rocket construction, though rudimentary machinery (such as powder-granulating machines to mix the powder, hand-operated "pile driver" rammers to press in the propellant, and steam-operated lathes to turn out wooden guidesticks) was introduced in Congreve's day. In addition, Congreve rockets, with their thin, sheet-metal cases and sometimes tarred, canvas-covered warheads, were difficult to store. (Hygroscopic saltpeter in the powder readily picked up moisture in the atmosphere, especially when the rocket exhaust vents were left open or were not properly secured.)

Yet in the first half of the nineteenth century, these flaws were largely offset by the rocket's equal or greater range and lightness compared to guns of similar caliber. Moreover, smooth-bore, muzzle-loading cannons of the time were themselves inaccurate and inefficient. In range alone, rockets were quite competitive with conventional artillery. In addition, rockets could be quite destructive considering their small size, and they possessed the singular feature of lacking recoil—a great advantage when discharged from boats and ships. Ponderous cannons had to be mounted on wheels and secured with pulleys so that they could be rolled back on deck every time they were fired. On land too, cannons had to be dragged back into position after each round. Moreover, cannons were cumbersome and required teams of horses to move them in battle; rockets were more portable. Finally, rockets were relatively inexpensive compared to other ordnance, one of Congreve's favorite selling points.

By mid-century, however, as the Industrial Revolution began to introduce major technological advances in conventional artillery, the weaknesses of the rocket became more manifest. The most prominent artillery improvements were breech-loading and rifling. Breech-loading speeded up the loading of guns, and rifling made cannons far superior in both range and accuracy compared to rockets. (The introduction of the breech-loading, rifled gun in the 1860s was the most oft-cited reason for disbanding rocket troops.) In the same period, Bessemer's steel process provided stonger, more heat-resistant cannon barrels for handling heavier and more powerful projectiles. On the seas, vulnerable wooden sailing ships were being replaced by swift, steam-powered ironclads against which Congreve-type rockets were pitifully ineffective.

Although a few countries had already declared older, Congreve-type stick-stabilized rockets obsolete by the 1850s, the timely improvements of William Hale and his two sons prolonged the life of the gunpowder rocket in England and a few other nations for about half a century. Hale eliminated the cumbersome guidesticks and introduced more accurate "stickless," or spin-stabilized, rockets. He also incorporated the hydraulic press in driving the propellant into the motor cases, replacing the dangerous and inefficient hand-operated, pile-driver "monkey" presses. Hale's adoption of Bessemer steel for rocket cases and a new means of rolling steel added to the rocket's strength and reliability, though its range remained about the same. Another more subtle result of these improvements, which appear to have been unrecognized at the time, was that the thick metal cases of Hale's rockets provided greater protection of the propellant in storage. This must have considerably helped to ensure the use of these rockets up to the late nineteenth century. Another factor contributing to the longevity of the powder rocket was Great Britain's numerous colonial wars during the latter half of the nineteenth century, especially in Africa, where ample opportunities were presented to employ Hale rockets. The projectiles proved ideal for waging small wars or punitive expeditions in bush country against primitive, ill-armed opponents and where terrain was impractical for larger, wheeled artillery. Native superstitions about the self-moving "devil" rocket were not without their own effect.

The Franco-Prussian War (1870–71) marked the decline of war rockets in other countries, especially since in this war the combatants used rifled, breech-loaded guns as well as hydraulic recoil shocks. Cannons and other firearms now decidedly outclassed rockets in range and overall performance. There began an almost universal move toward conversion to rifled breech-loaders. Consequently, the decade of the 1870s witnessed the greatest number of countries ending their war rocket establishments and related activities.

The use of Hale rockets by Great Britain lingered in her African and Indian outposts until as late as 1899, by which time other European powers had long since abandoned rocket warfare. Apart from England, only Russia in her eastward expansion for empire used rockets (though of the Congreve type) as late as the 1890s. China, Egypt, and Brazil are known to have made or employed both types until at least the 1880s.

More powerful smokeless powders, based on nitrocellulose-nitroglycerine ("double-base powders") were not stabilized and adopted for guns until this period and therefore did not play as significant a role in phasing out the rocket in Continental Europe as other technological advances. Nonetheless, the appearance of the first successful smokeless powders underscored the real Achilles heel of the old powder rocket—its centuries-old reliance on gunpowder, which severely limited its energy potential. Gunpowder held back the performance of rockets and constrained their growth in size. It seems that nineteenth-century rocket technicians almost wholly overlooked the chemistry of the propellant in their experimental efforts. When efforts were made to produce double-base rocket propellants, principally by Wilhelm Unge of Sweden in the 1890s, they came too late; England did not adapt smokeless powders to rockets in the nineteenth century, except in their warheads.

Meanwhile, the ranges and overall performances of guns increased markedly with the use of smokeless powder. The British adopted a form of it called Cordite in 1890. Soon, even Britain's territorial forces in Africa and India were furnished with new Quick Firing (Q.F.) rifled guns using this propellant and recoil-absorbers. In addition, opportunities for using rockets greatly diminished as England's African colonies became more subdued around the turn of the century. Thus, the need for the old powder war rocket gradually disappeared. (Russia experienced an identical situation in the completion of her eastward conquests.)

Gunpowder war rockets became as anachronistic in warfare as the longbow and lance, but some earlier technology did survive into the next century. American rocket pioneer Robert H. Goddard conducted his first solid-fuel experiments with U.S. Navy Coston signal rockets, which were hydraulically driven and mass-produced much like Hale war rockets. Goddard's solid-fuel work led to a smokeless powder-propelled projectile that may have been a precursor to the famous antitank Bazooka weapon of World War II. This phase of Goddard's work ceased, however, upon the signing of the armistice in 1918 that ended World War I.

By 1920, Goddard had switched to experimenting with liquid propellants, which have vastly more energy potential than solid propellants, and on 16 March 1926 he launched the world's first liquid-propellant rocket, which used liquid oxygen and gasoline for fuel. The solid-fuel rocket was not forgotten, however; it underwent another phase of development from the mid-1930s and today both large and small solid-fuel rockets flourish in a variety of capacities, from weapons propulsion and boosters to launch vehicles and sounding-rocket power plants.

The colorful epoch of Congreve and Hale rockets may be gone, but in an albeit tenuous way, they provided the first steps toward the second great age of rocketry, that of the twentieth century.

CHAPTER 1

The Indian Heritage

William Congreve's and William Hale's places in the history of rocketry cannot be fully appreciated without an understanding of rocket development over the previous six centuries. As Congreve himself pointed out, he never invented the rocket; he was merely its "improver." Indeed, his interest in pursuing rocketry was sparked directly by his knowledge of its earlier use in India.

The First Rockets

The first powder rocket was probably the accidental discovery of thirteenth-century Chinese Taoist alchemists who were experimenting with various flame-enhancing materials. Ironically, the aim of their experiments was not the concoction of new incendiary weapons, but the search for mortal longevity—an elixir of life. These formulations often involved the mixing and heating of a wide variety of substances, including sulfur; charcoal; and eventually saltpeter, or potassium nitrate. The addition of saltpeter to the other ingredients made the mixture either an explosive or propellant, depending upon the mixture's strength and how it was used. The Chinese sages must have been astonished to learn that if the powder were confined in a container with a small fuse hole and then lit, it exploded. This was the first crude bomb. If the same mixture were put in the bottom of a paper or bamboo tube closed or unclosed at this end, the escaping combustion gases could propel something (a stone, for example) out of the top. These were the first guns. Most astonishing and inexplicable of all, if the powder (perhaps made a little weaker to prevent bursting) were placed in a tube closed at the forward end and lit at the bottom, the tube suddenly propelled itself forward. This was the first basic rocket.[1]

There is no indication that the Chinese knew the fundamental principle of rocket flight (reaction propulsion). Nor were they aware of the processes of combustion. As late as the seventeenth century, and probably long after, the Chinese still adhered to the ancient *yin-yang* philosophy to explain the burning of gunpowder. *Yin-yang* held that all forces in the universe resulted from the

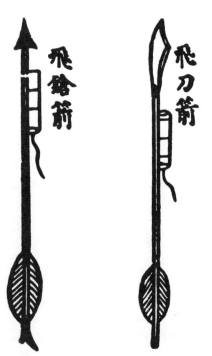

FIGURE 1.1

Chinese "fire arrow" war rockets. From the Wu Pei Chih (Treatise on Military Equipment) *by Mao Yuan-i, 1628. (S.I. A5372D)*

balance of *yin* (female, or passive) and *yang* (male, or active) elements. The union of saltpeter (*yin*) and sulfur (*yang*) thus produced fire. (Carbon, which chemically slowed combustion, was not included in the *yin-yang* explanation.)[2]

We now know that all chemical rocket propellants contain an *oxidizer*, which carries oxygen atoms for supporting combustion, and a *fuel,* the substance to be burned. Combined, they are called the propellant. Potassium nitrate (KNO_3) contains three active oxygen atoms per molecule, making it an ideal oxidizer that readily burns with the fuel of gunpowder—sulfur (S) and carbon (C) in the form of charcoal. However, it was not until the early nineteenth century that the Englishman John Dalton established modern atomic chemistry. A standard formula for gunpowder is KNO_3, 75%; S, 10%; and C, 15%. Rocket makers often varied the proportions according to their personal preference.

From China, knowledge of gunpowder and rockets may have spread to Europe via the Arabs, with whom the Chinese had close trade contact. We know that Europe and the Islamic Near East knew of gunpowder and rockets a little before 1300, but their rockets were primitive. The *Liber Ignium* (*Fire Book*) of ca. 1280 by Marcus Graecus (Mark the Greek) gives recipes for small, parchment-cased rockets that seem to have been a kind of firework. From the start, the gun was favored in Europe as a firearm, while the rocket, with rare exceptions, was used as recreational pyrotechnic or signal until the start of the Congreve era. In India, the situation was quite different.[3]

The Rocket in India

Like much of early Indian history, the development of firearms on the Indian subcontinent is poorly documented. Fantastic legends of the alleged antiquity and mythological origins of gunpowder and rockets in India abound but are unacceptable as historical proof. We do not know whether the Indians developed gunpowder indigenously or learned of it from the Chinese, from the Moslems who had long resided on the west coast of the Indian subcontinent, or from European visitors. We do know that European visitors in India reported seeing guns there from about 1450. In contrast to the low level of interest in war rockets in Europe, the war rocket flourished in India from at least the reign of the Mogul Emperor Akbar (1556–1605). But since our sources are European, it is conceivable that the rocket stretches back even earlier and was known under what is now obscure Indian terminology.[4]

As for the Chinese, they continued using both war rockets and firework

CONTRAFACTVR DES KVNSTLICHEN FEVRWERCKS SO BEY DES NEVGEBORNEN IVNGEN PRINTZEN FRIDERICHEN HERTZOG ZV WVRTEMBERG &. KINDTAVFFEN ZV STVETGART IM LVSTGARTEN DEN 12 MARTI ANNO 1616 GEWORFFEN WORDEN.

FIGURE 1.2
In the West, rockets were used mainly in lavish firework displays, such as this one in Germany in 1616. (S.I. 72–5743)

rockets from the thirteenth century onward, though technological stagnation set in and their rockets were little developed thereafter. The famous *Wu Pei Chih* (*Records of War Preparation*), compiled by Mao Yuan-I and variously dated at 1621 or 1628, depicts many types of interesting Chinese war rockets, all of them diminutive. Their tubes averaged 4 inches (100 mm) in length and were usually lashed to arrow shafts for stability, like firework rocket stabilizing sticks. The Indians went several steps beyond the Chinese in war rocket development and used the weapons quite extensively.[5]

The Indians called their war rockets *ban* or *bana*, perhaps from the Sanskrit *vana* ("arrow"), which may be a clue as to how they were originally made. (Sung to Ming Dynasty Chinese called their own rockets *fe-ho-tsiang*, or *flying fire arrows*, after their arrow guidesticks.) Haridas Mitra, in his *Fireworks and Fire Festivals in Ancient India*, speaks of the *Banua* peoples of Puri, Orissa state, who were well known for their rocket making; probably these were ordinary skyrockets. Edward Moor's *A Narrative of the Operations . . . Against . . . Tippoo Sultan* (1794) mentions that the fort of Toorkhunhooly, near Serringapatam, Mysore, was famous for making rockets; no doubt these were war rockets. Written instructions for both firework and war rocket manufacture in India were apparently never kept; these were probably family or caste trade secrets passed down orally.[6]

Mentions of *bana* in Indian military histories multiply almost indefinitely

FIGURE 1.3

Indian war rockets appear on the cover of a 1790 British account of the Mahratta wars. The fronts of the thick bamboo guidesticks were cut into deadly points. (S.I. 72–9884)

S K E T C H E S

CHIEFLY RELATING TO THE

HISTORY, RELIGION, LEARNING, AND MANNERS,

OF THE

H I N D O O S.

WITH

A concise Account of the PRESENT STATE of the NATIVE POWERS of HINDOSTAN.

L O N D O N:

PRINTED FOR T. CADELL, IN THE STRAND.

MDCCXC.

from the sixteenth century up to the Congreve era. In some battles, hundreds and even thousands of these rockets were fired; both adversaries were often armed with them. War rockets were used by such Indian peoples as the Mughals, Adhadanagars, Mysoreans, Marathas, Polygars, Sikhs, Rajputs, Rohillas, Jaipurs, Golcondans, Vijaynarans, the fighting monks called Naga Sannyasis, and the Vairagis. Mughals, Marathas, and Mysoreans strongly favored the weapons. War rockets were used mainly by a branch of infantrymen for anti-personnel purposes, fired against cavalry or opposing infantry troops. Occasionally they served as incendiary weapons, setting fire to forts, arsenals, and ammunition wagons. The fiery exhaust of the rocket itself served as the incendiary, so weapons were fired at close range in order to strike their targets before the gunpowder was consumed. Explosive warhead types, like those later made by Congreve, apparently were quite rare; only one mention of an experimental, late-eighteenth-century explosive Indian war rocket has been found.[7]

The eighteenth century was the apex of Indian rocket warfare. Their most reknowned engagements were against the British at the sieges of Serringapatam in 1791–1792 and 1799. A typical European description of standard Indian rocket weapons at the time appears in Quintin Crawford's *Sketches Chiefly Relating to . . . the Hindoos* (1790):

> It is certain, that even in these parts of Hindostan that were never frequented either by Mohammedans or Europeans, we have met with rockets, a weapon which the natives almost universally employ in war. The rocket consists of a tube of iron, about eight inches [20.3 cm], in length, closed at one end. It is filled in the same manner as an ordinary sky-rocket, and fastened towards the end of a piece of bamboo, scarcely as thick as a walking cane, and about four feet [1.3 m] long, which is pointed with iron. At the opposite end of the tube from the iron point, or that towards the head of the shaft that is shod with iron, to the object to which he means to direct it; and, setting fire to the match, it goes off with great velocity. By the irregularity of its motion, it is difficult to be avoided, and sometimes acts with considerable effect, especially among the cavalry.[8]

There are similar descriptions of Indian rockets weighing 6–12 pounds (2.7–5.4 kg), with the gunpowder propellant amounting to 1–2 pounds (0.54–0.9 kg). Captured Indian war rockets of this period had diameters of 1.5–3 inches (3.8–7.6 cm). The Europeans credited the rockets with ranges of from 1,000

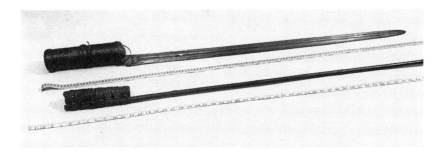

FIGURE 1.4

These specimens, captured by the British in the late eighteenth century, include (top) *a curious sword-blade rocket, which cut through the enemy; and* (bottom) *a rocket tube lashed with leather thongs to a thin bamboo cane.* (S.I. A1127A)

yards (900 m) to 1.5 miles (2.4 km); the former seems to have been the norm.[9]

The rocketeers were favored troops. In stately processions they marched close to the Sultan's personal retinue. In the Maratha kingdom, in the south of India, they proudly carried small triangular flags of green, white, and red tied to their rocket sticks. The significance of these colors is obscure, but they were probably not unlike Western military unit pennants. Hyder Ali of the Marathas is reputed to have mustered 2,000 rocket men in his army. His son Tippoo Sahib, whom the British defeated at Serringapatam in 1799, raised the number to 5,000.[10]

William Kirkpatrick translated and annotated the *Select Letters of Tippoo Sultan* (1811), which reveals the organizational structure of an Indian rocket unit in 1793. At that time there were 48,000 fighting men in Tippoo's army. These troops were divided into twenty-seven *kushoons* (brigades). Attached to each *kushoon* was one *jowk,* or company of rocket-men. Each *jowk* of rocket-men comprised thirty-nine soldiers, making a total of 1,026 rocketeers. Each *jowk* of rocket-men consisted of the following:

> one *jowkdaar* (captain), including horse
> two *surkheels* (lieutenants)
> four *jumaadars* (sergeants)
> thirty-two privates
> one *nujm-waleh* (tent man, who took care of the tent where the arms were
>   kept)
> Privates and *jumaadars* carried two rockets each, making seventy-two

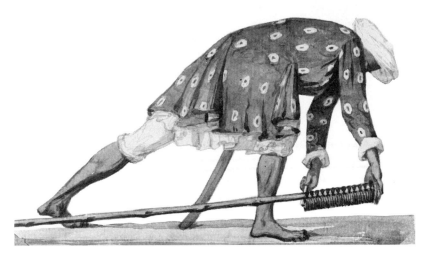

FIGURE 1.5

Late eighteenth-century watercolor showing one of Hyder Ali's rocketeers. Indian war rockets were lighted and thrown by hand-like spears, propped up against rocks or tree stumps, or placed on the ground and lighted. (S.I. A5134)

rockets in each rocket *jowk*. Tippoo's army thus had at least 1,944 rockets; bullock carts and camels also transported rockets.[11]

Another Englishman stationed in India during this period, Captain Charles Gold, gives a different number of rocket-men, or rocketeers, in Tippoo's army. According to Gold's *Oriental Drawings* (1806), Tippoo had sixteen *kushoons,* each with 200 rocketeers; this came to 3,200 rocketeers. It is interesting to note that if there had been twenty-seven *kushoons* (Kirkpatrick's figure) with 200 rocketeers each, the total would have been 5,400 rocketeers, a figure that agrees with the 5,000 rocketeers usually ascribed to Tippoo's army. Part of the confusion may be due to changes in Tippoo's army pay regulations over the years. Gold wrote that the rocket-men were omitted in the records because they were part of the irregular infantry and were paid different wages from ordinary soldiers.[12]

There is no disputing the fact that Tippoo's forces used rockets more extensively than previous Indian rulers. According to a list of the ammunition captured by the British at Serringapatam on 20 May 1799, there were 9,000 filled rockets of different sizes and 700 empty rockets. It is not specified whether these were ordinary paper signal rockets or metallic-cased war types. It is assumed they were war rockets, as 9,000 is considered an exorbitant number for signals. Also, signal rockets were made complete; they would not have been left empty. Moreover, the list also shows 600 "serviceable iron engines for throwing rockets." These were probably rail or tube launchers not unlike those made by Congreve and Hale during the nineteenth century.[13]

Why India Favored Rockets

There were several reasons for the popularity of war rockets in India. In the first place, progress in artillery development in India had been slower than in

FIGURE 1.6

Indian rocket troops assemble (at left of kneeling elephant) in front of Tippoo's palace, Serringpatam, in the 1790s. (S.I. 81–16706)

Europe. Indian cannons of the seventeenth and eighteenth centuries, with their lavish ornamentation, were more like works of art than efficient implements of war. Cannons of immense caliber were made, but were too immobile for combat as they had to be pulled by bullocks or elephants rather than horses. Beautifully ornamented handheld firearms were crude imitations of European guns. Indians thus preferred low-cost, hand-made war rockets over conventional firearms.[14]

Tactics of Indian fighting also dictated the need for rockets. The Marathas of southern India found the rocket ideally suited to their favorite maneuver of close-range hit-and-run skirmishes, in contrast to the long-distance sieges against walled cities or camps preferred by European strategists. Furthermore, the rocket lent itself to the southern Indian terrain of hill spurs and

FIGURE I.7

In England, William Congreve, Jr. (right), was later much taken with the Indian rockets displayed in the Royal Repository founded by his father, Artillery Captain William Congreve, Sr. (left). Both are shown near the practice range at Woolwich Arsenal in about 1780. (S.I. A5021; courtesy National Gallery of Ireland)

deep, stony-bedded rivers, impassible for cannons. In India the rocket was carried by individual men or "rocket boys," who required almost no training in comparison to artillerists, and who provided quick, portable concentrations of firepower. Guerrilla warfare, with plenty of rockets, was especially prevalent with the encroachment of the French and British who fought for dominance over Indian territories beginning in the mid-eighteenth century.[15]

The abundance of saltpeter (a mainstay in the East India Company trade) and bamboo were also factors in the popularity of the rocket in the East. Bamboo, found in India and China, made possible easily adapted rocket guidesticks that were light, strong, and straight; in Europe, pine or other wood sticks had to be specially shaped and balanced, a time-consuming job.[16]

Indian war rockets may have been simple, but they impressed eighteenth-century British soldiers so much that the East India Company made inquiries to find anyone who knew how to make them. Evidently the Company entertained the idea of making copies and retaliating against the Indians, but no expert could be found. A handful of these Indian implements had already been sent back to England as war trophies. They were the prized possessions of the Royal Artillery's Repository museum near the Royal Arsenal at Woolwich, founded in 1778 by Captain William Congreve, Royal Artillery. Congreve's son, William, Jr., was especially intrigued with them. It is likely that he listened attentively to firsthand accounts of the rockets in combat, related by veterans just returned to Woolwich from the battlefields of Mysore.[17]

CHAPTER 2

The Ingenious Mr. Congreve

William Congreve, Jr., was not immediately able to take up rocketry when the Indian specimens arrived at the Repository. He had recently graduated from Cambridge and was busily pursuing a business career. However, he often visited his father at Woolwich and there was always talk of weaponry and other military subjects, which young William had enjoyed since he was a lad.

Early Life

William Congreve the younger had a lifelong fascination with inventions of any sort. In 1785, at age 13, he sketched his own concept of a Montgolfier balloon while away at school and boldly wrote to his father that he was "fully bent on going to the Moon in an aerial balloon. I likewise send you a Balloon gun invented by myself," he added. "The force was great enough to fire a large marble 10 yards." In time, his contrivances became more well thought out and by 1800 he had compiled an enormous folio of his ideas, entitled *A Second Century of Inventions.*[1]

The younger Congreve developed his inventive bent from his father, a gifted man who rose to become a lieutenant general in the artillery. In 1812 he was bestowed with the title of baronet. General Congreve served with distinction in America during the Revolutionary War and was wounded in an engagement on Long Island. For this campaign, he designed a new type of light, 3-pound (1.3 kg) brass cannon that was easily packed on horseback for quick employment on the rough terrain of the colonies. At Menin, Flanders, during the French Revolutionary campaigns in 1794, he made a signal machine out of a windmill by removing its two opposite sails. In England he devised a more economical way of manufacturing gunpowder, prompting the epitaph on his tombstone: "He saves his country a million of money, but he died unenriched himself."[2]

The younger William Congreve was baptized and may have been born in the district of Homerton in the London borough of Hackney on 20 May 1772, while his father was stationed there as lieutenant. (Other sources cite only the county of Middlesex as his birthplace.) Due to an unknown early career disappointment, the father was determined not to raise his son in his own profession. The boy had a well rounded academic education, attending Free School in Shrewsbury and Singlewell School in Kent. At age 16, he entered Trinity College, Cambridge, to study law, and received a B.A. in 1793. Upon his matriculation with an M.A. at age 23, he became a member of the Inner Temple, one of the four mandatory societies of the Inns of Court, which gave its members exclusive right of admission to the bar. Perhaps because he then decided to use his legal training for a business career, however, he was not called to the bar and never practiced law.[3]

Congreve's activities from this time until 1803 are unknown, but from the latter year until 1804 he and another man published a small but outspoken newspaper, *The Royal Standard.* One editorial accused an admiral of cowardice in battle; the admiral sued for libel. Congreve lost the suit and gave up the paper, but the affair forced him to throw his considerable energies into other projects.[4]

The year 1804 was a frightening one for England. Napoleon Bonaparte was at the height of his conquests and threatened an invasion from Boulogne, 30 miles (48 km) across the Channel from Dover. Congreve, a member of the Society for the Improvement of Naval Architecture, proposed a 250-ton (227 tonne) floating iron-plated battery with sloping walls, carrying four 42-pounder (19 kg) cannons. The ship outwardly resembled the ironclad *Merrimac* of the U.S. Civil War, except that Congreve's proposed vessel was driven by oars rather than steam. Congreve's vessel never materialized, but he had another idea.[5]

Congreve Discovers Rockets

"In the year 1804," he later wrote, "it first occurred to me, that as the . . . rocket is exerted without any reaction from the point from which it is discharged, it might be necessarily applied, both afloat and ashore, as a military engine. . . . I knew that rockets were used for military purposes in India, but that their magnitude was inconsiderable, and their range not exceeding 1,000 yards [914 m]. I knew, also, that some years since, several experiments had been made in the Royal Laboratory by General Desaguliers, then Fire-Master, for the construction of large rockets; but that they had not succeeded, and that very few of them would even rise off the stand."[6]

It is likely that father and son knew Lieutenant General Thomas Desaguliers, Colonel Commandant of the Royal Laboratory and son of the famous French refugee physicist Jean Desaguliers. The younger Congreve's words indicate a close familiarity with General Desaguliers's experiments.

Here the question of Congreve's "originality" arises. In 1803, Irish revolutionary Robert Emmet made war rockets and was about to use them in an attempt to capture Dublin when his secret arsenal on Patrick Street exploded, rockets and all. Later, at least one of his assistants, Pat Finnerty, allegedly was hired to work at Woolwich making rockets, leading one historian to infer that Congreve freely borrowed Emmet's idea. There was also a claim made in 1808 by Scottish chemist James Hume that he had earlier presented war rocket plans to General William Congreve, Sr., and others, but that the plans were never returned. In his *A Concise Account of the Origin and Progress of the Rocket System* (London, 1807), Congreve was quite open about such claimants but dismissed them as "absurd," since the invention of the rocket "belongs to some of the heroes of Chinese antiquity. To claim the application of the rocket to the purpose of war," he went on, was "equally absurd, for this was the invention of the remote ages of the Mogul [Indian] Empire. The only merit I claim . . . is that I have obtained . . . the power of carrying weights infinitely beyond anything ever before conceived in this country, or known in India." Congreve might have added that he was the driving force in establishing a complete rocket system, which led to a minor revolution in artillery worldwide.[7]

Congreve began his research by buying a variety of firework skyrockets in

London, from the smallest, a few ounces in caliber, to the largest, probably one of the so-called 6-pounders (2.7 kg). In those years, European pyrotechnists still clung to the antiquated system of designating skyrockets by the weight of a lead ball that fit into the choke, or open end, of the rocket. The designation therefore did not refer to the weight of the rocket itself. When Congreve first started making his rockets, he chose to designate the caliber by the actual weight of the projectile, a more logical practice and one that has survived to the present.[8]

Congreve's largest skyrockets flew 600 to 700 yards (550–640 m), considerably less distance than Tippoo Sultan's war rockets. Congreve discovered that, like cannon balls, ranges of rockets could be increased and predicted according to the angles at which they were discharged. He worked out explosive and incendiary warhead compositions; made more powerful gunpowder; attached longer, stronger guidesticks; and fashioned special launchers by which firing elevations were adjustable. By the summer of 1805, he had prepared at least three combat-ready calibers of rockets: a 1-pounder (0.4 kg), a 3-pounder, (1.3 kg), and a 6-pounder (2.7 kg). Of these, only the two larger sizes were subsequently adopted for service; the 1-pounder was far too small. The range for the 3-pounder was 1,800 yards (1,645 m) when fired at 25 degrees elevation and 2,300 yards (2,100 m) for the 6-pounder fired at 35 degrees elevation. Effective ranges, however, were far less—600 and 700 yards (550 and 640 m), respectively. Since these models were incendiary, their warheads would have ignited whatever the rocket struck. Beyond the effective range, however, the accuracy of aiming would have greatly diminished. To ensure that the rockets would adhere to whatever they struck, Congreve designed the warheads with sharp points.[9]

Luck played a large role in the subsequent history of the Congreve rocket. William Congreve, Sr., was in a position to authorize the manufacture of the rockets in the Arsenal and had the right connections to help get them officially adopted. His son unabashedly availed himself of these opportunities. By the spring of 1805, the elder Congreve—now a General—arranged with the Master General of Ordnance, John Pitt, second Earl of Chatham, to initiate large-scale rocket production. Pitt's brother, William, was Prime Minister; both brothers favored the new weapon and were eager to see it tried in battle. Young Congreve meanwhile approached the Prince of Wales, the future King George IV, who also became an avid partisan of rockets and took a liking to Congreve, the two sharing common interests in politics, military affairs, and science. They became close friends, further broadening Congreve's contacts in promoting his rockets. The Prince introduced Congreve to Minister of War Robert Stewart, Viscount Castlereagh.[10]

A temporary rocket workshop was soon erected at Woolwich, and other departments of the Arsenal were requested to afford any aid they could. With the help of the Engineering Department and the Royal Brass Foundry, the workshop became the first factory in the West to mass-produce war rockets. It is unfortunate that apparently the papers explaining their manufacture no longer exist. From Congreve's later rocket treatises, it is known that within eight years, by 1813, the daily output reached thirty-six 32-pounder (14.5 kg) rockets.[11]

First Attempt in Combat—Failure

In early September 1805, the Prime Minister, accompanied by the Secretary of War and the Secretary for Foreign Affairs, witnessed a trial of Congreve's rockets conducted at the Woolwich marshes. Minister of War Castlereagh was so enthusiastic about the rockets that on another occasion he took the Prime Minister down the Thames in a small, flat-bottomed boat designed by Congreve to fire the rockets. It was a dark night, and as Castlereagh attempted to step from one boat to another, he slipped into the water and almost drowned.[12]

Prime Minister Pitt and his cabinet were so impressed with the rocket demonstrations that they wanted to proceed immediately with the inventor's plans. Congreve pointed out that Boulogne, Vimereaux, Calais, Dunkirk, French-held Genoa, and Cadiz might be considered as potential targets for rocket attacks. In the fall of 1805 the administration decided upon Boulogne for the first test. Commodore Sir William Sydney Smith was chosen to lead the expedition, accompanied by Congreve. For two months beforehand Congreve was kept busy making 3,000 6- and 8-pounder (2.7 and 3.6 kg) paper-cased rockets and a dozen newly created rocket boats, or "launches." Each launch, commanded by a Marine Artillery officer, carried forty-eight rounds. The rockets were discharged from ladder-like frames mounted to the boat masts; ranges of 2,000 yards (1,830 m) were expected. The long guidesticks of the rockets fit into hoops on top of the frames, which could be adjusted to fire the weapons at the desired angle. Ignition was achieved by a portfire or friction tube on a long stick. On 16 November 1805, the launches joined their respective gun brigs in Dover Roads. On the morning of 18 November, the squadron anchored abreast of Boulogne, about 3 miles (5 km) away.[13]

Accounts of what happened in the first Congreve rocket attack are some-what confusing. Wind and rough seas certainly hampered the operation. At about 9 p.m. on 20 November 1805, a reporter for the London *Times,* who trailed Smith's squadron in his own boat, observed that "two rockets were fired which we conceived to be signals for the leading ships to get under weigh [in Boulogne Harbor]." These were probably ordinary signal rockets rather than Congreve's. As soon as they were fired, according to the *Times* and official dispatches, the wind increased in violence and led to a halt of the expedition. The *Times* newsman noted that the large waves made it impossible to launch the rockets. The sea, he said, became "mountains high . . . and . . . a trifling accident occurred to one of the rocket boats during the gale . . . the rockets caught fire and went off in great numbers, and appeared to fall round one of our gun vessels. I never beheld such an illumination. I find the people at Dover saw it, and one and all set it down as the grand attack. Whenever the weather shall moderate, Sir Sydney will no doubt resume his station. I shall be close at his heels."[14]

The following day the weather calmed and the sea was almost as smooth as glass. At noon, gun brigs and rocket launches were sent forward once more and anchored abreast the Boulogne suburb of Ambleteuse. "By half past four [p.m.]," continued the newsman, "everything was completely arranged on board the gun brigs and rocket launches, under the immediate inspection of Mr. Congreve. . . . Upwards of a 1,000 shell and carcass [incendiary] rockets were fixed in frames from which they were to be fired in volleys; the shell-rockets, at a low angle, intended to pour into the French brigs at anchor; the carcass rockets each carrying as much carcass composition as is fired in one round by a 3-inch [7.6 cm] mortar, at 5° elevation, were to be reserved for throwing into the basin. The trains were laid that were destined to pour them, by hundreds in a volley. . . . All was yet well; but scarcely had the line got underway, scarcely was the first volley of rockets discharged, when, on a sudden, the wind shifted round to the north-west and in an instant blew a gale. . . . Victory was in a moment snatched from our grasp."[15]

Commodore Smith, Congreve's friend and a staunch advocate of rocket warfare, was reluctant to play up a failure that would also tarnish his own reputation. To his superior officer, Admiral Keith, commander-in-chief of the North Sea fleet, he reported it "impossible under the circumstances of wind and weather to place the rockets in the frame of the launches and use them aloft over the masts, or to row the launches with so much sea."[16]

Shortly thereafter, Smith confessed to Keith in person that the rockets did not work well despite the weather. On 25 November, Keith (who opposed the rockets) wrote to First Lord of the Admiralty, Lord Barham, with some satisfaction, that "the rockets were fired without effect; some of them burst in our boats, and none went in the intended direction."[17]

Even before the Boulogne attempt, Congreve faced critics of rocket warfare. Admiral Keith commented to Barham: "as for attempting to burn a few vessels in that extensive Road of Boulogne, it is nonsense; we shall get our ships crippled, fail of success, and be at great expense." Admiral Horatio Nelson, a few days before losing his life during his brilliant victory at Trafalgar, learned of the rockets and wrote to Castlereagh: "The rockets, if the account of them is true, must [be used to] annoy their [the French] fleet very much; but I depend more upon hunger for driving them out, and upon the gallant officers and men under my command for their destruction, than any other invention."[18]

After the abortive Boulogne attack, criticism of rockets was relentless. Fortunately, Congreve's chief supporters were the Secretary of War and the Prince Regent, who were willing to afford the weapon another chance. The second Boulogne attempt came a year later.

Second Attempt—Success!

The second expedition was led by Captain Edward Richard Owen. In the meantime, Smith took rockets on a little-known mission to the Mediterranean to aid Sicily and the Kingdom of Naples in their struggle against the French. It was perhaps at Gaeta, near Naples, in April 1806, that Congreve's rockets had their first successful debut in battle. The second Boulogne rocket expedition however is more famous and is usually considered as the first successful attempt.[19]

Rockets used on this occasion were Congreve's newer, iron-cased 32-pounder (14.5 kg) models, introduced in the spring of 1806. They carried as much carcass composition as a 10–inch (25 cm) spherical carcass and ranged upwards of 3,000 yards (2,750 m). Congreve discovered that he could reduce the length of the guidestick considerably and still maintain range. The 32-pounder (14.5 kg) dropped in length from 25 feet (7.6 m) to 15 feet (4.5 m). This also facilitated storage and handling.[20]

The second Boulogne attempt was postponed for several months while peace negotiations were being conducted by British Ambassador James Maitland, Earl of Lauderdale. Upon the collapse of this mission, preparations for the attack proceeded. Lauderdale and his suite were leaving Paris for London via Boulogne when Owen's squadron anchored in Boulogne basin. As soon as wind and sea were calm on the night of 8 October 1806, the attack was launched, with Lauderdale still in town.[21]

Twenty-four six-oared cutters had been fitted with frames at a "rocket depot" at Dover for simultaneously firing two rockets, but only eighteen of them went out to Boulogne. Within half an hour 200 rockets (one of Congreve's accounts says 400) were let off in the attack. "The dismay and astonishment of the enemy was complete," Congreve wrote, "—not a shot was returned—and in less than ten minutes after the first discharge, the town was discovered to be on fire. . . . the basin escaped without injury, from the rockets being thrown too much to the left: it was reported, however, that some vessels in the harbor had been destroyed, and it is certain a considerable range of buildings, supposed to be barracks or storehouses, were burnt—the fire indeed could not, from its duration, be trifling, having lasted from two o'clock in the morning to the next evening."[22]

"The ruins of eight buildings were . . . counted from the [River] Clyde," Congreve continued, "and there is every reason to suppose the damage . . . extensive, from the extreme caution with which Lord Lauderdale and his suite were guarded in their passage through the town a few days afterwards, not one of them having been suffered to leave the inn at which they were placed, nor any one permitted to have communication with them; even in passing through the streets they were conveyed in close[d] cabriolets [carriages]."[23]

The French papers presented quite a different story. *Le Moniteur* of 15 October 1806 said the British launched "a hundred incendiary rockets, a new invention which had no more success than all that the enemy tried against the [French] flotilla . . . most . . . rockets were without effect. Two fell on buildings and were extinguished without difficulty and without damaging those buildings. Someone found the next day on the beach in shallow water, many which had not been used." It is thus impossible to judge the true effectiveness of Congreve rockets in the second Boulogne attempt, but in British eyes, they were a resounding success.[24]

A Few More Experiments—Copenhagen to Waterloo

Congreve rockets were henceforth considered to be fit for further service. One sign of this was the fact that the Dover "Rocket Depot" continued to exist. England's protracted war with Napoleon offered many opportunities to use the rockets in action. During 2–4 September 1807, Copenhagen experienced a mass rocket bombardment designed to prevent the Danish fleet from falling into French hands. Various accounts say that between 10,000 and 120,000 rockets were thrown. Logistically, this would have been impossible. Production and supplies for such amounts were simply not available, and the Copenhagen operation had been hastily planned just weeks earlier.[25]

As Congreve himself wrote in *A Concise Account of . . . the Rocket System* (1810), "the rockets used at Copenhagen did very essentially contribute to the conflageration of that city; and if the weapon was able to accomplish anything where *only 300 were fired, and that only by the labour of sixteen men, partly uninstructed* [Congreve's italics], what more might not have been done by it, had it been previously adopted into our military system, and put into execution by the regiment of artillery, and navy." Other documents agree with these numbers.[26]

As at Boulogne, Congreve directed the rockets, which were fired by sixteeen Ordnance Department civilian employees rather than soldiers or sailors. This small crew could hardly have launched as many as 10,000 rockets,

FIGURE 2.1

William Congreve, Jr., is shown in 1807 at the bombardment of Copenhagen, where he directed the launch of about 300 of his own rockets. (S.I. A1126A)

much less 120,000, in two or three days; nor were there sufficient transport vessels on hand. Congreve came aboard the *Claudia* cutter accompanied by three sloops capable of carrying only a few hundred of his projectiles.[27]

On 5 September, after a three-day siege during which three-quarters of Copenhagen was destroyed, the Danish governor raised a flag of truce. Congreve went into the city in disguise to survey the damage. Much of the place was burned to the ground. Congreve and other British officials attributed this to the rockets. Danish accounts also attest to the devastating physical and morale effects of the new weapon. Indeed, the bombardment of Copenhagen dramatically established the efficacy of the naval rocket bombardment in major engagements. Further, it led to the spread of Congreve rocket technology and to the formation of the first non-British war rocket establishment on the Continent (see Chapter 5).[28]

The Copenhagen bombardment also prompted the Danish Academy of Sciences to pose a prize question on rocket motion. None of the participants won the prize, mainly because the judges felt that some of the necessary mathematics was lacking. But a mathematical instructor of the Royal Military Academy at Woolwich, William Moore, who probably personally knew Congreve, was led to produce his *Treatise on the Motion of Rockets* (1813), perhaps the world's first mathematical treatise on rocket dynamics (see Chapter 12).[29]

Meanwhile, Congreve applied his rockets against the French. He was present during Admiral James Gambia's rocket and shell assault on French shipping in the Basque Roads, off the Ile d'Aix, in April 1809.[30]

That same year, Congreve rockets were used in the Walcheren expedition and in the bombardment of Flushing, Holland, in which Congreve's first rocket-firing ship, the *Golago*, appeared. From 1808–1814, Spain and Portugal were introduced to Congreve's projectiles during the Peninsular War, an extension of the Napoleonic campaigns. The rockets did excellent service during the British expulsion of the French from Spain across the Bidassoa River, separating those two countries, and at the battle of Toulouse in 1814. In the Baltic, Danzig (now Gdańsk, Poland) was besieged with rockets in 1813.[31]

But the most celebrated employment of the weapon was at the battle of Leipzig, also called the "Battle of Nations," on 16 October 1813. Captain Richard Bogue and his Royal Artillery Rocket Brigade (later called the Rocket Troop) were the only British representatives among thousands of allied Germans, Russians, Swedes, and Austrians. Bogue and his 150 men were under the direct orders of the elected Crown Prince of Sweden, Jean Baptiste Bernadotte, a former marshal of Napoleon. At the moment that Bogue's rockets terrified 2,500 French infantrymen into surrender, he was killed. After the

FIGURE 2.2

Congreve rocket hero: Captain Richard
Bogue (1783–1813), commander of the rocket
troop that fought at the Battle of Leipzig in
1813. (S.I. 77–10206)

battle, in which Napoleon was defeated, Bernadotte personally thanked the Brigade, then under First Lieutenant Thomas Fox-Strangeways. In the great square of Leipzig, Fox-Strangeways was congratulated by all the allied sovereigns present. Tsar Alexander I of Russia bestowed upon him a medal of the order of St. Anne, which he took from his own breast. Afterwards, Charles XIII of Sweden awarded Fox-Strangeways and five others of the Brigade Swedish medals for valor; Bogue was posthumously conferred knighthood of the Swedish Military Order of the Sword, and his grave near Leipzig was honored with an imposing monument. Congreve also received the Order of St. Anne from Alexander I, and some years later (1821), he received the Swedish Military Order from Charles XIII.[32]

One hundred days after Napoleon's rout in 1813 and his banishment to the island of St. Helena, he escaped and quickly reassembled his *Grande Armée*. The battle of Waterloo on 18 June 1815 was his ultimate defeat. Eight hundred Congreve rockets, mostly 12-pounders (5.4 kg), were taken to Waterloo, where the Rocket Brigade was under R.A. Captain Edward C. Whinyates, but only fifty-two rounds were fired. (They were not nearly as effective as at Leipzig because of the tall corn in the area, which blanketed the explosions.) At Waterloo, a large frame launcher was used and several rounds were fired as "ground" rockets—simply laying them on the ground where clear and lighting them.[33]

The Duke of Wellington was biased against Congreve's rockets and almost prevented them from being taken to the battle. Earlier, while pursuing Napoleon's troops out of Spain, he had bluntly told the Secretary of War, "The only reason why I wished to have it [the Rocket Brigade] was to get the horses; but as we are to have them at all events, I am perfectly satisfied. I do not want to set fire to any town, and I do not know any other use of rockets." But Wellington tended to be against anything innovative.[34]

Congreves Come to the U.S.—War of 1812

Congreve rockets became famous in America during the War of 1812. They were used as far north as Bangor, Maine, and as far south as New Orleans. Yet in no single engagement were they so devastatingly effective as at the battle of Bladensburg, Maryland, on 24 August 1814.[35]

In reprisal for the American destruction of York (now Toronto), capital of the British colony of Upper Canada, in April 1813, the British decided to sack the American capital. At that time, Washington was a sleepy provincial town of comparatively little commercial value. Nearby Alexandria, Virginia, farther down the Potomac River, and Baltimore, Maryland, jutting into the Chesapeake Bay, were more significant targets. British plans called for a combined Army-Navy operation aimed at Alexandria and Baltimore, with a preliminary foray into Washington. As Captain James Alexander Gordon moved his fleet, which included Congreve's second rocket ship, *Erebus* (a converted 18- or 20-gun sloop), up the Potomac, Major General Robert Ross landed troops at Benedict, Maryland. Attached to Ross's army was the Royal Marine Artillery Rocket Brigade, commanded by First Lieutenant John Lawrence, and a Royal Artillery rocket detachment, under Second Captain Charles Deacon. Little resistance was encountered from the Americans and the British easily marched to Bladensburg, 5 miles (8 km) from the capital. In order to enter Washington, the British first had to cross the Bladensburg Bridge, which spanned the Anacostia River, a narrow eastern branch of the Potomac. The Americans were ill-prepared. Newly recruited troops, commanded by General William Henry Winder, hastily collected for the defense of the capital, faced professional troops seasoned by years of fighting Napoleon's *Grand Armée*.[36]

Surveying the movements of the opponents from afar were three men on horseback: President James Madison, Secretary of War James Monroe, and

Attorney General Richard Rush. Ross's troops approached the bridge and attempted to force their way across with a sudden discharge of rockets. American guns responded immediately and swept down almost an entire company of British infantry. The British survivors instantly took refuge behind a nearby warehouse; among them were the rocketeers, who again fired rockets. Secretary Monroe saw the projectiles "fall near the President" and Attorney General Rush afterwards wrote, "their rockets flew over us as we sat on our horses." President Madison discreetly advised his ministers to retire to the rear of the American lines. General Winder rode along the line encouraging his men to disregard the rockets, but instead, his troops panicked at the sight and the horrible hissing sound of the weapons as the British aimed them with increasing accuracy. The 5th and 24th Baltimore regiments, under lieutenant colonels John H. Schutz and John Ragan, simply fled the field. The British at once stormed over Bladensburg Bridge; Washington lay before them unprotected. In the subsequent courtmartial of General Winder for the American disaster at Bladensburg, Congreve rockets are often cited as a factor that led to the flight of Shutz's and Ragan's troops.[37]

The U.S. Capitol building was burned the night of 24 August 1814. Dolly Madison bravely retrieved some of the White House treasures before the British arrived. Law books and other combustibles were said to have been piled up against the White House and other buildings, and fired at by rockets. The State, War, and Navy buildings were all destroyed, and the Capitol was gutted.[38]

Following their assault on Washington, the British attacked Alexandria. Here, American opposition was stiffer. Captain David Ewen Bartholomew, commanding the rocket ship *Erebus,* was wounded. As it moved closer to get a better aim, the vessel came within range of American shore batteries and was badly damaged. The *Erebus* left and afterwards participated in the attempted strike at Baltimore. There, the principal obstacle was not a bridge but Fort McHenry, guarding the entrance to the city.[39]

The English troops, including Lawrence's and Deacon's rocketeers, landed at North Point on 11 September 1814. A battle ensued at the intersection of North Point and Trappe Roads. The British commanding general Robert Ross was killed as Congreve rockets and shells flew overhead (See Figure 2.3). The British advanced up North Point Road and camped 2 miles from the city. In the meantime, their fleet was compelled to sail past Fort McHenry.[40]

On the night of 12 September, *Erebus* and other ships moved into position. The following afternoon they commenced their attack. Bartholomew deluged the fort with Congreve 32-pounders (14.5 kg), but as at Alexandria, he found

FIGURE 2.3

Congreve rocket flying over head of dying British commander-in-chief Major-General Robert Ross at battle of North Point, near Baltimore, on 12 September 1814 in the War of 1812. (S.I. 72–7654)

that the rockets did not reach far enough. *Erebus* moved closer. American guns fired briskly, forcing several other English vessels to come to the aid of the rocket ship and tow her out. Smaller rocket barges also attempted to bombard the fort, but they were ineffective. Fighting continued into the night.[41]

Witnessing the bombardment was Francis Scott Key, an American lawyer seeking the release of a friend captured by the British at Bladensburg. Key, who was temporarily detained on his ship, was so moved by seeing the American flag "still there" after many hours' siege that he wrote "The Star Spangled Banner," later adopted as the U.S. national anthem. Congreve projectiles are alluded to in the line: "And the rockets' red glare, the bombs bursting in air, gave proof thro' the night that our flag was still there!"[42]

These immortal words were not the only poetic allusion to Congreve rockets in the war. When the inhabitants of Stonington, Connecticut, bravely defended their town during a series of British attacks from 9–13 August 1814, which included Congreves fired from several barges and a launch, an American composer was inspired to write "The Battle of Stonington," with the refrain: "The bombs were thrown, the rockets flew, But not a man of all their crew, (Though every man was full in view) Could kill a man at Stonington."[43]

The bravery of the Stonington villagers was amply proven when, according to *Nile's Weekly Register* (Baltimore) for 5 November 1814, some of them took hold of the external fuses of the explosive Congreve rockets (incendiary types were also used) and yanked them out "before the explosion . . . one or two persons received injury this way." Figure 2.4 shows a specimen of a Congreve retrieved from Stonington, perhaps handled in this brave, if foolhardy, manner.[44]

Congreve rockets also appeared in the last battle of the War of 1812, fought at New Orleans between December 1814 and January 1815. British rocketeers here included the detachments of captains Charles Deacon and Henry B. Lane. The dashing American commander and future president General Andrew Jackson is said to have strode among his men during the height of the battle, shouting, "Don't mind these rockets, boys. They are mere toys to amuse children!" But after the battle he privately confided to his friend, Revolutionary War veteran Roberts Hays: "It appears that the unerring hand of providence shielded my men from the shower of . . . rockets."[45]

Another American soldier provided this eyewitness account: "During the whole day [of 28 December 1814], the enemy incessantly threw Congreve rockets, which wounded some of our men. But one of these, Major [Daniel] Carmick of the Marines, had his horse killed and was himself wounded in the

FIGURE 2.4

Americans captured Congreve rockets from the British in the War of 1812. This one was fired in the battle of Stonington, Connecticut, on 10 August 1814, and is now in the possession of the Museum of Stonington. (S.I. 74-4425; courtesy Museum of Stonington)

hand. The British had great expectation from the effect of this weapon, against an enemy who had never seen it before. They hoped that its very noise would strike terror into us; but we soon grew accustomed to it, and thought it little formidable; for in the whole course of the campaign [in New Orleans], the rockets only wounded ten men, and blew up two caissons. That weapon must doubtless be effectual to throw amongst squadrons of calvary, and frighten the horses, or set fire to houses; but from the impossibility of directing it with any certainty, it will never be [but] a very precarious weapon to use against troops drawn up in line of battle, or behind ramparts."[46]

Close of a Versatile Career

The inventor of the Congreve rocket achieved fame for many other inventions, prompting newspapers and popular scientific journals to refer to him as the "ingenious Mr. Congreve." During his lifetime, he took out eighteen patents, two of which pertained to rockets (see Chapter 12). He never ceased promoting his rockets, but after accompanying the British fleet to the Basque Roads in 1809, he no longer participated directly in rocket actions, except in the planning stages. In 1811, he was made an equery, or honorary officer of the royal household. That same year he was elected a Fellow of the Royal Society and given the commission of lieutenant colonel of the Hanovarian Artillery, an honorary title that evolved from the personal bodyguard of the Hanovarian kings of England. Eventually, Congreve was elevated to the position of major general. His Hanovarian commission aroused no small amount of resentment by members of the regular Royal Artillery, who felt that he was not a professional soldier.[47]

Congreve also maintained an interest in politics, and in 1812 was elected Member of Parliament for Gatton, Surrey. In 1820, he became an M.P. for Plymouth and was reelected in 1826, serving until his death.[48]

In 1814, Congreve's father died. His son consequently became known as Sir William Congreve, 2nd Baronet. The younger Congreve also assumed his father's post of Comptroller of the Royal Laboratory and Superintendent of Military Machines; these were life positions. As Comptroller, one of his most enjoyable duties was the direction of a grand fireworks display in 1814 celebrating the victory over Napoleon. The following year he introduced his patented improvements in gunpowder manufacture at the Arsenal. In 1816, he was one of the official party that accompanied the visiting Grand Duke Nicholas of

Russia (later Tsar Nicholas I); he delighted in showing the Duke the facilities at Woolwich, which included rocket practice on the firing range.[49]

With artillerist Lieutenant James Nisbett Colquhoun, Congreve adapted his rockets to whaling in 1820–21, patenting and manufacturing a rocket-propelled whaling harpoon. This particular venture, tested by whalers in the Arctic Ocean, proved to be a commercial failure (see Chapter 12).[50]

In 1824, at age 52, Congreve married the young widow Isabella Carvalho M'Envoy in Wessel, Prussia. This union produced two sons and a daughter: William Augustus, William Frederick, and Isabella Christine. So far as is known, none of the Congreve children had any connection with rockets, though after Congreve's death Lady Congreve tried to obtain compensation for models of her husband's rockets.[51]

Congreve's final days were sad. In 1826, he was among those accused of fraudulence in the conduct of the Arigna Mining Company, of which he was one of the directors. The court proceedings dragged on and a decision was not announced until 1828. By then, Congreve was living in the warm climate of southern France, at Toulouse, in order to regain his health; he had developed paralysis in the lower part of his body. On 15 May 1828, at 56 years of age, he died and was buried in the Protestant Cemetery with full military honors by the French garrison of the city.

The sentence in the Arigna Mining Company case was passed shortly after. The company was declared "clearly fraudulent," but the Chancellor of the court refrained from giving any opinion as to the conduct of Congreve and his associates, who were recognized to be "respectable."[52]

CHAPTER 3

The Congreve Rocket After Napoleon

The British did not cease using Congreve rockets after Napoleon was crushed in 1815; on the contrary, the "Congreve era" had just begun. The Royal Navy carried rockets into action around the globe until the advent of William Hale's stickless or "rotary" rockets in the 1850s. Following are some examples of these actions.

The earliest post-Napoleonic Congreve engagement was an effort to suppress piracy along the ill-famed Barbary Coast of North Africa. An English fleet under Admiral Edward Pellew, later 1st Viscount Exmouth, set sail towards Algiers from Plymouth on 28 July 1816 to negotiate with the leader of Algiers, known as the Dey. The Admiral insisted upon the rockets for his expedition. Congreve himself worked on the plans but did not accompany the fleet, which included the transport *Trafalgar* laden with 2,500 rockets. Each line frigate and battleship had a rocket boat or "flat" assigned to it, making eight flats manned by a total of twenty men from the 2nd Rocket Troop in addition to midshipmen and sailors.[1]

At Gibraltar, the British fleet met a Dutch frigate squadron under Vice-Admiral Theodore Frederik Van der Capellan. He begged that his forces be permitted to join the expedition, since Dutchmen numbered among the Dey's slaves; Pellew consented. The Dutch Admiral also wanted Congreve rockets and requested instructions in their use. Accordingly, Steven Gaze and other officers went aboard a Dutch frigate after dark and fired 32-pounder carcass rockets from one of her boats. British accounts of the ensuing battle do not mention Van der Capellan's men using rockets, but there is evidence that the Dutch were indeed supplied with them (see Chapter 6).[2]

Upon his arrival at Algiers on 27 August 1816, Pellew sent a note to the Dey demanding the abolition of slavery and the immediate release of all slaves. By 2 o'clock in the afternoon, no answer had been received and Pellew, in the *Queen Charlotte,* made the signal for an attack. At half past two *Charlotte* anchored 100 yards (90 m) from the Mole-Head jutting from the city into Algiers Bay while other ships took their appointed positions and opened fire.[3]

Damage inflicted upon the enemy fortification and shipping by the

FIGURE 3.1

Clearing a pirates' nest with rockets at the bombardment of Algiers in 1816. (S.I. A5293)

FIGURE 3.2

Britain's colonial expansion was a dominant factor in the spread of Congreve rocket warfare. At right is a curious launcher for Congreve's rockets at Rangoon, Burma, in 1824 during the Anglo-Burmese War. (S.I. 72–9762)

rockets was severe. As at Copenhagen nine years before, fires were seen breaking out everywhere the rockets fell. One rocketeer was cited in Pellew's dispatches: "A gallant young midshipman in Rocket Boat No. 8 [Aaron S. Symes], although forbidden . . . [followed] in support of the barge in which attempt he was desperately wounded, his brother officer and nine of his crew killed." After eight hours of intense bombardment, the Dey's batteries were silenced and in ruins, as was a great part of the town. The next morning the message was received that all Pellew's demands had been granted and 3,000 slaves had been liberated.[4]

In recognition of their services, several rocketeers earned Naval General Service medals with clasps for Algiers. Midshipman Symes, now permanently disabled, was promoted and given a pension for life. In gratitude for Pellew's part, he was made a viscount and hailed as a liberator for Christendom.[5]

Colonial Campaigns

Following Algiers, the majority of Congreve rocket actions took place in British colonies. One of the earliest actions was the first Burmese War of 1824–26, which involved a border dispute between Burma and British colonial India. One unusual aspect of this campaign was the role of the East India Company's rocket establishment, which was supplied by Congreve's private rocket factory in Bow, England. Special Anglo-Indian rocket units, formed earlier (see Chapter 8), were deployed for the first time and included Captain Charles Graham's Bengal Rocket Troop.

Unfortunately, rough country roads and extreme heat caused the rocket propellant to deteriorate during land transport, and many rockets were found to be unreliable. The Burmese campaign typifies one of the major drawbacks of nineteenth-century powder rockets; namely, their low tolerance to extreme temperatures. Part of the problem lay in the manufacture. Gunpowder propellant could not be compressed tightly enough. In contrast to modern castable, case-bonded, solid propellants, prepared under controlled temperatures, poured into rocket tubes, and allowed to harden, at that time gunpowder had to be mechanically compressed into the rocket tubes and was therefore relatively loose. An additional problem was that although Congreve mass-produced his rockets, the iron cases were still largely fabricated by hand and were not always as strongly or uniformly bound as they should have been. Under poor transportation conditions, particularly in extreme climates, cracks could develop within the propellant. Cracks increased the burning area, generated more gases, and led to explosions. It is not surprising that early gunpowder rockets often failed in extremely hot or cold countries. In the Burmese campaign one attempted solution was water transport wherever possible, minimizing the chance of propellant cracking encountered in land transport.[6]

Yet Captain Graham's rockets performed well enough against the flimsy, combustible stockades of Burmese forts and river craft. Perhaps the greatest damage was inflicted when a solitary rocket killed Burmese chief Maha Bundoolah on 1 April 1825 at Dalla. Congreve rockets also saw action during the storming of Melloone in January 1826, after a treaty had been signed, but before it had been communicated to the combatants.[7]

In another colonial campaign, the Canadian rebellion of 1837, excessive cold rather than heat was the problem. Congreve rockets were taken out of old storage cases at British forts and given to the expeditionary force leaving Montreal. Long-term storage of the rockets in the Canadian climate could have caused propellant cracks. Alternate spells of freezing and thawing could make the powder unstable and, when cold, prone to cracking with the slightest movement. When fired during a Canadian winter, rockets were also likely to experience ignition delays and slower burning. On 15 December 1837, at Saint Eustache, about 20 miles (32 km) west of Montreal, one rocket in particular misbehaved, probably due to slow burning. When fired at a rebel-held church, it dipped rather than climbed, hitting a nearby fence, which broke its guide-stick. The rocket continued to burn, but, according to one account, without its stick it flew wildly out of control "all over a ploughed field in a most frightful manner . . . headquarter staff, Rocket Troop, and all, took flight." It finally burst within a few feet of the general-in-chief. The incident seems to have been enough to halt the subsequent use of rockets in this particular campaign, though not in Canada altogether.[8]

In the Opium War in China (1839–42) during fighting because of Chinese disruption of the British opium trade, both sides used rockets. Chinese rockets were no more than crude rocket-propelled arrows (see Chapter 8); British Congreves were far superior and more destructive. Throughout the campaign the steamship *Nemesis* was especially effective, with Congreve rockets fired from tubes mounted on her bows. At Chuenpee on Ansons Bay in January 1841, for example, one eyewitness reported: "The first rocket fired from the *Nemesis* passed through the side of a [Chinese] junk into her magazine, when she blew up with a most tremendous explosion, hurling the unfortunate crew in the air, not one of whom escaped; and very shortly the whole flotilla of junks were either shattered to pieces or burnt."[9]

The annals of Britain's conquest of the Maori aborigines of New Zealand contain numerous mentions of Congreve rockets, especially during the 1840s to 1860s. Yet British belief that these weapons were bound to terrify a primitive people proved to be unfounded. The Maoris derided the sometimes erratic rockets and demonstrated a cleverness and skill in guerrilla warfare. In one of the first engagements, in 1845, Maori chieftain Hone Heke ordered the roofs of the *pa*, or stockade, at Okaihu to be covered with flax so that they could not be burnt by the rockets. This was also done at the battle of Puketutu at Lake Omapere. Says one account: "The rocket-tube from which so much was expected was now placed in position on the northwest side of the *pa*, at a distance of about 150 yards [137 m]. Twelve rockets were fired by Lieutenant [Charles] Egerton, [of H.M.S.] *Northstar* . . . without any effect." Perhaps because the Maoris showed little fear of rockets, nothing is heard of the weapons' use in New Zealand after the 1860s, though the Maori wars continued until the 1870s.[10]

FIGURE 3.3

Rocket battery on the Parana River, near San Lorenzo, Argentina, in 1846, against the forces of Argentine dictator Juan Manuel de Rosas. (s.i. a5319)

Congreve rockets were much more effective in the Franco-British attempts to crush Argentine dictator Juan Manual de Rosas in 1846. The most notable rocket action took place at San Lorenzo, Argentina, on the Parana River. The British and French commanders agreed to secretly land a party of English sailors armed with rockets on a grassy island opposite the batteries of San Lorenzo. Rocket tubes were highly portable and, as Congreve had said years before, provided the firepower of conventional artillery without the encumberance of guns. The rocket-men at Saint Lorenzo dug trenches and made small embankments for cover and protection. The plan called for the rockets to be discharged on a signal given by the commander-in-chief upon the approach of the allied fleet, "thus causing a double-banked fire of great force," from the rockets and ships' guns.[11]

The plan was not so easily executed. Twenty-three men carrying three 24-pounder (10.8 kg) and three 12-pounder (5.4 kg) Congreve rocket tubes landed on "Rocket Island," as it was now dubbed, and stealthily took up their positions right under the noses of the enemy. On the morning of 4 May 1846, H.M.S. *Gorgon* gave the signal; the rockets blazed away. According to one account: "One went twenty feet [6 m] over their [the enemy's] heads . . . another just cleared, two fell short, and two appeared to plow the crowd up, and bounded into the calvary in the rear. It is quite impossible to describe the panic and confusion this caused amongst the enemy." However, while the rockets' performance was excellent in this engagement, Rosas remained undefeated and it was not until 1852 that he was finally overthrown. Yet he was so impressed with the weapons at St. Lorenzo that he obtained some for his own army and used them in his final battle (see Chapter 7).[12]

Crimean War

Contrasted with the small scale of rocket action in Argentina, the Crimean War of 1853–56 was the first real "rocket war." Three nations—England, France, and Russia—used the projectile in the most extensive employment of Congreve-type rockets in the nineteenth century. British rocket production alone at the height of the war totalled 500 a day, compared with thirty-six a day reported by Congreve in 1813. The Crimean campaign also marked the intro-

FIGURE 3.4

The Crimean War of 1853–56 saw extensive employment of rockets against the Russians.

(s.i. 72–10664)

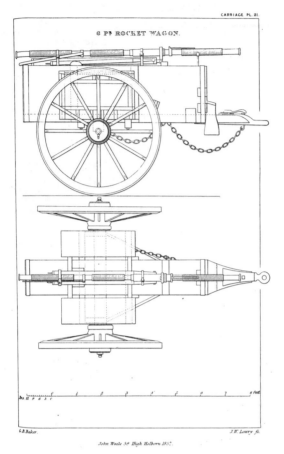

CARRIAGE PL. 21.

6 P? ROCKET WAGON.

G.B.Baker. J.W.Lowry fc.

John Weale 59 High Holborn 1852.

FIGURE 3.5

Crimean War-vintage 6-pounder (2.7 kg) rocket wagon with mounted launcher. Part of launcher is wrapped in hemp to prevent overheating during firing. (S.I. 72–10664)

duction of the Hale rocket, which was used on an experimental basis.[13]

The British used Congreve rockets in almost every major action in the Crimean War, from the bombardment of Odessa and the battles of the Alma, Balaklava, and Eupatoria in 1854, to the bombardment of Sweaborg in 1855 and the siege of Sebastopol from October 1854 to September 1855. One reason for this extensive employment of rockets was the insistence of the British Commander-in-Chief, Lord Raglan. In a *Memorandum for Generals of Divisions,* dated 16 October 1854, he ordered that "each division will also have with it [besides standard equipment] a detachment of twenty artillerymen, under an officer of artillery, with rockets." Many British ships and boats were armed with Congreve rockets. William Hale went to the Crimea as a private citizen and pursuaded Navy officers to try out his own projectiles in combat.[14]

Various accounts of rocket actions in the Crimea describe both successes and failures. At the battle of Eupatoria on the Black Sea, in February 1855, a witness observed the following:

> While [the Russian] General [Stefan] Chruleff was forming his Greeks [volunteers aiding the Russians] and Cossacks for the assault, the *Furious* British war-steamer landed a rocket party on the extreme right of the town, who, coming round among the windmills opened their fire precisely on the head of the Russian column as it emerged from the broad gate of the cemetery. The discharge was point blank, the rockets tearing through the column, which nevertheless endeavored to deploy, but was so broken by the inequalities of the ground and the various impediments met from the tombs of every size and shape, that the necessarily last time under the unexpected and destructive fire of the little rocket brigade; a portion of the column never left the burial ground, or came out only in a struggling and confused mass.[15]

FIGURE 3.6

Launchers on a boat, firing against Russian fort of Taganrog in 1855 during the Crimean War. (S.I. 72–3133)

FIGURE 3.7
Rockets used against Nystad, Crimean campaign, 1855. (S.I. 79–7373)

On the other hand, Commander Robert Jenner of the *Basilisk* wrote to a fellow officer on 10 June 1855 that "the rockets I have been supplied with do not range their proper distances, and burst most unsatisfactorily."[16]

But just as the Crimean War was a high point in the history of the nineteenth-century powder rocket, it also marked the end of an epoch of the use of conventional artillery. This was the last European war in which all combatants used muzzle-loaders. Technical difficulties with breech-loading mechanisms were being overcome (mainly by providing gas-tight breech closures). The Crimean War also saw (during the siege of Sebastopol) the first crude rifled ordnance in the British Army.

Artillery developments were now rapid, and the Sepoy Mutiny in India in 1857–58, ended the smooth-bore period for the British. In rocketry, the Mutiny became the last major conflict in which British Congreves were deployed. Two Royal Navy "Rocket Brigades" were formed for the occasion; one was composed of men from H.M.S. *Pearl*, the other of men from the *Shannon*. Usually, Naval rocket troops confined their operations to coasts. But because of the shortage of troops due to the sudden outbreak of the revolt, sailors from the *Pearl* and *Shannon* were forced to drag heavy guns, in addition to rockets, several hundred miles inland. The *Shannon* had eight Congreve rocket tubes. Under the command of Captain William Peel (son of former British Prime Minister Sir Robert Peel) the *Shannon's* Rocket Brigade distinguished itself in the relief of the beseiged British garrison at Lucknow, then capital of Oudh Province (now capital of Uttar Pradesh state), in November 1857.[17]

According to one historian, "the rockets unexpectedly proved to be a battle-winning factor. A salvo of rockets was lobbed over the great wall and fell, hissing, into the enclosure, causing loud detonations and clouds of smoke within. Meanwhile Sergeant Paton, continuing his exploration round the walls, had come across a crack on the far side of the enclosure, just wide enough to admit one man at a time. He . . . promptly led about fifty men to the spot. . . . The only enemy to be seen were apparently in a panic, struggling to get out of the place as fast as they could."[18]

However, as in Burma, India's climate inevitably affected many of the Congreves. One soldier wrote: "The sticks had got too dry, and [the rockets] burnt so quickly, as in many cases, to fall or explode far short of their range. Whether it was an older batch of rockets, or whether their having been exposed to the sun for some months was the cause of their misdoings, I do not know, but they were a great failure."[19]

Other Conflicts

In addition to major conflicts, there were innumerable minor wars and colonial punitive expeditions in which Congreve rockets played a part. Rockets were used frequently in Africa. Perhaps the beginning of this employment occurred in the First Ashanti War on the Gold Coast (now Ghana) in 1825–26. At the decisive battle of Akantamasu, near Accra (the present capital of Ghana), on 7 August 1826, according to one historian, "a few [Congreve] rockets fired at the right moment, spread terror and confusion into the ranks of the Ashantis."[20]

Elsewhere in Africa, disturbances of the Mandingoes, an Islamic tribe inhabiting the territory inland from the Gambia River in Sierra Leone, promulgated the "Barra War" in 1831. On 17 December of that year, British rockets were used in the attack on the enemy's capital at Essaw, but the natives shrewdly removed the thatched roofs of their huts and the rockets had little effect.[21]

In 1837–42, hundreds of old Congreves were taken out of storage and accompanied the British Army fighting in the First Afghan War in Afghanistan. They were effective in the siege of Herat in 1837 and in the defense of Kabul in 1842. At Herat, Sir John Kaye observed that: "the rockets ranged too widely to work any serious mischief to the besieged; but their grand fiery flight as they passed over the city struck terror into the hearts of the people, who clustered upon the roofs of the houses, praying and crying by turns."[22]

At the opening of the second Anglo-Chinese War (1856–60), Captain Charles Govan's Rocket Battery of the Royal Artillery was dispatched from India and Captain Guy Rotton's Rocket Battery, consisting of sixty-seven men and three officers, was brought from England. Captain Henry Hicks's Madras Artillery, also of the British colonial establishment in India, was armed with Congreves. Considering the fact that French forces in this allied campaign in China likewise included rocketeers, and the Chinese used crude "rocket arrows," the second Anglo-Chinese War ranks as the second "rocket war" after the Crimean conflict. Congreve rockets saw excellent service in the attacks against the Taku forts on the Pei-Ho River.[23]

Japan also felt the effects of Western war rockets when in 1864 the British sent a reprisal force against a Japanese war lord for his attacks against European shipping in Japanese harbors. Congreve rockets bombarded the seaport of Shimonoseki, in southwestern Honshu, on 5 September of that year.[24]

On the other side of the world, in British Honduras, 12-pounder (5.4 kg) rockets helped to burn the rebel town of San Pedro early in February 1867. The following month, a Royal Artillery rocket party was sent to Marajal, near Hondo, where the rebels made their last stand. The rockets, it is said, left traces of blood; perhaps they struck and wounded the enemy as they sped in their flight. It is not certain whether the rockets in the Honduran campaign were Congreves or Hales. The same is true of engagements in the late 1860s and 1870s. In 1867 Hale rockets officially supplanted the older and less reliable Congreves in both major and minor wars.[25]

Having glimpsed Congreve rockets in action in a variety of circumstances, in the next chapter we will focus on the technology of the weapons themselves, gaining insight into their general success for more than half a century.

CHAPTER 4

The Congreve Rocket System

Clearly, Congreve rockets were not wholly reliable in battle, even by nineteenth-century standards, so Congreve must have been a superb salesman for them to have been adopted and widely accepted. Toward these goals, he exploited his father's considerable connections and published several promotional booklets extolling the virtues of his "Rocket System."

These publications have proven invaluable in quite a different way than Congreve intended. They offer contemporary military and technology historians excellent coverage of the calibers, supporting equipment, performances, and costs of the rockets, in addition to organizations of rocket troops. Unfortunately, they do not offer manufacturing and other technical details. This type of data has come down to us in fragmentary form from other references, such as artillery manuals and captured specimen reports. The following is an analysis of the Congreve Rocket System based on these few available sources.

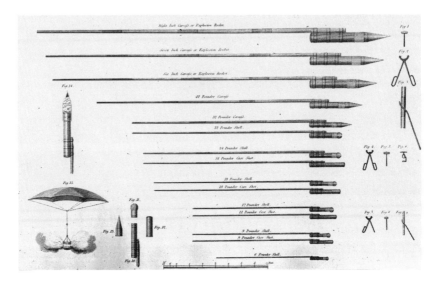

FIGURE 4.1

Congreve's "rocket system." Shown here are a typical incendiary rocket; rocket parts; a battle-field illumination rocket; and tools for handling rockets. (S.I. A4462)

Calibers and Performances

Congreve developed, in modern military parlance, a "weapons system." He himself called it the Congreve Rocket System. This consisted of a series of calibers with warheads designed for different types of missions and support equipment for carrying and launching the weapons, including firing stands for use on land and sea; carriages; tools for servicing the rockets; the organization of rocket-armed troops; published tactical instructions and range tables for different calibers; and the standardization of rocket manufacture for mass production.

As far as is known, such a system had never before been created, at least in the West. In India, rocket-armed fighting forces had been organized, but Indian rocketeers ("rocket boys") were largely irregular, non-professional soldiers. Moreover, Indian rockets of the sixteenth to eighteenth centuries appear to have been limited to one or two basic calibers with few modifications.[1]

By contrast, through Congreve's tireless efforts, two Royal Artillery Rocket Troops had been organized in the British Army by 1814, and ten basic calibers of war rockets existed with all the requisite equipment—the 6-, 9-, 12-, 18-, 24-, 32- and 42-pounders, plus the 6-, 7-, and 8-in. models (2.7, 4, 5.4, 8, 10.8, 14.5, and 19 kg and 15.2, 17.7, and 20.3 cm). They ranged from 800 yards (730 m) to 3,000 yards (2,740 m). The Royal Navy were regularly issued 32-pounders and other calibers, and temporary Royal Marine rocket artillery units were formed.[2]

The 6- to 42-pounders (2.7–19 kg) were the most commonly used rockets throughout the British services. They were further divided according to their warheads: 6-pounder (2.7 kg) shell or explosive rocket; 9- to 24-pounder (4–10.8 kg) shell and case shot, or scattering lead ball rocket; 32-pounder (14.5 kg) shell and carcass, or incendiary, rocket; a 42-pounder (19 kg) carcass rocket; and 6–8 inch (15.2–20.3 cm) carcass or shell models. Hence, the system expanded to at least fifteen rocket types to meet all military needs, from antipersonnel skirmishes to bombardments of ships and fortified towns. For

FIGURE 4.2

Congreve side-mounted stick rockets. Bottom: shell or explosive rockets. Note external fuse channels leading to warheads. Top: 32-pounder (14.5 kg) incendiary, or "carcass," rocket with internal fusing. (S.I. A1128B)

Table 1

Ranges of the Congreve Rockets (After Congreve)

Firing Elevations and Respective Ranges

Caliber	Point Blank, or Ground Practice	20–25°	25–30°	30–35°	35–40°	40–45°	45–50°	50–55°	55–60°	60–65°
6–8 in (15.2–20 cm)	—	—	—	—	—	—	—	—	—	2,100–2,500 yds (1920–2285 m)
42 pr (19 kg)	—	—	—	—	—	—	—	2,000–2,500 yds (1,830–2,285 m)	2,500–3,000 yds (2,285–2,745 m)	—
32 pr (14.5 kg)	1–1,200 yds (915–1,100 m)	—	—	1,000–1,500 yds (915–1,370 m)	1,500–2,000 yds (1,370–1,830 m)	2,000–2,500 yds (1,830–2,285 m)	2,500–3,000 yds (2,285–2,745 m)	3,000–3,200 yds (2,745–2,925 m)	—	—
24 pr (10.8 kg)	Nearly the Same	—	—	—	—	—	—	—	—	—
18 pr (8 kg)	1,000 yds (915 m)	—	1,000–1,500 yds (915–1,370 m)	1,500 yds up (1,370 m up)	2,000 yds up (1,830 m up)	2,000 yds up (1,830 m up)	—	—	—	—
12 pr (5.4 kg)	Nearly the Same	—	—	—	—	—	—	—	—	—
9 pr (4 kg)	800–1,000 yds (730–915 m)	1,000–1,500 yds (915–1,370 m)	—	—	2,000 yds up (1,830 m up)	2,200 yds up (2,010 m up)	—	—	—	—
6 pr (2.7 kg)	Nearly the Same	—	—	—	—	—	—	—	—	—

Source: William Congreve, Details of the Rocket System (London, 1814).

ease in classifying the calibers, Congreve further categorized his rockets into: *heavy* (6–8 in), *medium* (24- to 42-pounders), and *light* (6- to 18-pounders). Table I, modified from Congreve, shows different ranges and respective firing angles. It should be noted that in Congreve's day rocket performance was measured not by thrust, but by range. This was eminently practical, as soldiers needed only to know which types of rockets to use on given occasions and the best way to aim them. Congreve must have spent hours on the Woolwich firing field determining launch elevations for achieving optimum ranges before arriving at what was probably the world's first rocket range table.[3]

Why were smaller Congreve rockets designated in pounds and larger ones in inches? And why did Congreve choose the denominations 6-, 12-, 18-, 24- and 32-pounders? The answer to both questions is that he borrowed standard artillery nomenclature of the day. Smaller guns bore weight designations, while the heavier mortars and howitzers were classified by diameter.[4]

Early nineteenth-century rockets compared very favorably with guns in range. The short range of guns was due mainly to their smooth bores, or barrels, and their round ammunition. There was a considerable air gap ("windage") between the round, loose-fitting projectile and the barrel wall, so that air pressure slowed the velocity of the projectile; this also cut back range. The blunt, round shape of the projectile itself encountered much air resistance, and this too hindered speed, range, and accuracy. Additionally, the smooth barrel gave the ammunition an indiscriminate path, also destroying its accuracy.

It should be noted that guns were restricted in their firing elevations, which affected their ranges. However, this was mainly a matter of tactics (the desirability for long, flat ranges). Mortars were always aimed at high angles since they were meant for closer ranges from steep locations. Rockets, by comparison, were not as restricted in their firing elevations, because by being self-propelled they did not follow strictly parabolic curves. Nor did rockets face the problem of recoil, as did guns. For massive, large guns, recoil was not a great problem, but it could be troublesome for smaller pieces or with any gun mounted on a ship (recoil caused vessels to sway, which interfered with maintaining aim). All recoiling artillery had to be rolled back into position as quickly as possible after each firing, besides being reloaded. Rockets faced no recoil problem at all. Congreve rightly cited this as a major advantage over conventional artillery that made rocket weapons especially attractive for use on boats and ships, even though rockets did require protection from stray sparks.

Cannons were also generally very cumbersome. A typical 9-pounder field gun used during the Napoleonic wars weighed 2 tons (1,800 kg) with its

Table 2

Ranges of British Smooth Bore Artillery 1750–1860

Brass Guns in Land Service

32-pr (obsolete by 1816)	1,900 yd (1,700 m) at 5°
24-pr (obsolete by 1811)	1,700 yd (1,550 m) at 5°
18-pr (obsolete by 1811)	2,000 yd (1,830 m) at 7°
12-pr (heavy)	1,100 yd (1,000 m) at 3°
12-pr (light)	1,400 yd (1,300 m) at 4°
9-pr (in use after 1808)	1,400 yd (1,300 m) at 4°
6-pr	1,400 yd (1,300 m) at 4°
3-pr	1,200 yd (1,300 m) at 4°

Iron Guns

42-pr (coast artillery)	3,100 yd (2,850 m)
32-pr	2,900 yd (2,650 m)
24-pr (the most popular gun in the siege train)	1,900 yd (1,740 m) at 5°
18-pr	1,800 yd (1,650 m) at 5°
9-pr (coast artillery after 1800)	1,800 yd (1,650 m)
6-pr	1,500 yd (1,370 m)
12-pr	1,800 yd (1,650 m)

Mortars (brass and iron)

13-in (33 cm)	4,100 yd (3,750 m)
10-in (25 cm)	1,300 yd (1,200 m)
8-in (20 cm)	1,600 yd (1,460 m)

Howitzers (brass and iron)

10-in (25 cm)	2,000 yd (1,830 m) at 12°
8-in (20 cm)	1,700 yd (1,550 m) at 12°

Source: Compiled from Major-General B.P. Hughes, British Smooth-bore Artillery: The Muzzle-loading Artillery of the 18th and 19th Centuries *(1969): 28–31, 37, 39.*

limber, while a 24-pounder siege gun required teams of bullocks or horses to move it 7 miles (11 km) a day over good roads. There were lighter pieces, but their calibers were correspondingly smaller. Rockets required no limbers and were light enough to be carried individually by hand, if necessary, though several were usually borne in small caissons.

In comparing guns to rockets, weaponry in general was then woefully backwards and suffered from static development. For example, the most prominent firearm in land warfare was the muzzle-loading smooth-bore flintlock musket, introduced around 1700 but still in use by the time of Waterloo and only effective when fired *en masse* at very close range. Artillery was not much more advanced. Cannons had become more mobile in the eighteenth century with the introduction of improved Gribeauval and other transport carriages. Otherwise, artillery had remained basically unchanged since the seventeenth century, in that they too were smooth-bore muzzle-loaders. Muzzle-loading, in which the gun was loaded from the front of the barrel, was a slow and inefficient process that required ramming, sponging, and loading with each round. Unpredictable as they were, Congreve rockets were free from such encumbrances and held their own in range and firepower. They seemed to many artillerists a "new" and welcome advance that, in time, promised great improvement in accuracy.

Congreve himself sought a way to compensate for the inaccuracy of the rocket. Early in his experiments on the firing range, he found that the rockets' low energy output did not produce full force (thrust) upon ignition, which made it difficult to keep them on target. Maximum thrust was reached only after a slight delay. Soon after a Congreve rocket was fired, it "dipped" in its trajectory, rose again, and arced in a ballistic curve before striking its target. Congreve compensated for the "dip" by adding a few more degrees of firing elevation. The rocket returned to a more suitable trajectory when full power was reached and headed on the right course towards the target. Even with the range tables, rocket-firing in Congreve's day was largely empirical, since there were many unknown ballistic variables. Lateral dispersions were often very wide, especially during winds.[5]

Thrust, now taken for granted as a measure of rocket performance, was not measured for Congreve rockets, but may be estimated from known values. The 32-pounder (14.5 kg) Congreve rocket contained about 10 pounds (4.5 kg) of gunpowder that burned for approximately 3 seconds. We may use *specific impulse* (I_{sp}), a modern rocket propellant performance parameter expressed in seconds, equal to the thrust in pounds divided by the propellant consumption rate in pounds per second. Since gunpowder has a specific impulse of 80–100 pounds per second per pound (36–45 kg/sec/kg), we can transpose to find that the thrust for a Congreve 32-pounder rocket was about 250 pounds (113 kg) for 3 seconds, maximum. If a rocket of this size used a modern solid propellant with an I_{sp} of 200–250, the corresponding thrust would more than double, though modern solid-fuel rockets require super-strong, lightweight, heat-resistant materials in addition to exactingly designed exhaust nozzles and other motor elements. By comparison, modern liquid fuels possess even greater I_{sp}s of around 400.[6]

Velocities of Congreve rockets were not measured either, but may be easily estimated from results of firing trials at Dum Dum, India, on 22 June 1816. Launched at elevations of 55°, 32-pounder rockets attained ranges of 2,036–2,874 yards (1,832–2,586 m) with flight times of 20–25 seconds. Average flight velocities, therefore, varied from 243–303 feet/second (74–92 m/sec), or 165–206 miles per hour (266–332 km/hr). The rocket was, of course, more streamlined than roundshot, but this was offset by the low impulse from gunpowder and the air drag over the guidestick.[7]

Payloads

One gauge of rocket effectiveness commonly used both in Congreve's time and our own is payload capability, though by no means can present-day warhead contents or capacity be equated with what was available in Congreve's day. Congreve's rocket system does not reflect a perfect adaptation of artillery nomenclature of the period, since incendiary rockets were not fitted with shells nor did they exactly correspond in caliber with shells. Neither did warhead weights of shot and shell rockets always match their designated calibers. Despite assigned rocket caliber designations, overall weights varied widely depending upon payloads.

The normal payload for a 6-pounder (2.7 kg) rocket was a 3-pound (1.3 kg) shot or shell. The 9-pounder (4 kg) rocket was usually fitted with a grenade of unspecified weight; the 12-pounder (5.4 kg) with a 6-pound (2.7 kg) shot or shell; the 18-pounder (8 kg) with a 9-pound (4 kg) shot or shell; and the 24-pounder (10.8 kg) with a 12-pound (5.4 kg) shot or cohorn shell. (The latter was a seventeenth-century light mortar shell named after its Dutch inventor, Baron Menno van Cohorn.) Nine- to 24-pounders (4–10.8 kg) were also armed with case-shot heads. These were spherical, hollow warheads holding up to 200 carbine balls (forty-eight in the 12-pounder rocket). Bursting powder was at the bottom of the heads to facilitate the scattering of balls among cavalry or infantry, similar to the shrapnel shell, invented in 1804 by artillerist Henry Shrapnel.[8]

The 32-pounder (14.5 kg) rocket was considered to be too large for case-shot warheads because it was rather heavy for an antipersonnel weapon, but in other respects it was the most versatile of the calibers. Congreve called it the "mean point" (i.e., intermediate, or middle caliber) of the rocket system. It was the smallest rocket used as a carcass (incendiary) in bombardment "and the largest armed with [explosive] shot or shell, for field service." However, "the 24-pounder [10.8 kg] rocket is very nearly equal to it in all its applications in the field; from the saving of weight, therefore, I consider it preferable."[9]

Because of its versatility, Congreve subdivided the 32-pounder (14.5 kg) rocket into *small* carcass (incendiary) models containing 8 pounds (3.6 kg) carcass composition; *medium* carcass, with 12 pounds (5.4 kg) composition; and *large* carcass, with 18 pounds (8 kg) composition.[10] The 32-pounder was also "armed with bursting cones [i.e., conical warheads], made of stout iron, filled with powder, to be exploded by fuses, and . . . used to produce the explosive effects of shells." These explosive rockets were classified as *small* shell rockets, carrying 5 pounds (2.2 kg) of powder; *medium*, with 8 pounds (3.6 kg) of powder; and *large*, with 12 pounds (5.4 kg) of powder. The 32-pounders could also be fitted with 5.5-inch (14 cm) howitzer shells of 18- or 24-pounder (8–10.8 kg) solid shot.[11]

Congreve said almost nothing of the less popular 42-pounder (19 kg) rocket introduced about 1807, which could convey about as much carcass composition as the 32-pounder carcass model.[12]

Congreve's largest rockets, with diameter designations, weighed 100–300 pounds (45–136 kg) and each was "loaded with not less than a barrel of powder." They carried combustibles of 25–50 pounds (11–22 kg) of bursting

FIGURE 4.3
Congreve's larger models were designated in inches. This 6-inch (15 cm) carcass or incendiary rocket, weighing 100 pounds (45 kg), is incorrectly labeled as a 100-pounder. (S.I. 82–14787)

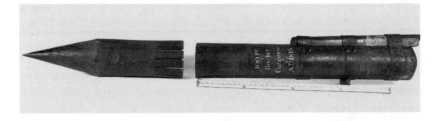

FIGURE 4.4

Same rocket as in Figure 4.3 is shown disassembled prior to being displayed in the National Air and Space Museum. Note the fabric-covered holes around the cone, which communicated the incendiary fire to the target when the rocket struck. (S.I. A3733)

powder and were "equally efficient for the destruction of bomb proofs, or the demolition of strong buildings." However, none of the giant rockets were ever used in combat, perhaps because of their expense. There may have also been technical problems in their manufacture.[13]

In his 1814 and 1827 rocket treatises, Congreve optimistically foresaw much larger models: "Rockets from half a ton [450 kg] to a ton weight [905 kg] . . . driven in very strong and massive cast-iron cases, may possess such strength . . . that, being fired . . . against . . . any fortress . . . with one explosion of several barrels of powder [could] . . . complete a practicable breach."[14] He also experimented with other configurations, including clustered rockets of three, four, or six 32-pounders or other calibers "well lashed together, with the sticks in the centre also strongly bound together" (see Figure 4.5). These were apparently troublesome to make, expensive, and offered no significant increase in range over standard, single-cased rockets.[15] Discharging them was another problem. "The great art of firing these," cautioned Congreve, "is to arrange them . . . to take fire contemporaneously, which must be done either by priming the bottoms of all thoroughly, or by firing them by a flash of powder, which is sure to ignite the whole combination at once."[16]

Congreve also made tiny rockets for antipersonnel use. He called them "a species of self-motive musket-ball cartridges" that were discharged from a 4-pound (1.8 kg) musket. Congreve wrote that these rockets were "twice the weight of a musket ball," yet their range and penetration was "at least equal." Rockets of up to half a pound (0.2 kg) were also made and were fired from a shoulder-held gun. One-pounders (0.4 kg) were "projected from light tubes, formed as lances, either for infantry or cavalry. . . . The one-pound Rocket posseses all the range, weight, and force of the one-pound shot, so that a regiment of lancers, each man being so armed, would possess a tremendous fire, and carry 15,000 or 20,000 rounds of this ammunition into action without incumbrance!!!" Despite his exuberance, these weapons were never made use of, probably because they were not cost-effective.[17]

Besides "rocket ammunition," a non-offensive "light-ball" was developed. This was a 42-pound (19 kg) or other caliber rocket fired vertically into the air where it ejected a ball of slow-burning composition. Upon release at peak altitude, the ball was ignited by a fuse and produced a brilliant light while floating back to earth by a parachute on a chain. Depending upon wind conditions, the illumination lasted for about 10 minutes. This was one of the earliest forms of battlefield flare for facilitating nighttime military operations. According to Major Charles James (Royal Artillery Drivers) in his *Military Dictionary* of 1810, Congreve's light-ball was a great improvement over the gun-fired light-ball, which shed its light too briefly.[18]

Related to this device was Congreve's floating rocket carcass, described by James as a 32-pounder carrying combustible matter by parachute to "far beyond the range of any known projectile force." James suggested that it might be thrown from a blockading squadron "in great quantities with a fair wind against any fleet or arsenal, without the smallest risk, or without approaching

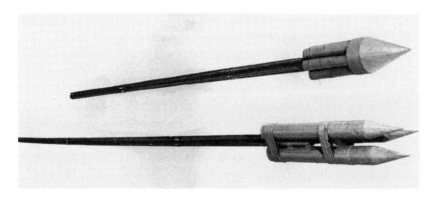

FIGURE 4.5
Congreve experimented with multiple-cartridge models, but they were never used due to their expense and difficulty to produce. (S.I. 78–5943)

within range of either guns or mortars." Congreve says almost nothing about the floating carcass in his treatises; presumably it never materialized as a viable weapon.[19]

Designs

In their outward appearance, Congreve rockets resembled large skyrockets. Closer analysis shows that there were marked differences, particularly in the design of the guidestick. The first rockets used in the 1805 Boulogne expedition were actually large cardboard skyrockets with warheads. The following year Congreve switched to metal cases and heavier calibers, necessitating longer guidesticks—up to 25 feet (7.6 m) long for 32-pounder (14.5 kg) rockets. Although workable, this arrangement was cumbersome. A postscript in Congreve's 1807 edition of *Concise Account of the . . . Rocket System* indicates that he experimented with fins, spiral vanes, and perhaps other means for dispensing with the stick altogether. These devices apparently proved to be unsatisfactory, because they were never made use of. (Other rocket-fin designs in the nineteenth century also proved to be unsuccessful, mainly because of ignorance of aerodynamics and low rocket power.)

By 1810, Congreve had shortened the sticks to 15 feet (4.5m) for 32-pounder (14.5 kg) rockets. For convenience in stowing land-service rockets, Congreve also sectioned the sticks, which were assembled prior to launching. Assembly was accomplished by ferrules (metal bands). Tools for jointing and fixing the sticks consisted of hammers, pincers, vices, and wrenches. Sticks for larger rockets of 6–8 inches (15–20 cm) caliber came in four sections. Sticks for smaller calibers were usually divided into half that number. Each stick section was 3 feet 6 inches (1 m) long and was shaped and beveled where it fit the rocket case.[20]

For sea service, said Congreve, sticks "are made in the whole length." Perhaps the reason for this was that there was more room to stack entire lengths of rockets on ships. It also simplified manufacturing and ensured that the sticks remained straight. All sticks were made of the "straightest white deal" or Riga fir that was free of knots.[21]

In 1815, Congreve made his most important change in the rocket's configuration. He shifted the guidestick away from the side of the case (the so-called side-mounted stick rocket) to the center of the long axis of the rocket (the center-mounted stick rocket). This was achieved by attaching a circular base-

FIGURE 4.6
One of Congreve's major improvements was the shifting of the stick to the longitudinal axis of the rocket in 1815. (S.I. A1129C)

plate to the rear of the rocket. The center of the plate had a threaded socket into which the guidestick was screwed. The exhaust gases issued from five equidistant holes around the central, socketed guidestick hole. The first center-mounted stick rocket was fired on 30 December 1815. Its superiority was immediately evident and the pattern was officially adopted the same day. British Congreve rocket specimens can therefore be dated, according to their stick arrangement, as before or after 1815.[22]

Congreve never spelled out the advantages of the central stick over the side-mounted arrangement, though upon analysis it is apparent that there were several. The side-stick rocket was heavier on one side and had a tendency to yaw towards that mass, particularly if a lateral cross wind was blowing. The yawing probably caused wide dispersion. By shifting the stick towards the thrust line, pitching and yawing movements were significantly decreased. All forces were in greater equilibrium with the centering of the stick down the thrust line. Another advantage, probably not realized by Congreve, was that less air drag was encountered by the center-mounted stick rocket compared to the side-stick pattern. Also, shifting the stick to the center of the long axis of the rocket, in line with its thrust, tended to produce better aerodynamic stability by keeping the center of pressure behind the rocket's center of mass. The exterior and interior ballistics of Congreve and other side-stick gunpowder rockets is still not well known, so there may have been other stabilizing factors achieved by the center stick.

The arrangement of the exhaust gases issuing from the equidistant holes around the axis of the center-mounted stick rocket had benefits too. The thrust line still ran down the axis of the rocket, but the gases were more evenly and equally distributed (providing that all exhaust cavities were free of dirt, rust, and displaced pieces of powder). For ignition, a single fuse line was placed in one of the cavities. The center-mounted pattern was very popular and was adopted internationally. Generally, it was conceded that the accuracy of the rockets had greatly improved. Center-mounted stick rockets could be shot easily through tubes, whereas this was difficult with side-mounted types. However, other factors, such as low impulse and poor storage qualities still made nineteenth-century gunpowder war rockets quite unreliable.[23]

Another of Congreve's important but little-discussed rocket innovations was fusing for regulating the explosions of shell warheads. Congreve's incendiary rockets required a simple powder train from the top of the propellant charge to the incendiary composition, so it would burn almost immediately after the propellant had been consumed. Upon this secondary ignition, the incendiary warhead material burned for 5 minutes. Explosive rockets were trickier to manage. If a shell burst too soon or too late, the purpose of the rocket would be lost; the target would not be destroyed.[34]

In Congreve's day, the commander of a rocket detachment alone determined by experience and rough "eyeball" sighting from one round to the next which fuse or aiming adjustments to make. Approximate range tables helped, but precision was hardly possible.

Congreve's original explosive or case-shot rockets (side-stick pattern) were furnished, in his words, with "an external fuse of paper, which is ignited from the vent the moment when the rocket is fired." Adjustment of the timing of the bursts was made by cutting the fuse length with "a pair of common scissors," thereby shortening fuse burning times. Congreve's description is incomplete, however, and it is not clear if the rocket propellant and fuse were lighted separately or if the cut (shortened) fuse was retied and then ignited.[25]

With the introduction of the central-stick pattern, the external fuse was discarded, probably because it became an encumbrance. An internal fuse similar to standard artillery shell fuses was introduced. The internal fuse was more efficient, though it underwent refinements over the years.[26]

By the 1840s, according to the *Description of an Alteration in the Construction of Rockets* by James Cockburn, the Director of the Royal Laboratory, "every [explosive] rocket is fitted with a fuse screwed into the base of the shell." The elliptical warhead shell contained a hollow cavity in the center of which was a channel filled with slow-burning fuse composition. A metal plug fit into the nose of the shell and was closed with a screw. According to the bursting time desired, this plug was unscrewed before firing the rocket. The fuse composition was bored out to a specified height above the cone (i.e., the cone caused by the cavity in the propellant). To make drilling easier and prevent friction leading to premature ignition, boring bits were greased; grease was furnished in the artillerist's kit. A brass scale was available for ensuring that the correct depth of bore had been made. A funnel was used to pour bursting powder into the void left by the boring. The top plug was then screwed back on and the rocket was ready to fire.[27]

Typical guidelines for boring rocket fuses in the 1840s are as follows: "If the whole length of the fuse be left in the shell of the 24-pounder [10.8 kg] rocket, it may be expected to burst at about 3,300 yards [3,000 m], elevation 47 degrees. . . . If the rocket composition be bored into, to within 1.5 inches [3.8 cm] of the top of the cone, the shell may be expected to burst at about 700 yards [640 m], elevation 17 degrees."[28]

Igniters and Launchers

Congreve initially used slow match, specially primed paper rolled very tightly into a string, for rocket ignition similar to pyrotechnic fuse. But he felt this to be dangerous and inconvenient and devised a portfire, a thin iron stick about 3 feet (0.9 m) long with a pistol lock igniter on its end. Congreve wrote that it was "lighted in action by a flash of powder" from a pan. The portfire was carried in the rocket trooper's holster.[29]

FIGURE 4.7
The easiest technique of launching was the "ground volley," as in old Indian style (cf. Figure 1.5). This illustration dates to 1854, showing the central-stick pattern. (S.I. 79–7372)

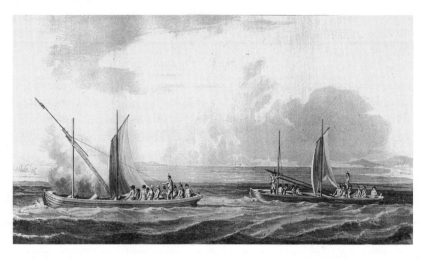

FIGURE 4.8

Congreve rockets were also fired from boats. The launcher was the same as used for bombard-ment on land, minus its legs. Rockets were stowed under tarpaulins or tanned hides. (S.I. A4462B)

Congreve's first rocket launchers were for sea service. They were 12-foot (3.6 m) ladder-like frames with loops into which were slung the rockets and could be mounted on boats. From these evolved large land-frame launchers, used at Waterloo and in other Napoleonic campaigns. Later, perhaps after the introduction of the centrally mounted stick rocket in 1815, these unwieldly frames were replaced by more convenient portable tubes set on adjustable tripods and weighing 20 pounds (9 kg) or more. In time, graduated slides for fixing the firing elevations were added and this became the basic style of rocket launcher internationally. Single- or multiple-tube launchers were sometimes mounted on carriages, boats, and ships. On vessels, the tubes were raised or lowered by ropes and pulleys.

Congreve also designed a small, iron-plate trough about a foot (0.3 m) in length and 6 pounds (2.7 kg) in weight that he called *bouche à feu* ("fire mouth"). It had four short legs "so that the rockets may be discharged parallel to the surface [of the ground] and close to it." The *bouche* anticipated the later trough for firing Hale rockets at low elevations. However, tubes on tripods became the standard means of launching Congreve rockets.

Occasionally, rockets were fired without any launchers at all. These "ground volleys" were rockets simply placed on level ground and lit, as the Indians used to do.[30]

Rocket-firing Ships

Undoubtedly Congreve's most spectacular launching platforms were his rocket-firing ships. These could be manned or unmanned "fireships." Fireships were usually abandoned ordinary vessles stripped of their useful furnishings, loaded with combustibles, and rigged with rockets. The ships were then towed to battle position, ignited, and cast adrift towards the enemy fleet. The rockets went off as the vessel burned. "I had an opportunity," said Congreve, "of trying this experiment in the attack of the French fleet in Basque Roads [in April 1809], and . . . the greatest confusion and terror was created by it in the enemy [camp]." He also said that 1,200 rockets were distributed in different parts of the riggings of the fireships, some "placed very high in the yard arms, others to the mastheads."[31]

According to an intercepted letter written by one of the French captains, Guilluame-Marcelin Proteau, rocket fireships caused little real damage on this

FIGURE 4.9

Detail of boat launcher shows loops for insertion of rockets (up to 12- or 18-pounders, or 5.4 or 8 kg). (S.I. 81–12155)

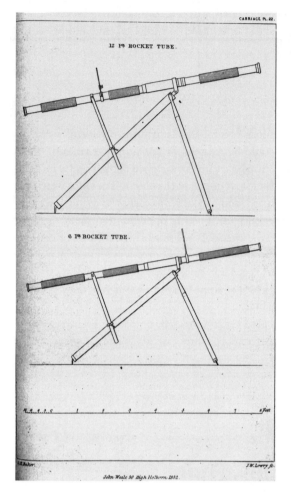

FIGURE 4.10
Standard 12-pounder and 6-pounder (5.4 and 2.7 kg) rocket launchers, 1853.
(S.I. 72–10665)

occasion: "I was in a position three and a half cables [650 m] from my squadron when I saw . . . something floating at the boom. Suddenly there was an explosion; a quantity of rockets, grenades and shells exploded in the air without doing us the least harm, although we were within half a cable's length [93 m]." Elsewhere in his dispatch, however, Captain Proteau noted that "the French could not make any counter movement or do the slightest harm [for fear of coming within range of the rockets]."[32]

In the same engagement were the rocket cutters *Nimrod* and *King George* and the rocket schooner *Whiting*. (Congreve himself came from England on the *Aetna* bomb vessel, towed by the copper-plated *Cleveland* transport carrying the rockets.) *Whiting, Nimrod,* and *King George* were not true rocket vessels but merely had frames installed. Shortly after the Basque Roads expedition, the first bonafide rocket ship appeared. This was the *Golago* (sometimes written as *Galgo* or *Golga*), possibly a captured Spanish vessel. It had been fitted at Deptford with twenty-one "rocket scuttles" in her broadside. The scuttles were square openings with little iron shutters that stayed closed when the rockets were not being deployed, protecting the rockets within from stray sparks and the effects of inclement weather and rough seas. The rockets were poised, complete with sticks, on ramps built between decks at 50°–55° discharge angles. As with boat-fired rockets, ignition was accomplished by a trigger line or lanyard leading to individual gun locks. Congreve offers no explanation as to how smoke and fire were deflected from inside the ship, nor other details. *Golago* served in the battle of Walcheren Island, an expedition off the Netherlands, in August 1809. Congreve was also present at this engagement and commanded five land frames.[33]

Congreve's second rocket ship was the *Erebus* of Fort McHenry fame. It

FIGURE 4.11
Rare photo of a rocket exercise launcher in the 1860s at Woolwich. (S.I. 79–1749)

FIGURE 4.12

Royal artillerists insert a large central-mounted Congreve or Boxer rocket in a firing tube.
(s.i. 79–1750)

was an 18- or 20-gun sloop originally built about 1808 and refitted like the
Golago with about twenty rocket scuttles for firing 24- or 32-pounders (10.8 or
14.5 kg). It retained its twenty guns. An existing log of *Erebus* shows that on
29 December 1813 Lord Castlereigh boarded her, perhaps to inspect the ship as
a potential rocket vessel. On 2 February 1814, "two commissioners of the Navy
and Colonel Congrave [sic] came aboard," and on 13 February *Erebus* docked in
Woolwich, where she was fitted for firing rockets. The work was completed by
late March, when she embarked for America. Congreve hoped for other rocket
ships, but his plans never reached maturity. Later rocket-firing vessels merely
carried tubes.[34]

Accoutrements and Carriages

Beginning in 1811, when Congreve began instructing artillerymen in the use of
rockets at Woolwich and Bagshot, he also began developing accoutrements for

rocketeers, tactics, and carriages. Since the men were part of the Royal Horse Artillery and Congreve did not wish to offend the fierce pride of the regiment, the dress of the rocket troops was kept the same. Their uniforms consisted of the identical blue jackets braided with yellow, with large semicircular crests of black bearskin on their helmets. However, their accoutrements were distinctive. Rocketeers carried leather holsters on both sides of their mounts for bearing two 12-pounder (5.4 kg) rockets each. The sticks fit into a strapped bundle supported in a bucket suspended from the flap of the saddle.[35]

Ammunition horses carried special packs for holding eighteen evenly distributed rockets fit into special pockets closed "by a flap . . . and padlocks." Other pockets contained "small stores, such as portfires, slow match &c." An adjoining leather case held a bundle of unassembled stick sections. The whole was protected from the weather by a "painted canvass." Besides rocket artillerymen, Congreve also proposed the formation of rocket infantry, one infantryman to carry a frame and the rest each carrying three rounds, though rockets were not turned over to this branch.[36]

FIGURE 4.13

Two other naval rocket uses. Top: unmanned fireships with combustibles and rockets set towards an enemy fleet. Bottom: manned rocket-firing ships, like the Golago, *shown here.*
(S.I. A4462D)

FIGURE 4.14
Model of side of the Golago,
*built around 1809. The ship
launched 32-pounder (14.5
kg) rockets. Model in the Rotunda Museum, Woolwich,
England. (S.I. 72–9880)*

By 1814, Congreve had built two types of transport carriages called "rocket cars." These were for 32- or 24-pounders (14.5 or 10.8 kg) (heavy car), the other for 18- or 12-pounder (8 or 5.4 kg) rockets (light car). The heavy cars conveyed forty rounds of 24-pounders (10.8 kg); the light cars conveyed sixty 12-pounders (5.4 kg) or fifty 18-pounders (8 kg). Each car was pulled by four horses, and each discharged "two rockets in a volley from a double iron plate trough," probably making them the world's first mobile rocket launchers. Troughs could be adjusted to different fighting positions without being detached from a carriage, but over the years carriage designs changed.[37]

Manufacture

Only rudimentary details of Congreve rocket manufacture survive. Official written manufacturing records may have disappeared during the heavy bombings of the Woolwich military works during both world wars. Fortunately for historians, Congreve rockets were captured by the French in 1809 (see Chapter 5) and they subsequently published some of their analyses, although the findings are mainly from chemists' points of view. The "Congreve Rocket Commission" appointed by the French Government in 1814 was composed mainly of chemists, the most prominent of whom was Jean-Pierre-Joseph d'Arcet. The French also conducted a number of experiments based upon the captured specimens, the findings amounting to almost 120 pages of illustrated manuscript notes, but these have not been examined. Nor have the highly detailed notes on Congreve rocket manufacture taken by a "mole" (informer) working in Woolwich and furnished to the Swedish Captain D.W. Silfverstophe for his 1829 report to the Swedish military. (The Silfverstophe report has only recently been translated into English by the Science Museum, London.) Thus, the two best available sources used here for details of authentic British Congreve rocket manufacture are d'Arcet's published "Notice sur les fusées incendiares de Congreve" ("Notice on Incendiary Congreve Rockets") of 1814 and the lengthy article "Of Iron Rockets" in the "Pyrotechny" section of David Brewster's *Edinburgh Encyclopedia* of 1830.[38]

By 1814, there were two 70 by 46 foot (21 × 14 m) rocket-driving houses at

FIGURE 4.15
Rocketeers were uniformed like the regular Horse Artillery, with minor modifications. Rocket sticks were carried in special leather scabbards. (S.I. 79–7376)

ROYAL ARTILLERY

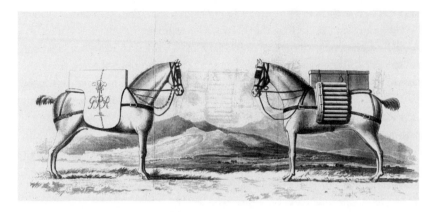

FIGURE 4.16

Transporting rocket ammunition. "GPR" stands for George Prince Regent (the Prince of Wales, later King George IV), who did much to promote rocket warfare. (S.I. A570A)

Woolwich, plus two 59 by 23 foot (18 × 7 m) workshops for finishing the rockets. On 18 March of that year, a steam engine made by Henry Maudslay, apparently of 8–10 horsepower, was installed and probably drove lathes used to make guidesticks and rammers for pressing in the propellant. The ramming process itself was still done by manual labor, for Congreve initially borrowed manufacturing techniques for making skyrockets. The principal differences were the substitution of metal for pasteboard for rocket motor cases; an increase in propellant proportions (many pounds instead of ounces); improved powder mixing (perhaps including Congreve's powder-granulating machine, installed at Woolwich in 1816); and the substitution of incendiary or explosive compositions in place of innocuous but beautiful "stars."[39]

Major steps in making a Congreve rocket included: (1) preparing the rocket tube; (2) brazing on a metal cup at one end; (3) ramming in a layer of clay down the capped end; (4) ramming in the propellant powder; (5) ramming in the "wadding" on top of the propellant; (6) drilling a hole through the clay and filling it with mealed gunpowder; (7) attaching a baseplate to the clay end; (8) attaching the warhead; and (9) painting the rocket and fixing on the guidestick.

To prepare the tube, soft sheet iron was first hammered around a mandrel for forming the rocket cylinder. A Congreve 24-pounder (10.8 kg) central-stick rocket of 1815 had a case thickness of 0.16 inch (0.4 cm). The outside diameter of the tube was 4.5 inches (11.4 cm). The length of the rocket, minus its head, was 22.87 inches (58 cm).[40]

The case was dovetailed in the longitudinal joint. Four rings or hoops of iron were then driven on the case to prevent it from splitting. An iron wire was also wound around it. The tube was then ready for brazing along the joint. (Before 1812, Congreve rockets were apparently only riveted; after this date they were brazed and riveted.)[41]

Following this, according to Brewster, the inside of the case was "lined with a single fold of cartridge paper pasted on." This was to protect the propellant from deteriorating due to moisture or rust. (Years later, the practice was to additionally apply anticorrosive paint to the lining paper.)[42]

At one end of the tube, which was to serve as the exhaust or "vent," an iron or copper cup was brazed on. A vent hole was drilled. The tube was then placed in the propellant rammer, called the "monkey press," a kind of pile-driver. The origin of the term "monkey press" is uncertain, but one etymological dictionary indicates that a drop-weight pile-driver called a "monkey" had been known since at least the mid-eighteenth century.[43]

FIGURE 4.17

Left to right: *Volley carriage with thirty-four tubes; 6-pounder (2.7 kg) volley carriage with ten tubes holding seventy-two rounds; and 12-pounder (5.4 kg) volley carriage with ten tubes holding forty rounds. In Rotunda Museum, Woolwich, England.* (S.I. A1126B)

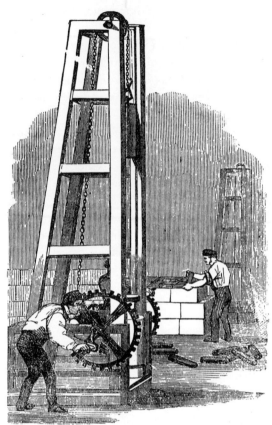

WAR-ROCKET MAKING.—THE MONKEY-DRIVING PROCESS.

FIGURE 4.18

Prior to the introduction of Hale rockets, war rockets were manufactured using the laborious "monkey press," a heavy weight that was lifted then dropped on wooden rocket rammers in successive blows to ram in the powder. (S.I. A4671)

The similar, manually operated "monkey" rocket press was the most important part of the manufacture. It was also slow and inefficient. On several occasions Congreve recommended an alternate means of powering it to the Board of Ordnance. On 27 November 1810 he wrote: "I have before stated that a very great saving would arise in the manufacture of the rocket, if the force of water or steam were introduced instead of manual labour." His plea was ignored. On 11 November 1813 he tried again and even recommended a 10-horsepower steam engine, but was again unheeded. It was not until four decades later that the conversion to steam (i.e., hydraulic) presses was finally made (see Chapter 11).[44]

In Brewster's account of rocket making in the 1830s, he starts with a description of the mold for holding the rocket tubes: "a very different apparatus is required from those used for paper rockets. A block, or more, of tough oak or elm, must be provided, in which semi-cylinders are cut, of such sizes as to

FIGURE 4.19

Rocketry was not without accidents. A large explosion of Hales occurred at Woolwich Arsenal in September 1883. Other arsenal rocket explosions took place in 1830, 1842, and 1855. (S.I. 77–14260)

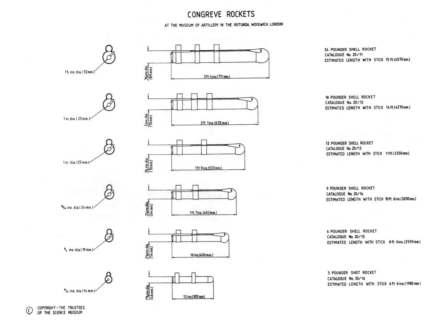

CONGREVE ROCKETS

AT THE MUSEUM OF ARTILLERY IN THE ROTUNDA, WOOLWICH, LONDON

FIGURE 4.20

Dimensional drawings of Congreve rockets, 3- to 24-pounders. Specimens in the Rotunda, Royal Artillery Museum, Woolwich, England. Drawings by John West, Science Museum, London, 1987. (S.I. 89–16662; courtesy Dr. John Becklake, The Science Museum, London)

take in each diameter . . . to each scale of rocket. . . . Besides these there are required all the tools of a brazier and worker in sheet-iron, such as scissors, hammers, anvils, files, vices, drills, &c."[45]

"The first operation in filling the rocket," Brewster continued, was to put the tube "into the mold . . . then to drive down . . . a layer of fine clay, about half an inch [1.2 cm] thick. This is carefully rammed, first by light and then by harder blows, the workmen turning the rammer round frequently till it is beaten as hard as a stone." The clay served as a guard to the vent, preventing the metal from being destroyed by "the burning torrent of fire." The tube was then removed from the mold, and a funnel-shaped hole was bored through the clay disc, equal to the diameter of the vent hole.[46] Without realizing it, Congreve and other early rocket makers were forming a crude flaring nozzle, permitting exhaust gases to flow more evenly and efficiently out of the rocket than if the vent were a simple hole.

The tube was returned to the monkey mold for propellant loading, which was done by a series of metal spindles and wooden rammers, in the same manner ordinary skyrockets had been made for centuries. A tapering spindle on a stand was first placed down into the base of the mold cylinder. The rocket casing was fit over the spindle so the spindle's needle pierced through the clay vent hole. The ramming was then done. Eight or ten different-sized rammers with varying proportions of conical holes were used successively to hold down the propellant over the spindle during the driving by the drop weight of the press. Gradually, a cone-shaped cavity was formed throughout two-thirds of the driven propellant.[47]

The old pyrotechnists called the cavity the "soul" of the rocket because, for reasons they could not adequately explain, it seemed to be the source of the

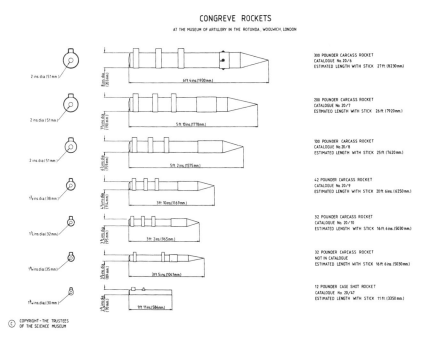

FIGURE 4.21

Dimensional drawings of Congreve rockets, 12- to 300-pounders. Specimens also in the Rotunda, Royal Artillery Museum, Woolwich, England. Drawings by John West, Science Museum, London, 1987. (S.I. 89–16661; courtesy Dr. John Becklake, The Science Museum, London)

rocket's flight. In a sense it was, since the cavity exposed a large burning surface, resulting in a greater initial thrust than if the rocket were driven solid. This ensured sufficient energy in the weak propellant for a good takeoff, provided everything else was done right.

Over the centuries, tradition-bound pyrotechnists developed elaborate rules as to how many blows were required for each rammer and rocket size. Congreve and his associates liberally borrowed these methods and expanded upon them. For example, according to Brewster, "As soon as the composition is settled a little . . . four or five blows with the monkey must be given from a height of five or six inches [12.7–15.2 cm]. . . . It is then ready for the full force of the engine; and the monkey being raised to six feet [1.8 m], the composition is to receive sixty strokes." In his leaflet *General View of a Complete Course of Experiments* of about 1810, Congreve adds another rare detail of this important phase of the manufacturing: "One man is allowed to attend each mold, and four to drive, taking alternate spells . . . and 45 spells make a rocket—each rocket, therefore, requires 2 hr. 38 min. for driving . . . 3 rockets may without difficulty be made in 8 hr."[48]

"The last operation in driving," wrote Brewster, was "to ram the wadding at the end of the composition . . . to prevent it from blowing out at the head before it is burned out." Brewster prescribed two methods. One was to "lay a coating of clay about three quarters of an inch [1.9 cm] thick on the top of it" then cover with an iron plate with a hole in its center and fix in place by two pins riveted through on the outside of the case. Next, a hole was drilled through the center of the clay and filled with mealed powder, or fuse composition. The powder within the center of the clay enabled the warhead composition to be ignited following the burnout of the propellant. The second method was to place a similarly perforated and filled cylinder of beechwood in the center of the clay.[49]

French chemist d'Arcet found in his captured 1809 Congreve specimen that the insert was yellow or "stove clay" and had a weight of 6.3 ounces (181 g) and a thickness of about 0.7 inch (2 cm). Also, on this clay, he said, "there is a little bitumen scattered." Congreve apparently borrowed a practice used in making artillery shells. The bitumen (coal grains) provided a tighter fit for the clay disc, similar to the way bitumen was used to ensure a tight fit when packing shell fuses.[50]

Following this procedure, the baseplate was attached. This operation varied according to the type of rocket. In central-stick models, the base was closed by an iron disk welded on. The disk was a baseplate with a threaded socket into which the guidestick was screwed and had five equidistant exhaust holes around its circumference. The latter were 0.5 inch (1.2 cm) in diameter each. In the old side-stick rocket, a baseplate with a single vent in the middle was welded on.[51]

Next, warheads were attached. These differed widely but those for incendiary Congreve rockets, according to Brewster, consisted of a plate-iron cylinder six inches long "with two inches more for gores on which the cone is fixed."[52]

D'Arcet noted that after the conical incendiary warhead was snugly fit into the propellant tube by means of these gores, fifty-five turns of tarred string were carefully wrapped around the joint "in a solid manner." Brewster added another interesting detail as to how warhead and bodies were attached: "This is done by means of a hammer and a wooden block, with a hollow cone in it, made to receive the conical part of the head."[53] Brewster also says that four nails or wooden screws fixed the head firmly on. The upper part of the rocket was further secured by a winding of twine, then covered with pitch.[54]

As a chemist, d'Arcet took particular interest in the warhead and its incendiary composition. He noted six small, slightly flared holes around the conical warhead. These holes were for issuing fire from the incendiary. According to Brewster, they were easily formed with small spindles, when the newly prepared combustible matter was "still soft."[55]

The incendiary composition was called "rock fire" because it hardened after its preparation. D'Arcet and other French chemists took great pains to discover its formula, as did the Americans during the War of 1812. The Russians, too, examined it from a sample rocket they obtained in 1813. French analysis indicated a formula of resin, 20%; saltpeter, 54%; sulfur, 18%; antimony, 5%; and inert or other additives, 3%.[56]

French analysis of Congreve rocket propellent revealed saltpeter, 58%; sulfur, 18%; carbon (charcoal), 22%; and additives, 2%. This formula agreed with Brewster's, who, however, said that one to half an ounce (about 42.5 g) of turpentine oil was added to each pound (0.4 kg) of the propellant composition. Details of the manufacture of other Congreve warheads are given neither by Brewster nor d'Arcet.[57]

Following the attachment of the warhead, according to d'Arcet, the "entire rocket was then painted with oil paint with a bluish iron grey color."[58]

The final step in Congreve rocket manufacture was fixing the guidestick.

Brewster said this was not done "till the rocket is about to be used." In side-stick rockets, the guidestick was secured with sheet-iron or copper strips. In some extant specimens, the strips are riveted to the rocket case. In central-stick rockets, the sticks were simply screwed to the baseplate flanges prior to firing.[59]

Linear dimensions of Congreve rockets are as rare as manufacturing details, but in 1987, for the first time, dimensioned drawings by John West of the Science Museum in London were made of thirteen models of Congreve rockets at the Royal Artillery Museum and published in the *Journal of the British Interplanetary Society*. The drawings are presented here (Figures 4.20 and 4.21) with the kind permission of John Becklake and Peter Turvey of the Science Museum and the British Interplanetary Society.[60]

Brewster provides further dimensions. Average weights of empty 24- to 32-pounder (10.8–14.5 kg) Congreve rocket cases were 6 pounds (2.7 kg); weights of the empty cases and warheads combined were 10.25–15 pounds (4.6–6 kg). Loaded weights of the rockets, minus their sticks, varied from 17–33 pounds (7.7–15 kg). Stick weights were 5.5–10.5 pounds (2.5–4.7 kg) for the same calibers.[61]

Congreve rockets remained in the British armament until 1864 when they were supplanted by Boxer's pattern, invented by General Edward M. Boxer, Comptroller of the Royal Laboratory. The Boxer rocket was essentially an improved Congreve. Its main feature was a stronger rocket case made by repositioning and reducing the number of vents to three. Boxer also employed a stronger rocket composition.[62]

The Troops

Another important phase of Congreve's rocket system was the establishment of rocket-armed troops. Ironically, although the Royal Navy baptized Congreve's rockets in battle, no official Naval troop organization was ever formed. In the Boulogne attacks of 1805 and 1806 (and presumably other early rocket actions), Royal Marine Artillerymen were temporarily assigned to or volunteered to handle the new, experimental weapon.

Following the bombardment of Copenhagen in 1807, the Master General of the Ordnance, Lord Chatham, ordered an examining committee of field officers of the Royal Artillery to report on the efficacy of the weapon. Their findings were positive, though the original document has not been found. They concluded that the Congreve rocket could become "a powerful auxilliary to the present system of artillery." Upon this recommendation, several Royal Artillerymen were trained to use the rockets. Some of the men apparently were sent to Sweden in the summer of 1808 as part of Lieutenant-General Sir John Moore's expedition to help in the fight against Napoleon. Rockets were sent in the *Ceres* transport to the Swedish port of Gothenburg for Moore, but the despotic and unbalanced Swedish king, Gustavus IV, proposed grandiose schemes of conquest to the English general and imprisoned him when he disagreed with his plans. Moore escaped, disguising himself as a peasant. The *Ceres* had not been allowed to unload and was sent back. Moore's army then departed for Iberia and apparently it was here, during the Peninsular campaign in 1808–12, especially in Portugal, that the first Royal Artillery rocket troop first saw action on the battlefield. This group of men, which Congreve called a "Field Rocket Brigade," was really an experimental artillery unit of two noncommissioned officers and twelve gunners under the command of First Lieutenant William Fullerton Lindsay-Carnegie.[63]

The history of the first official Rocket Troop of the Royal Horse Artillery begins in September 1811. The Board of Ordnance placed a detachment of thirty-two Royal Horse Artillerymen, under Second-Captain Richard Bogue, at Congreve's disposal for further integrating rockets into the Artillery. This detachment experimented with the weapon both at Woolwich and at Bagshot, helping Congreve refine his system for eventual use by mounted or horse artillery.[64]

In May 1813, the detachment was inspected by a committee of Royal Artillery officers who recommended that it be tried in combat. On 7 June 1813 came orders designating Bogue's unit The Rocket Brigade. Before being sent overseas to Germany, more troopers were added. When the brigade departed Ramsgate on 11 June, it consisted of one captain (Bogue); two first lieutenants; two sergeants; an assistant surgeon; five corporals; a trumpeteer; a wheeler; two collar (horse harness) makers; three farriers (blacksmiths); five bombardiers; twenty-four drivers; and eighty-two gunners. An additional sixteen men followed and left by way of Woolwich, making a total of 144 men plus eight officer's horses and ninety-seven troopers' horses.[65]

The distinguished services of Bogue and his men have already been covered. Bogue died a hero at the "Battle of Nations" at Leipzig in 1813. The Brigade also fought well at the battles of Göhrde, Wittenburg, Frederiksfort, and Glückstadt.

On 3 October, another Royal Artillery detachment trained in firing rockets debarked from Woolwich. This group, called the Rocket Company, consisted of almost sixty men under Second-Captain Henry Boyer Lane.

Lane's Company was sent by the Prince Regent directly to the army of Marshal, the Duke of Wellington, in France. The Regent personally helped to organize the early Artillery rocket troops. With only three days of training in firing rockets before they left, Lane's Company showed poorly at first, but afterwards did its share to enhance the reputation of Congreve rockets at the crossings of the Bidassoa and Ardour rivers in chasing the French out of Spain. Lane's rocketeers fought gallantly at the battle of Toulouse, but when sent to America for service during the War of 1812, they did not fare as well, especially at the battle of New Orleans.[66]

Shortly after Lane left for France, another body of artillerymen was organized to use rockets. This group, under Captain William G. Elliot, received its instructions at Woolwich in December 1813. By then, it was apparent that a more formal structure was needed. By a General Order of 18 December 1813, the Regent "was pleased to approve . . . two troops to the establishment of the Royal Artillery to be attached to the service of rockets." A further order of 24 December 1813 clarified the nature of these troops. As of 1 January 1814, Elliot's and Lane's detachments collectively became the 1st Rocket Troop. On the same date, Bogue's old detachment, now commanded by his surviving First-Lieutenant, Thomas Fox-Strangeways, became the 2nd Rocket Troop. This Troop remained in France as part of the Army of Occupation after Waterloo in 1815 and did not return to England until January 1816.

On 4 July 1816, the British Army was reduced, including rocket troops. One rocket unit was to remain; it was not specified which one, causing no end of controversy among Royal Artillery historians. Since the 1st Troop was already below strength, it was the one that was completely reduced, or rather, abolished. Some of the men were transferred to the 2nd Troop, including Captain Elliot, who became its commander.[67]

This troop existed for many years but was abolished as I Troop, Royal Horse Artillery, in 1847. However, a Royal Army directive of 16 June of that year ordered that "each of the Troops in Great Britain shall have a Rocket Section as a part of its equipment . . . with a view of extending the knowledge of the rocket service." This system was strengthened in 1858 when rocket training became part of regular gunnery courses; before this, troops evidentally received rocket-firing instruction in the field. Further, Army regulations for 1864–65 called for one rocket carriage of unspecified caliber to be assigned to different horse artillery and field batteries.[68]

Thus, instead of a disbandment of rocket troops in 1847, there was a de facto expansion in which Congreve rockets (and, later Hale rockets) came to be more widely supplied than before. Earlier, Congreve had drawn up elaborate schemes for the establishment of "Royal Rocket Troops." A later champion of Congreve rockets, writing in *Colburn's United Service Magazine* in 1852, went even further and proposed the establishment of a rocket battalion. In practice, the British Army and Navy never followed Congreve's rigid organization plan, which would have been vulnerable to changes and reductions anyway. The flexible system that did evolve was one reason why the British "Rocket Service," as it may be called, enjoyed a long life, even in the face of rapid progress in the development of other artillery after the Crimean War. Another reason was that the Rocket Service greatly benefited from Britain's expanding empire with its attendant colonial wars. In short, the rocket was beginning to become very much a colonial weapon for reasons such as its lightness and cheapness.[69]

In addition to the wider distribution of rockets throughout the artillery, the Royal Navy deposited stores of Congreve rockets almost everywhere the Union Jack flew. At the first sign of an uprising, or colonial expedition, rockets were taken out of storage—albeit sometimes misbehaving because of local weather conditions or long-term storage—and turned over to the artillery or Royal Marine Artillery unit on duty.

Table 3 is not a completely accurate reflection of the extent of the British Rocket Service overseas, since rockets (and attendant equipment) were also sent with Army and Navy expeditionary forces departing from England.

Rockets and rocket boats were also assigned to ships. The larger rocket-firing vessels *Erebus* and *Golago* evidently saw service only during the War of 1812 and the Napoleonic campaigns, though rocket-armed steamers and other ships were employed long after the Napoleonic period (notably in the Crimean War) and carried their own rocket ammunition. Nonetheless, by the 1850s the 32-pounder (14.5 kg) rocket was replaced by the 24-pounder (10.8 kg) as the largest caliber in overseas service. Hong Kong was a major depot for the rockets and South Africa was the rocket-supply region for that continent.

Assessments of Congreve Rockets

Advantages of rockets vis-à-vis conventional artillery claimed by Congreve and others up to this period may be enumerated as follows: (1) competitive ranges to field guns (early to mid-nineteenth century); (2) portability; (3) absence of recoil; (4) impressive physical and psychological effects; (5) rapidity of discharge and operation (with minimal preparation, like screwing in sticks, rockets were always ready to fire, whereas muzzle-loaded guns required

Table 3

Serviceable Congreve Rockets in Storage during the 1850s

Foreign Stations	Congreve Rockets				
	24-pr.	12-pr.	6-pr.	3-pr.	Totals
Bermuda	120	72			192
Cape Town (S. Africa)		171	329	27	527
Columbo (Ceylon)		10			10
Fort Beaufort (S. Africa)		222	334	190	746
Gambia (W. Africa)	66	282	300	258	906
Gibraltar		80		350	
Graham's Town (S. Africa)		99	439	249	787
Halifax (Canada)		100	100		200
(British) Honduras			93		93
Hong Kong	3,689	2,787	2,054	1,980	10,510
Jamaica	83		76		159
Kingstown			300		300
King Williams Town (S. Africa)			355	17	372
Mauritius		100	100	70	270
Montreal	200	400	180	736	1,516
Natal		483	146		629
Malta		28			28
Quebec	300	1,271	107	222	1,900
Sierra Leone	21				21
Simon's Town (S. Africa)		14		620	634
Sydney	99	84			183
Trincomali (Ceylon)	542	195		156	893
Totals	5,120	6,105	5,330	4,671	21,226

Source: From an unpublished list, Army of Great Britain, Royal Artillery Institution Library (Woolwich, 1859).

loading, sponging, and priming with every round); (6) simplicity of operation and maintenance; and (7) low cost vis-à-vis field guns and shells (the 32-pounder rocket cost £1 1s. 11d., said Congreve, compared to £1 2s. 7d. per 10-inch mortar round—irrespective of the mortar piece or mortar bed, while a Congreve launcher cost only £5). For most of these reasons, especially its light weight and firepower, Congreve rightly saw the rocket as the "soul of artillery without its encumbrance." Congreve did not mention that some disadvantages of the rocket included (1) unpredictability and sometimes erratic behavior; (2) inaccuracy; (3) susceptibility to misfiring or even explosions after long-term storage, especially in extreme climates; (4) liability to misfire when transported long distances overland; and (5) slow, often dangerous and inefficient manufacture that was still largely done by hand. As we saw, some of these problems were due to the poor performance, handling, and storage characteristics of gunpowder in which saltpeter was hygroscopic (i.e., it picked up moisture, which made it cake and burn improperly).[70]

Nonetheless, Congreve's rockets received approbation from the most distinguished generals of the age. Marshal Marmont, Duke of Ragusa, former aide-de-camp to Napoleon and Inspector General of the French Artillery, extolled Congreve rockets at length in his classic *Spirit of Military Institutions* (1845). "I repeat it," he concluded, "Congreve rockets must produce a revolution in the art of war; and they will assure success and glory to the genius who shall have been the first to comprehend their use." Marmont's words were not fulfilled, but his tone typified the clamor by many other nations to follow Britain's suit and introduce Congreve rockets into their own armies.[71]

CHAPTER 5

European Nations with Major Rocket Establishments

From the moment of their debut in battle, Congreve rockets created a minor sensation within international military circles. Apart from their advantages in portability, firepower, range, and low cost contrasted with conventional firearms, they possessed a colorful mystique due to their novelty. Though rockets faced severe criticism by those who saw them as unreliable or "uncivilized," most military men recognized their usefulness in tactical situations and believed that the weapon showed great promise. Some glorified the rocket, characterizing it as a "romantic" mode of warfare. The fact that England, then the most powerful nation outside Napoleonic France, originated Congreve rockets greatly enhanced this mystique. Hence, soon after its introduction, many other nations sought to emulate the British in the creation of their own rockets and elite rocket-armed troops.

A fierce competition developed, faintly presaging the missile race of the next century. Despite Congreve's avowed secrecy, as typified in the preface to his 1807 *Concise Account of the . . . Rocket System* in which he said: "I have cautiously avoided any disclosure which might lead to a discovery of the interior structure . . . of the rocket," the projectiles became widely adopted and the technology global. The spread was effected several ways. Some countries engaged professional pyrotechnists to begin making rockets from scratch. In other instances, countries sold or gave them to their allies. There were also individuals claiming to have been former employees of Congreve who offered to sell the "secret" of rockets. "Dud" (i.e., unburned) Congreve rockets were occasionally recovered in battle by the enemy; these were analyzed, then duplicated.[1]

Regardless of the source of other rocket systems, Congreve's priority was recognized and the term *Congreve rocket* became an accepted generic for *war rocket* throughout Europe.

Denmark

Not surprisingly, the history of Danish rocketry in the last century began with the spectacular British bombardment of Copenhagen in 1807. Second-lieutenant Andreas Anton Frederick Schumacher, Danish Army Engineers, was fascinated with the unburned Congreve rocket he found, and in 1809 he attempted to copy it. To ensure secrecy, a workshop/laboratory was erected on the remote island of Hjelm, in the Kattegat Sea. Danish King Frederick

FIGURE 5.1
Lieutenant Andreas Schumacher (1782–1823), Danish Army Engineers, established the Danish Rocket Corps and developed its rocket ammunition. The Danish unit was the first on the European continent. (S.I. A5143A; courtesy Tøjhusmuseet, Copenhagen)

FIGURE 5.2

In 1816, the Danish Raket
Corpset *wore their own
distinctive uniforms.*
*(S.I. 71–1505; courtesy
Tøjhusmuseet,
Copenhagen)*

supported the research and assigned several men, possibly convicts, to assist.[2]

By 1811, Schumacher developed his own "rocket system," which was comparable to Congreve's. The Dane said his rockets were even more portable and powerful. A rocket production plant was established at Frederiksvaerk and a "Rocket Flotilla," consisting of rocket-armed lugger boats and a schooner, was stationed at Isefjorden. Soldiers and sailors were taught how to operate the rockets, but not how to make them. Like Congreve, Schumacher was fanatical about keeping the "secret" of his rocket construction.[3]

On 16 February 1813, newly promoted Captain Schumacher was made head of the new Danish *Raketkompagniet* ("Rocket Company"). It was manned by eighty-five men, including four officers, eight noncommissioned officers, a trumpeter, and seventy-two privates. The men wore a distinctive uniform of dark green with grey trousers, light blue collars, and yellow buttons.[4]

There was little opportunity to try the rockets in combat. In the spring of 1813, however, a few were fired from Langeland Island against British men-of-war. No other engagement is known, but the Danes continued to maintain their rocket organization and even upgraded it to a *Raket Corpset* ("Rocket Corps") by a royal decree of 17 March 1816. At full strength this unit consisted of 114 men. The original company uniform was retained with some modifications.

Schumacher commanded both the corps and the flotilla, which created service frictions comparable to Congreve's difficulties as a civilian in charge of artillery and naval rocketeers. Some of the resentment was caused by the severe discipline imposed by Schumacher and by his mania for secrecy. He entrusted his "secrets" to no one and never saw fit to write down instructions. Workers were told only of the phase of the operation that concerned them individually. If the work was poor, part of a man's payroll was deducted. Schumacher himself labored so hard in perfecting his system that he became physically and mentally exhausted. He died on 3 January 1823, at the age of 41.[5]

From our viewpoint, Schumacher's rockets differed little from Congreve's. They varied from 1.5–3.5 inches (3.8–8.8 cm) in caliber and carried 6- to 24-pounder (2.7–10 kg) shells, incendiaries, or grapeshots. Effective ranges were from 400–1,000 meters (about 400–1,100 yd), though the rockets could cover two to three times these distances. Launchers were trestles or tubes that were sometimes mounted on four-wheel carriages. Schumacher also invented an eight-tube carriage launcher pulled by four horses and known as the "rocket organ."[6]

Following Schumacher's death, the command of the *Corpset* was assumed by artillery major Andreas Brun Meyer. By this time, the strength of the organization had grown to 132 men. From time to time improvements were made, necessitated by rapid advances in conventional artillery. During 1831–33, Meyer and Danish artillery captain Jacob Scavenius Fibiger conducted an ambitious program of seventy-two experiments, resulting in the development of an improved grenade, battlefield illumination, finned and rotation-stabilized rockets, and even rockets meant to fire underwater. Nevertheless, in 1842 Denmark's King Christian VIII decreed that the standing army be changed to a militia. The *Raket Corpset* was thus abolished, although part of it survived as a small auxiliary unit. It remained relatively inactive for a few years, until Denmark's war with Prussia over the sovereignty of Schleswig-Holstein in 1848–50. Danish rockets appeared at the battles of Frederica and Isted on 6 July and 25 July 1849, respectively. They were probably the last Danish war rockets of the nineteenth century. At the close of the conflict, most of the

FIGURE 5.3

Danish war rockets from about 1848, of 3.5-inch (8.9 cm) caliber. Left: a rocket with its "fire cap" or incendiary warhead detached. Right: one with a 24-pounder (10.8 kg) explosive shell. (S.I. 71–1507; courtesy Tøjhusmuseet, Copenhagen)

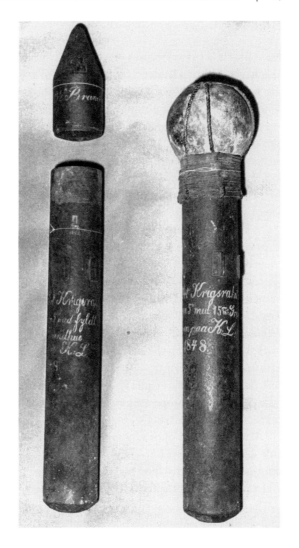

Danish army units disbanded and the remaining rocket section was abolished, though in the 1850s the Danes may have procured Hale rockets for experiments (Copenhagen's Tøjhusmuseet has a Hale rocket, but there is no record of its origin). Nonetheless, judging from military journals, in the latter half of the century the Danish Army was far more critical of Congreve rockets and no new rocket organizations were created.[7]

Austria

Austrian rocket development was directly influenced by the Danes. At its height, the Austrian *Kriegs-Raketen Anstalt* ("War Rocket Establishment") was the largest and most sophisticated rocket organization on the European continent, far surpassing in size its parent, the Danish *Corpset*.

As early as 1808, under the orders of the Austrian artillery, Chief Fireworks Master Anton Mager fabricated twenty-four sheet-iron-cased war rockets, similar to those fired by the English against Copenhagen. Mager's rockets were successful in tests on the Simmeringer Heide (Heath) before Archduke Karl, but nothing further was done until the pioneering work of Major Vincenz Augustin.[8]

This able artillery officer (later made a baronet, entitling him to the aristocratic addition of "von" to his name) first encountered Congreve rockets when he witnessed Bogue's rocketeers at Leipzig in 1813. Following the Allied victory and peace of Paris in May 1814, Augustin was sent to the Netherlands, France, and England on diplomatic missions. While in London, he visited the Royal Arsenal at Woolwich and may have met Congreve, but was refused manufacturing details. Subsequently, Augustin's superiors sent him to Denmark, which was then the only other country possessing a war rocket system. This mission resulted from negotiations at the highest level, including the Austrian minister of foreign affairs, Clemens Metternich, political architect of post-Napoleonic Europe. Augustin traveled under an assumed name to ensure the secrecy of the mission.[9]

Only through political pressure did Schumacher finally consent to provide details of his work to the Austrians, though he would only convey the information verbally. Upon his return to Vienna in March 1815, Augustin was given a Royal Grant to produce Austria's own rocket system and was approved by Denmark's King Frederick VI. The negotiations had not been in vain, for as early as May 1815, Augustin reported that a rocket laboratory staffed by forty-six men had been established at the military works of Wiener-Neustadt, a few kilometers southwest of Vienna. Progress continued rapidly. By the end of May, the completed rocket battery was eqipped with 2,400 rockets of different calibers. By the middle of 1815 the Austrian Army's first *Raketenbatterie* (Rocket Battery) had already been formed. Four new companies of artificers were created for servicing the rocket battery. The troops were distinguished from the regular artillery and bombardiers by their own uniforms, which were similar to those of General Staff officers. The rocketeers wore dark green trousers and jackets with black collars and cuffs with yellow buttons. Collars

FIGURE 5.4
Artillery General Vincenz
von Augustin (1780–1859),
the Austrian rocket pioneer,
developed his own rocket sys-
tem. He also commanded the
Austrian rocket corps from
1814 to 1838. (S.I. A4762B)

were adorned with flaming brass shell emblems and hats were of the shako style with shell emblems.[10]

Augustin was commandant of what came to be called the *Kriegs-Raketen Anstalt* ("War Rocket Establishment") at Wiener-Neustadt until 1838. He never commanded individual rocket batteries, but he saw his rocket troops fight for the first time at the siege of Huningue, on the left bank of the Rhine, in Alsace, France, during the summer of 1815. The siege was brief and marked one of the last engagements of the Napoleonic wars. Austrian rockets were then of 2-, 3-, and 4-*zoll* calibers (a *zoll* equalled about an inch, or 2.5 cm). Eighteen munitions carts were available. Augustin continually improved his rocket system, which in time warranted being named the "Augustin system." The *Anstalt* also grew and in 1817 was renamed the *Feuerworks-Corps* ("Fireworks Corps"). By

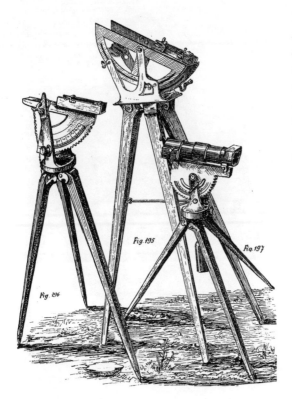

FIGURE 5.5
*Austrian rocket launchers,
Augustin system.* Center:
*old-style launcher with iron
sight.* Left: *12-pounder
(5.4 kg) launcher for stick
rockets.* Right: *an Austrian
stickless rocket launcher from
the late 1860s.* (S.I. A5070B)

1825, with the addition of new buildings, Wiener-Neustadt became known as *Raketendorf,* literally "Rocket Town."[11]

One reason for the growth of Austria's rocket establishment as well as its army in general was that, like England, it greatly expanded its empire after the fall of Napoleon. The Austro-Hungarian Empire stretched from Bohemia, Croatia, and Slavonia in Eastern Europe to Lombardy and other Italian states in the south. These holdings required a large standing army and a light, portable artillery capable of quick transport and easy deployment in a variety of terrains. Rockets fit the need very well, especially during later uprisings in some of the most mountainous country in Europe.

Noncolonial campaigns also occurred. In 1821 Austrian *raketeurs* helped put down an uprising in Naples, and reportedly in 1823 an Austrian frigate was armed with rockets when it bombarded the Moroccan city of Mequine in a punitive expedition against Riff pirates. In 1838, Austrian rocket teams successfully helped to quell a minor Serbian revolt in Montenegro. Two years later, a *Raketeur* detachment accompanied a small Austrian fleet assisting the British in the bombardment of Beirut, Syria (now the capital of Lebanon).[12]

Meanwhile, Augustin's career advanced rapidly. By 1831 he was a major-general and in 1838 he was made a field-marshall-lieutenant. He became the general director of artillery in 1849, and in the same year received his baronetcy. Augustin's rocket system was so well admired that in 1831 the Swedes signed a private contract with Martin Westermayr, a former pyrotechnist, who had worked under Augustin, to help them start their own rocket establishment. In 1852, the Swiss adopted the Austrian system outright, turning down the efforts of one of their own countrymen. Contractual arrangements for the "Augustin system" were also made with Bavaria, Württemberg, and one or two other German states.[13]

Although Austrian rocketry was widely exported, at home a rigorous secrecy was maintained. The Kaiser himself made periodic inspections of Wiener-Neustadt's rocket works and decreed that no outsider should be admitted without his personal consent. The men of the laboratory swore to reveal nothing.[14]

In 1831, the Fireworks Corps began a major expansion with the addition

FIGURE 5.6

Austrian rockets. Fig. 198 is a stick rocket with shell, Schumacher pattern; Fig. 199 is an illumination head for a spin-stabilized model; Fig. 200 shows a grape shot warhead, rotation model; Fig. 201 is the first Austrian Hale model; and Fig. 202 is a rotation rocket with 6-pound (2.7 kg) hollow shell. (S.I. A5070C)

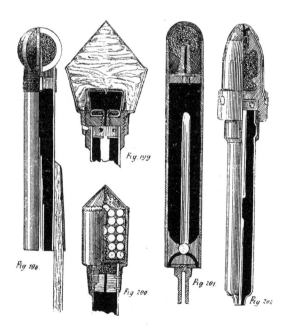

of new companies. Ultimately, in 1850–1851, the entire organization was converted to the *K.K. Raketeur Corps* ("Royal Imperial Rocket Corps") with about fifteen *Raketenbatterien* (one for each army corps) in addition to an ordnance company, a staff company, three reserve companies, and a staff school. An even larger *Raketeur Regiment* was formed in 1854. It consisted of eighteen batteries that in time of war could be expanded to twenty, with a slight reduction in the relative size of each battery. Augustin's establishment thus had swollen from roughly 100 men in 1815 to about 4,000 in 1854, becoming far larger than the rocket force established in Congreve's own country, England. As early as 1829, the Austrian rocket establishment totaled 475 troops. In comparison, the rocket establishments of other nations usually consisted of one special rocket battery or corps of about 160 men.[15]

The sweeping organizational changes in the Austrian rocket establishment were largely in response to the bloody Italian and Hungarian revolutions of 1848–49. *Raketenbatterien* were already stationed in Venice-Lombardy at the

FIGURE 5.7
Austrian war rocket practice (stick rockets) fired in Italy during Austro-Italian War of 1848.
(S.I. A773)

outbreak of the revolution. According to Major H. Reisner, the Rocket Armament Commandant during the Italian campaigns, Austrian rockets proved to be invaluable in the mountain engagements of Curtatone, Custoza, Monte Castello, Pastrengo, Aquilla, and Udine, and in the bombardment of Venice. They could be brought to spots accessible only to foot soldiers. Austrian rockets also did very well in Hungary, particularly at Petervasar and Szegedin (Szeged). Excellent service was also obtained from the rockets at Temesvar (or Timisoara), now in west Rumania.[16]

In 1859, another Austro-Sardinian war flared up, but von Augustin did not live to see his troops in action again. He died on 6 March 1859 at the age of seventy-nine. (His position was assumed in 1860 by Major-General Friedrich von Schmidt, a former captain-lieutenant in the old Fireworks Corps.)

The Austrian Army faced military reverses in the Italian campaign, particularly at the battles of Magenta and Solferino. Austrian artillerymen must have learned the value of rifled guns since France, allied with Italy, successfully used old bronze muzzle-loaders converted to grooved rifling.[17]

The Austrians thereafter followed the French practice of modifying their muzzle-loaders, but still maintained their faith in rocket weapons. It is true that the *Raketeur-Regiment* was reduced to twelve *Batterien* in 1860, but this was apparently just an economy measure. Furthermore, the Englishman William Hale, with his knack for timeliness, approached the Austrians in 1858 with his more accurate stickless rockets, and after several trials (presided over by Schmidt) succeeded in selling them the secrets of his projectiles as well as his hydraulic presses. A switch was made to stickless rockets but at the same time rifled guns were in the ascendancy and in 1863 the *Regiment* was given new, light 3-pound (1.4 kg) steel rifled mountain guns to augment its overall firepower. With the guns came a change in name to *Raketeur-und Gebirgs-Artillerie-Regiment* ("Rocketeer and Mountain Artillery Regiment") and a reduction to eight *Raketenbatterien*. In effect, rifled guns and rifled rockets were competing with each other in the same unit.[18]

However, the real showdown for the Austrian rocket establishment came in 1866 in the Austro-Prussian War. Nine *Raketenbatterien* (two at the start) took to the field, but they were no match for the powerful and precise Prussian Zündnadelgewehr, or "needle guns" (named for the method of shell detonation). The main asset of these weapons was their breech-loading mechanisms, which enabled the Prussians to fire them quickly from prone positions, unlike the standing Austrians with their muzzle-loaders and rockets. The terrain was another factor working against the *raketeurs,* who formerly enjoyed the advantage of fighting in mountains, which were prohibitive to conventional

FIGURE 5.8
Austrian Raketeur *(rocketeer), ca. 1862. (S.I. A5070A)*

wheeled artillery pieces and where they could easily hide. The relatively flat lands of Bohemia annulled these advantages. This was especially treacherous to Austrian *raketeurs* using stick or Hale projectiles, who traditionally fought at close range. The Austrian Army was decisively defeated, thanks largely to the enemy's *Zündnadelgewehr.*

In the light of artillery progress in general, the days of the *Raketeur Regiment* seemed numbered. Its rapid demise had already commenced in 1864, when the men began to be transferred to other units, but several batteries were raised again for the wars of 1866. *Raketenbatterien* were formed temporarily in 1869 to put down rebels in Krivosije, Dalmatia (Hungary). After this, they ceased altogether.[19]

As for the rockets, in their day, Austrian spin-stabilized rockets acquired an excellent reputation for reliability and accuracy. This was achieved by careful fabrication and firing at close ranges. Standard calibers were 1.9 and 2.3 inches (5–6 cm), the exterior warhead diameters. The rockets were classified into field (or light) rockets, and siege (or heavy) rockets. The former were 6- and 12-pounder (2.7 and 5.4 kg, or 5 and 6 kg) models with grenade, shot, incendiary, flare balls, and shrapnel rockets—much like Congreve's system. The latter were 16- and 28-pounder (7.3 and 12.7 kg) bomb, grenade, shell, flare ball, and "blasthead" (explosive) rockets. Austrian Hale rockets, called *Rotations-raketen,* generally retained the older caliber nomenclature. Usual sizes were the 4- or 6-pound (1.8 or 2.7 kg) hollow, shell, incendiary, and lightball rotation models. Ranges of Austrian stick and rotation rockets were comparable; mean ranges were 2,460 feet (750 m), effective ranges about 1,970 feet (600 m), maximum ranges 2,953–4,675 feet (900–1,425 m). The Austrian rocket systems represented the epitome of this nineteenth-century technology due to their use of both Congreve- and Hale-type projectiles and their reputation for craftsmanship in rocket manufacture. But the Austrians also adhered to the practice of limiting the propellant to gunpowder, and therefore limited the growth potential of the powder rocket as the age of modern ordnance began to emerge.[20]

FIGURE 5.9

Austrian rocketeers attacking fort of Peschiera, Italy, against insurgents in the Austro-Italian War of 1866. (S.I. A4826)

Poland

Poland was introduced to Congreve rockets at the British siege of Danzig (now Gdańsk) from January to November 1813, which was witnessed by Lieutenant Josef Bem of the Polish Horse Artillery. Bem became intensely interested in developing his own rockets but it was not until after the war, in 1818, that he received permission to conduct experiments at the artillery school at Warsaw, since the Polish Army was then in a state of modernization and reorganization. Bem summarized his results in his paper *Uwagi o rakietach zapaloajacych* (*Remarks on the Subject of Incendiary Rockets*) of 1819. He presented his report to the grand duke of Russia, Constantine Pavlovich, who was also commander-in-chief of the Polish Army, since Poland was then a territory divided between Russia, Prussia, and Austria.[21]

The Duke was pursuaded to establish rocket troops in the army and Bem was rewarded with a captaincy. But because of his outspoken political views concerning Poland's future, Bem was dismissed from his post in 1821 and then imprisoned, tortured, and released. Eventually, he rose to national prominence and became a dominant figure in the subsequent military and political history of Poland and neighboring Hungary.[22]

Although Bem ceased his rocketry experiments almost as soon as they had

FIGURE 5.10
Josef Bem (1795–1850), Polish rocketry pioneer, depicted in his general's uniform. As a captain, in 1819, he undertook experiments that led to the founding of Polish rocket troops.
(S.I. A5167)

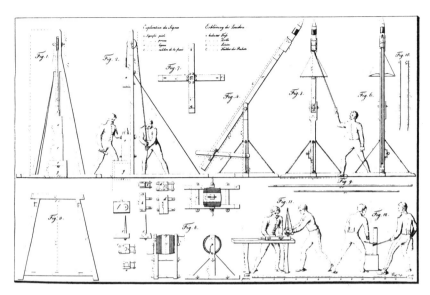

FIGURE 5.11

Plate from Bem's book Erfahrung über die Congreveschen Brand-Raketen (Experiments with Congreve Incendiary Rockets), *published in 1820, showing manufacturing details and a novel launcher. (S.I. 79–14194)*

begun, his report was expanded and published in Weimar in 1820 as a bilingual (in German and French) work titled *Die Erfahrungen über die Congreveschen Brand-Raketen bis zum, Jahre 1819 in der Königlichen Polnischen Artillerie (Experiments with Congreve Fire Rockets up to 1819 in the Royal Polish Artillery)*. The book is now of great interest, especially in light of Bem's later prominence. However, his rockets were little more than imitations of Congreve's incendiary rockets with central guidesticks.[23]

Bem's friend and superior officer, French-born General Piotr Bontemps, directed further experiments beginning 1822. He was aided by an Austrian pyrotechnist who had worked at Weiner-Neustadt, possibly Martin Westermayr. With the encouragement of Tsar Alexander and the Duke, the Polish *Raketekorpusu* ("Rocket Corps") was established several months later, and Bontemps played a major role in organizing it. In addition, a rocket factory was built in Warsaw. The Corps was divided into two sections, a half company of infantry and a half company of cavalry. There were 174 men in the former and 157 in the latter with an aggregate of 331, plus horses. Each section had its own uniforms. The troops continually trained and marched in parades but did not fight using their weapons until Poland's insurrection against Russia in 1831. The rocketeers fought with distinction at the battles of Wawer and Grochów, but the Russians ruthlessly suppressed the insurrection and Poland once more failed to gain independence. The Corps was consequently dissolved the same year.[24]

Russia

Count Feodor Rostopochin, accused of burning Moscow in 1812 on the heels of Napoleon's invasion, is alleged to have used rockets to start the fires. No evidence has been found to support either charge. Russian leaders had always been interested in rockets, though their progress was often slow. In 1810, a Russian "Military Study Committee" investigated the rocket's potential. Tsar Alexander was certainly aware of both Congreve and his rockets, because in 1813 he personally congratulated the British rocket battery at Leipzig and afterwards bestowed honors upon Congreve *in absentia*. In 1814, the future Tsar Nicholas I visited England and, with other Russian nobles, viewed a Congreve rocket practice at Woolwich, directed by Congreve.[25]

That same year, a member of the Study Committee named Kartmazov succeeded in constructing explosive and incendiary rockets, but Lieutenant Alexander Dmitriyevich Zasydko of the Artillery is recognized as the man who really established Congreve rockets in Russia. Zasydko saw extensive service during the Napoleonic campaigns and was well acquainted with rockets according to reputation, but he later wrote that he "never had any opportunity to see, much less obtain information as to how the English manage to use them." Upon his return to Russia in 1815, he designed his own "fighting rockets." Like Congreve, Zasydko began by studying firework and standard Russian Army signal rockets of 1–3 inches (2.5–7.6 cm) in diameter. By 1817, then Colonel Zasydko succeeded in making incendiary and demolition (explosive grenade) models of three calibers: 2-, 2.5-, and 4-inch (5, 6.3, and 10 m) models with ranges of 2,180–3,390 yards (1,990–3,100 m). Zasydko presented these to the Minister of War, along with detailed descriptions of plans for mass production. The Minister ordered trials to be held and they were carried out between July and December of that year at the St. Petersburg Artillery Grounds. The results were favorable and Zasydko was sent to the headquarters of the Second Army at Mogilev, in east Byelorussia, commanded

FIGURE 5.12
Alexander Zasydko (1779–1837), Russian
rocket pioneer. (S.I. 72–1195)

by Field-Marshal Mikhail Barclay de Tolly. Here, Zasydko's task was to train some of de Tolly's men in the use of rockets even though no permanent Russian rocket establishment had been decided upon. De Tolly praised Zasydko's efforts, rewarding him with a promotion to major-general. Meanwhile, Zasydko's rocket-manufacturing machines were installed at the St. Petersburg Technical Gunnery Laboratory (later called Ohktensk Gunpowder Works) on a trial basis. In 1820, Zasydko himself was stationed at St.

FIGURE 5.13
Zasydko explains his war
rocket to Field-Marshal Bar-
clay de Tolly at Mogilev,
Byelorussia, around 1817,
leading to the introduction
of his rockets in the Caucasus
campaigns. (S.I. 72–1196)

Petersburg when he was appointed first chief of the newly founded Mik-hailovskaya (Michael) Artillery School, where he took the opportunity to promote his rockets further.[26]

During the same period, an Englishman named Massingbird-Turner (who is said to have tried to bribe someone in the Royal Arsenal to procure Congreve rocket secrets) was also undertaking rocketry experiments in Russia. These were 2-, 3-, and 4-inch (5-, 7.6-, and 10 cm) models built at Okhtensk. They differed from Kartmazov and Zasydko rockets in having centrally mounted rather than lateral guidesticks. Massingbird-Turner rockets were tested satisfactorily in 1824 on the Volkova firing field and gave the Minister a basis for reconsidering the adoption of military rockets.[26]

In August of that year, General Alexei Ermolov, commander of the Caucasus armies, agreed with the chief of staff that war rockets could be used against tribes in the Caucasus for Russia's expansion in this region. Ermolov said they promised to be "of great help to us in the mountains, but even more against enemies whose cavalry greatly outnumbers ours." He twice requested rockets for his Caucasus campaigns, but only a few were available because the rocket work was still experimental. Finally, in March 1826, the government decided to create a permanent rocket establishment—one author says this move was prompted by Ermolov's repeated requests while another source says Zasdyko went directly to Tsar Nicholas and suggested the idea.[28]

Initially, the rockets were made at Okhtensk. Then construction was shifted to the old St. Petersburg Rocket Institute, founded in the 1680s by Peter the Great for the purpose of making military signal and firework rockets intended for victories and celebrations. Lieutenant-General Piotr Kozen, who had earlier been "lent" by Russia to assist Bem in Poland in making his rockets, was named director of the Institute. Massingbird-Turner was appointed manager of its day-to-day production, a position he maintained until as late as 1850, while artillery second-lieutenant Piotr Kovalyevsky was chosen as commander of the first official Russian rocket battery, or *Rakettnaya Rota*. The first order of the Institute was the manufacture of 3,000 rockets for the Caucasus armies. Kovalyevsky's men first deployed the rockets in August 1827 at the battle of Ushagan and against cavalry near Alagoz. According to Soviet historian Victor N. Sokol'skii, "these are apparently the first instances of the use of military rockets against an enemy by Russian troops." It was discovered, however, that rockets could not be satisfactorily transported over great distances. Rockets dispatched from St. Petersburg were ruined, while those made in the field performed well.[29]

The first large-scale use of Russian military rockets occurred during the Russo-Turkish War of 1828–29, particularly at Silistria and Shumla and during the sieges of Braila, in Walachia on the lower Danube (now part of Rumania), and Varna, a major Black Sea port now in Bulgaria. On the field, Kovalyevsky's company consisted of twenty-three officers and 303 privates. But it was evident that rockets could barely stand the lengthy transport; the Turkish front was more than 2,000 miles (3,200 km) of unpaved roads and trails from St. Petersburg. Almost 2,400 rockets were expended during the 1828–29 campaign, but they very often fared poorly. It was therefore decided to make rockets in the field. Captain Vasily Vnukov, another of Bem's former co-workers, was chosen to head field production. In March 1828, Vnukov, with members of the Institute and rocket-manufacturing machinery, was sent to Tiraspol, where he set up a model of the factory.[30]

Following the campaigns against Turkey, Russian rockets were dis-

FIGURE 5.14
Zasydko rockets were first used in the Russo-Turkish War of 1828–29. Shown here is an attack on the fortress of Varna in 1828. (s.i. 79–6016)

patched to help subdue Poles in the Polish insurrection of 1830–31. However, Konstantin Konstantinov, a Russian who became a foremost rocketry pioneer, admitted that "the failure of rockets in two consecutive campaigns completely cooled the zeal for that projectile in Russia." Compounding the transportation problem, many of the rockets were made too hastily. Manufacturing in the field did not always produce good results. Adverse weather conditions were also to blame. Lieutenant-General Zasydko (appointed in 1829) and his assistants had no control over most of these conditions; even after his retirement in 1834, he continued to try to solve these problems, until his death in 1837.[31]

It was still believed that military rockets had great potential. In 1832, to facilitate coordination of the various rocket programs, all existing rocket factories were consolidated. There were also numerous progressive experiments carried out in the mid-1830s to 1840s, principally by military engineer General Karl Schilder. Among Schilder's accomplishments was the adaptation of multiple rockets for firing large weights. In 1834, he designed and constructed the world's first rocket-firing ironclad submarine, a remarkably advanced idea, although in those years the vessel could adequately derive its

FIGURE 5.15

Rocket-armed barge and submarine tested by Russian engineer Karl Schilder. The man-operated submarine submerged about 40 feet (12 m), but was not effective. (S.I. 72–1198)

motive force only from muscle power. Schilder also tried rocket-firing, flat-bottomed ferry boats or pontoons (first used during the Russo-Turkish War of 1828–29). In other respects, the development of rocketry in Russia was slow during this period because of antiquated, hand-manufacturing methods.[32]

In the mid-1840s, military rocket production rose because of the increased use of rockets in the Caucasus, owing to the insistence of commander-in-chief and governor of the region, Prince Mikhail Vorontsov, who had first seen rockets at Leipzig in 1813. Vorontsov ordered thousands of them.[33]

But the Golden Age of nineteenth-century Russian rocketry began in earnest with the appointment of Colonel Konstantin Ivanovitch Konstantinov as chief of the St. Petersburg Rocket Institute in 1847. Konstantinov was one of Russia's greatest artillerists and scientists. A brilliant graduate of the Mikhailovskya Artillery School, he traveled abroad from 1840 to 1844 studying rocket-production techniques. He met Augustin, who allowed the Russian to witness Austrian rocket practice. Konstantinov wrote the first manual for war rocket manufacturing in his own country. One of his most outstanding achievements was the design and construction of an electrical ballistic rocket pendulum for measuring the performance of rockets with the aim of improving their construction. The first was made in 1846; an improved version was started in 1849 and completed in 1854. In addition, Konstantinov created or ordered the creation of new and advanced rocket-production machinery, such as hydraulic rocket presses; introduced central-tail configurations in Russian military rockets; and redesigned rockets scientifically. Konstantinov also conducted extensive research on rocket ballistics, made sighting devices for gauging rocket altitudes, lectured extensively on rocket technology at the Mikhailovskaya School, and published the best books written on rocketry during his lifetime. In short, the quality of Russian rocketry increased enormously due to Konstantinov, becoming one of the most advanced systems in Europe.[34]

Meanwhile, Hale of England attempted to sell the Russians his spin-stabilized rockets. In October 1848, he sent his agent, patent attorney Matthew Nottingham, to St. Petersburg. However, the results of comparative tests between stickless and stick rockets on Volhkova Field did not satisfy the Russians and they refused the offer, mainly because Nottingham asked for a "moderate compensation" of 189,000 Russian pieces of silver![35]

Konstantinov later wrote that rockets were not fully established in Russia until 1857, when the greatly improved models he had designed were introduced. This is one reason why rockets used in the Crimean War of 1853–56

FIGURE 5.16
Konstantin Konstantinov (1817–71), another Russian rocket pioneer, tried to make rocketry into a science by studying rocket dynamics using his electrical ballistic pendulum.
(S.I. 72–1199)

were of inferior quality, though beginning in the early 1850s the weapon was widely supplied to stations throughout the expanding Russian Empire, from the Trans-Ili region of Kirghizia, Armenia, and Western Siberia, to fortresses at Orenburg, Kerch, Bucarest, Revel (Estonia), and Helsingfors (now Helsinki, Finland). Still, the St. Petersburg plant turned out 20,358 rounds between 1853 and 1856 although French war rocket production was 20,000 in 1853–54 alone. The use of Russian rockets in the Crimean campaign occurred in almost every major engagement, from the sieges of Silistria and the Turkish forts of Kurouck-Dara, Karadach, and Kars, to the prolonged bombardment of Sebastopol.[36]

After Russia's defeat in the Crimea, the Russian Army underwent a modernization program. The enlightened war minister, Dmitri Milyutin, did not neglect rockets and supported Konstantinov in his endeavors. From 1857 to about 1859, Konstantinov was again sent abroad, this time to France, Prussia, Spain, and perhaps other countries to gather the latest data on rocket-production techniques. From an industrial firm in Paris, he ordered new rocket presses and other equipment. Moreover, Konstantinov realized that the St. Petersburg rocket plant was both antiquated and strategically poorly located. Through his efforts, a new central Russian rocket factory was established at the port of Nikolayev, east of Odessa, also the site of a large naval fortress with sprawling military supply warehouses. He felt it to be an ideal location for the rocket factory in the event of another war with a European power. The closing of the St. Petersburg plant and move to Nikolayev was made in 1864.[37]

Russian war rockets continued to be fired in the long, drawn-out (1864–81) mountain operations in the western Caucasus, known as the Turkestan War. Typical campaigns were in Bukhara and Khivinskii during 1868 and 1874–81, respectively. Konstantinov died at Nikolayev in 1871. He was succeeded by his faithful subordinate for 20 years, Major-General Victor Nyechayev. By 1882, the Nikolayev factory staff consisted of the director (always a major-general), two draftsmen, six noncommissioned officers, three artillery officers, two master artificers, two master pyrotechnists, six clerks, one "junior dresser" (apparently a valet), a medical attendant, 152 laboratory workmen, and seventeen servants, making a total of 181 people.[38]

A limited number of rockets were employed in the Russo-Turkish War of 1877–78, perhaps the first time war rockets with "guncotton" warheads were used. Nyechayev developed these rockets at Nikolayev in collaboration with Lieutenant Fridrihs of the Russian Navy. They were supposed to have much

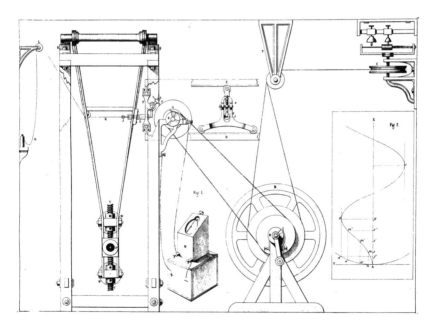

FIGURE 5.17

Konstantinov's pendulum, 1847, for measuring rocket thrusts. At right is a thrust-time curve from one of his tests. (S.I. 79–9595)

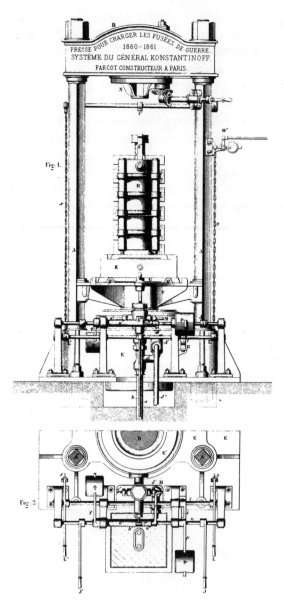

FIGURE 5.18
Konstantinov's hydraulic
rocket press, constructed in
Paris, 1860–61. (S.I. A4495A)

more powerful explosive effects than those with gunpowder-based compositions; but at the battles of Pleven, Ruschuk, and Sulnia the new rockets showed
"no particular success," according to historian Sokol'skii.[39]

Writer Willy Ley said that Russian nineteenth-century war rockets were used for the last time in 1881 during the Tekke expedition against the Turkoman stronghold of Geok Tepe. General Mikhail Skobelev used rockets successfully here, completing the Russian subjegation of Turkestan. But Russian war rockets were employed for a long time after. They saw action after 1887 in several Central Asian and Far Eastern expeditions and in Turkestan as late as 1899. After the Crimean War, the Russian rocket establishment was much like that of England in that the weapons were issued indiscriminately to troops who requested them rather than being alloted to fixed rocket units. This explains why Russia, like England, used rockets up to the eve of the twentieth century. For example, although the Artillery Committee requested the discontinuation of war-rocket production in January 1886, the commanders of the Caucasus, Turkestan, Omsk, and Irkutsk regions urged that a supply of rockets be kept at hand in case of any further outbreak of conflict. The Nikolayev plant continued to manufacture signal, flare, and lifesaving rockets until 1910 and

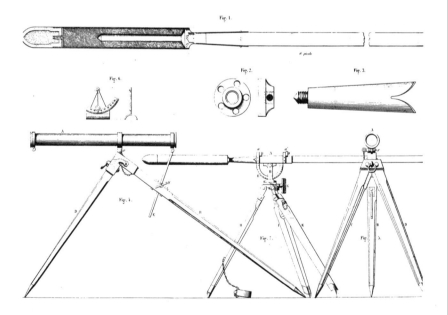

FIGURE 5.19

Different views of a Konstantinov 2-inch (5 cm) war rocket and launcher. (S.I. A4495B)

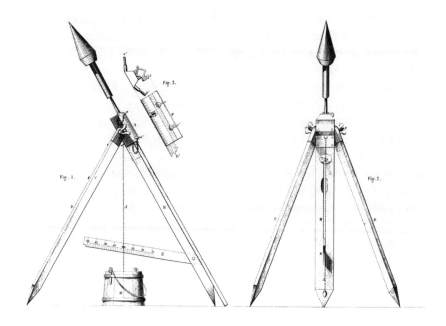

FIGURE 5.20

Konstantinov made many other types of rockets, including this 2-inch (5 cm) flare or illumination rocket. (S.I. 79–9597)

new designs for war rockets were proposed from time to time. The original founders of Russian rocketry, Zasydko and Konstantinov, have not been forgotten; in the 1970s the Soviet Government named lunar craters in their honor.[40]

France

The history of nineteenth-century French war rocketry can be divided into two periods: 1810–26, the exploratory phase; and 1827–72, the duration of the war rocket establishment and rocket troops. The French had many opportunities to become well acquainted with the details of Congreve rockets used against them, beginning in 1804 with the first Boulogne attempt. A specimen fell into French hands in 1809 when the British attempted to destroy French ships at the Ile d'Aix in the Basque Roads. A 32-pounder (14.5 kg) incendiary Congreve was recovered from an English fireship that ran aground. Colonel Marie François Récicourt, engineer-in-chief of the defenses of the Isle, boxed-up the rocket and sent it to Paris after he himself had examined it, and it was forwarded to the Société d'Encouragement (Society of Encouragement).[41]

Society member chemist Jean d'Arcet thoroughly analyzed the rocket and published his results. Napoleon was apprised of the find and ordered a commission of artillery officers to study and duplicate it. Other eminent scientists involved in the investigation included physicist Gaspard Monge and chemists Claude Bethollet and Louis Guyton de Morveau. In 1810, Marine Artillery Captain Pierre Frédéric Bourée and Army Artillery Captain Charles

FIGURE 5.21
Russian war rockets in action—fired from the window of a government building—during the Crimean War, 1853–56.
(S.I. 72–1200)

FIGURE 5.22

Drawings accompanying a French report of a rocket captured during an 1809 British attack off the French coast. (S.I. 80–1750)

Moreton de Chabrillan began making French copies of the rocket at the Vincennes military works near Paris.[42]

The copies compared very closely with Congreve's but were capable of greater ranges: 3,280 yards (3,000 m) for 3-inch (7.6 cm) models and 4,592 yards (4,200 m) for 3.5-inch (8.9 cm) models. They were, however, for experimental purposes only. Similar trials were made from 1810 to 1812 at Toulon. The difference was that here the rockets were to be battle-tested in the French siege of Cadiz, Spain. French war rockets were also made at Seville, which was then under French control. Captains Bourée and Moreton were ordered to establish war rocket factories at four naval arsenals: Lorient, Rochefort, Cherborg, and Brest. But these ambitions were excessive. Before long, more than 2,000 3-inch (7.6 cm) rockets were made at Toulon but at 30,258 francs, the cost was enormous. As a result, the government did not encourage further work. Some rounds from Seville and Toulon were sent against Cadiz, but they failed to reach the ramparts.[43]

Denmark was then an ally of France. Like Austria, in 1813 France also sent an officer to visit Danish Captain Schumacher to learn about rockets. The French ambassador to Denmark, Baron d'Alquier, insisted that Schumacher write a complete memoire on his rocket system. Again, the Dane agreed to relay only verbal information to the officer, artillery captain Brussel de Brulard. Like Augustin, Brussel de Brulard traveled clandestinely; even the embassy people believed his business was nothing more than making meat purchases for the French Army. But Schumacher turned out to be more cooperative than anticipated, giving the Frenchman five or six samples of his rockets. These were let off in a firing test in January 1814 before French artillery officers at Hamburg, Germany. One rocket behaved erratically but

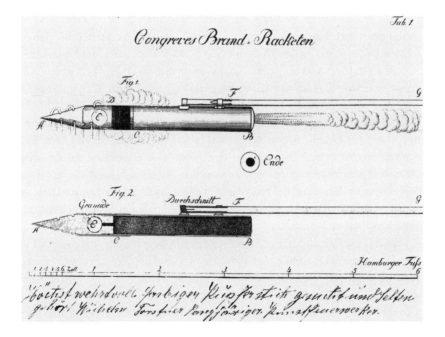

FIGURE 5.23

The same model in action, depicted in an 1820 German translation of a Congreve rocket treatise. (s.i. 84–11003)

the others flew well. French rocket production began again, this time based on the Danish pattern, in Hamburg. However, the French commander at Hamburg, Marshal Louis Davout, was too demanding, and the men were pushed to such a limit that explosions were frequent. On 12 April 1814 Napoleon abdicated and soon after, Hamburg fell. Most of the remaining rockets and equipment were turned over to the Allies, who discovered that the rockets often rebounded. The rest, wrote one historian sarcastically, "were good for the defense of a ditch."[44]

Not until the close of 1826 was progress finally made. It was initiated by an Englishman, Robert Bedford, who claimed to have worked with Congreve. He convinced inspector-general of artillery Marshall Silvain Charles to try out his rockets even though the expense for some 500 firing experiments was "fairly costly." The investment seemed justified. The artillery commission concluded: "The progress of the rocket is sufficient for a special corps to use this kind of firearm . . . within the limits of a moderate wind." From then on, the School of Pyrotechnics at Metz became the official rocket-making body for France's armed forces. Bedford was assigned to manage production and he stayed until 1845. Under his influence, French war rockets during this period followed an essentially British design, particularly the central-stick pattern.[45]

At first, there was no "special corps" of rocketeers and rockets were given experimentally to standard artillery batteries and naval units. The first appearance of rockets in battle was supposed to have been in the Morea, in the Peloponnesus, Greece, in 1828 during France's intervention against the Turks in the war for Greek Independence, but it was not a moment of glory. The pyrotechnist who was assigned to fire them was discovered asleep—and drunk—at the foot of the temple of Bacchus. By default, perhaps, the true debut of post-Napoleonic French war rockets occurred two years later, in Algiers, in the first of many engagements that led to the establishment of this French colony.[46]

In 1833 the French Marine Artillery officially began using war rockets, but it was not until 18 December 1840 that a naval school of pyrotechny was created at Toulon on par with the Army's school at Metz. The protracted Arab campaigns in Algiers probably had much to do with this since Toulon is on the southern coast and an embarkation point for North Africa. From 1836 to 1837, rocket-armed vessels were regularly supplied for the Algiers campaigns. One of the major rocket actions was the naval bombardment of Constantine in 1837. Another occurred in 1844, when French naval rockets were thrown from ships against Tangier and Suerah in the war against Morocco.[47]

Although the French increasingly employed rockets, the formal structure of an elite rocket corps was not adopted until the Minister of War permanently assigned the 6th Battery, 5th Artillery Regiment, to the Pyrotechnic School at Metz on 28 March 1842. These troops were known as the *Fuséens* ("Rocketeers"). In 1845 a section of this unit, consisting of twenty-five men under the command of First-Captain Pierre Rouge, was assigned to Algeria. This came to be their de facto headquarters. With reorganizations came new battery designations and increased field strengths. By 1855 they were known as the "4th Battery (*Fuséens*) of the 12th Artillery Regiment" and consisted of four officers, 154 men, thirty-four horses, and seventy-two mules.[48]

In 1845, the Englishmen Bedford quit the pyrotechnic school in a dispute over a new phase of manufacturing and reorganization. After his departure, French war-rocket design changed considerably. On 5 August 1848 a monstrous explosion took place in the Metz rocket works in which Captain Rouge was killed. The disaster led to greatly improved safety measures in French war rocket manufacture.

The same year, French artillery major Louis Auguste Susane was named new director and commandant of the Metz pyrotechnic school. During the next twenty years of his tenure, Susane instituted vast improvements both in safety and quality of manufacture. For example, like Konstantinov of Russia,

FIGURE 5.24

General Louis Susane, (1810–76), French
rocket pioneer, who directed the French
war-rocket establishment. He also wrote
Les Fusées de Guerre (War Rockets),
1863. (S.I. A4826A)

he abolished the archaic and dangerous hand-driven, pile-driver presses, replacing them with hydraulic presses.

By 1853, the start of the Crimean War, twenty-two presses had been installed in addition to other new equipment. Emperor Napoleon III, an authority on artillery, requested the production of heavy rockets with unprecedented ranges of 4,000 yards (4,570 m) or more. "Confident in his hydraulic presses," wrote French rocket authority Auguste Pralon, "Commandant Susane didn't hesitate to respond affirmatively." These ranges were indeed reached and even exceeded by the end of the Crimean War.[49]

The start of the campaign saw an increase to three batteries of *Fuséens.* Both the Army and Navy deployed war rockets extensively in Russia. During the last phase of the war, 7–8,000 large siege rockets were dispatched from Metz for the Black Sea flotilla; some also came from Toulon's School of Maritime Pyrotechny. Early in 1854, it was reported that Metz produced 3.5-inch (9 cm) models that were "a magnificent success" and reached 18,370 feet, or 3.4 miles (5,600 m). The large Navy rockets from Toulon tried earlier went from 4,360 to 4,700 yards (4,000–4,300 m), with one ranging 8,746 yards (8,000 m). This was probably the longest distance ever reached by a nineteenth-century gunpowder war rocket. The largest French siege rockets were of 4.7 inch (12 cm) caliber and could attain 7,500 yards (6,860 m, or 4.2

FIGURE 5.25
French war-rocket battery before Russian fort of Sebastopol in 1855, during Crimean War.
(S.I. A5052B)

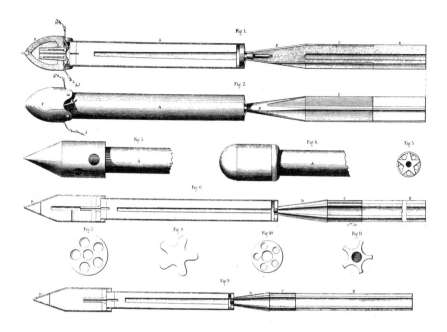

FIGURE 5.26

French war rockets ca. 1854, with calibers of 1.9-, 2.7-, 3.5-, and 4.7-inch (5, 7, 9, and 12 cm).
(S.I. A4495)

mi). The purpose for these rockets was to batter the walls of the great Russian fort of Sebastopol.[50]

After the war, these large rockets were probably little used, if at all. Besides, smaller calibers like the 2.3 inch (6 cm) were easier to transport and quite suitable for desert fighting in Algeria and Morocco. Algerian-based *Fuséens* were also dispatched to Italy in 1859 to assist the Sardinians in their war for independence against the Austrians. However, the 234 men, twenty-four horses, 114 mules, and 2,000 field rockets arrived a day *after* the decisive battle of Solferino on 25 June. Back in North Africa, they returned in time to help quell an uprising in Morocco, with one eyewitness marvelling at the excellent service of the *Fuséens* despite sweltering heat, sandstorms, and difficult terrain. Available French records do not speak of any detrimental effects of the desert heat upon rocket performance.[51]

Not long after the Moroccan disturbance, in 1860, war broke out with China. The *Fuséens* sailed for the Orient, but their ship caught fire off Macao in

June. Luckily the men were saved, as were their rockets, which were on another vessel. The *Fuséens* were able to fight side-by-side with a British counterpart rocket battery at the Taku fort of Sinho; they also did well at Tang-ku. Then, in 1862, after returning to Algeria and fighting in the Kayberlie campaign, they were sent to Mexico as part of the French force protecting "Emperor" Maximillian of Mexico. The *Fuséens* performed poorly against the rebel Mexicans, who often fought guerilla-fashion. Only a handful of rounds were fired in the affair of Vintilla and the siege of Puebla. After the Mexican fiasco, in which the unfortunate Maximillian was overthrown, the French army returned home. The *Fuséens* returned to Algeria, where they probably fought their last land battles with rockets against insurgent Kayberlies in May 1865. French naval rockets were lobbed against the citadel of Vinh-Long, Indochina (modern Vietnam), in June 1867.[52]

In 1870, when the city of Metz fell to German hands during the Franco-Prussian War, the pyrotechnic school and laboratory was moved to Bourges. All equipment was saved and sent out just before the German soldiers marched in. By then, however, the factory mainly made signal rockets. No French war rockets saw action in the Franco-Prussian campaign, although on 19 November 1870 the Minister of War sent an urgent telegram to the school: "Tell me by telegraph if you have any war rockets." It was too late.[53]

The *Scientific American* of 3 December 1870 reported that a "distinguished civil engineer and chemist" by the name of Laurent had invented a rocket that he christened *Fusée Satan* ("Satan Rocket"). It was so-named because on striking, it spread sheets of unquenchable flame over a space of 172–258 square feet (16–24 sq m). The fire came from the rocket's petroleum-filled warhead. Experiments were conducted at St. Cloud in front of an artillery committee that was "apalled by the terrible nature of this engine of destruction." "However this may be," continued the magazine, "the Committee of National Defense has given the inventor a large building on the Batignolle (formerly a girls' school), and has ordered the immediate manufacture, on a large scale of *Satan* rockets." But despite the hyperbole and promises, no further word was heard of the *Fusée Satan*.[54]

Finally, in 1872, the Committee of Artillery bluntly asked the War Minister: "Is there an interest to conserve war rockets . . . in service?" To this the Minister replied: "The French artillery had in no way employed war rockets in the last war [of 1870–71] and likewise hadn't knowledge that the German army themselves used engines of that nature against us." On 15 July 1872 the Committee concluded that rifled artillery such as the Germans used was "incomparably superior" to war rockets. "To sum up, there is no reason for keeping war rockets." The Minister approved the decision on 27 July 1872 and the *Fuséens* were abolished.[55]

Sweden

The history of Swedish rocket troops of the nineteenth century is a short one. Swedish interest in Congreve rockets dates back to 1807 when they were used by the British to attack the capital of Denmark. In the summer of 1810, the famous Swedish chemist Jons Jakob Berzelius visited some friends in Copenhagen, where he met the Danish physicist Hans Christian Orsted and several Danish officers. Soon, their discussion was about the Copenhagen bombardment and Congreve rockets. Berzelius was then given the opportunity to study some specimens that had been picked up by the officers. He took these rockets back to Stockholm where they were turned over to Swedish military authorities. In the spring of 1811, the Royal Academy of Military Sciences appointed a commission to study them. "Even though Berzelius and his colleagues succeeded in improving the performance of the rockets," writes Swedish science historian Sigurd Strandh, "it seems, nevertheless, that the Royal Academy of Military Sciences had great difficulty in convincing the army authorities in Sweden of the practicability of the new weapon."[56]

Many Swedish officers found the weapon to be repugnant and "inhumane." Master of Ordnance Colonel Paul Schroderstierna, on the other hand, saw great promise in the rocket and began his own experiments in 1813. Much later, in 1829, Captain D.W. Silfverstolpe wrote an excellent report of Congreve rockets he saw at Woolwich and suggested the formation of a Swedish rocket brigade. Still there was no governmental support.[57]

Then, on 14 April 1831, Martin Westermayr, the pyrotechnist who had worked in Austria's Wiener-Neustadt rocket plant, wrote a proposition to the Swedish ambassador in Berlin, where Westermayr then resided. He informed the ambassador that he was on his way to St. Petersburg to try to interest the Russians in his rockets. He would stop in Stockholm, he said, and if the Swedes agreed, would stay for three months, giving full instructions on how to make rockets and demonstrating them. Crown Prince Oscar (later King Oscar I) was delighted and accepted the offer mainly because of his role as Commander of the Swedish Artillery. The contract was signed on 18 May 1831. Based on his own experience, Westermayr added the stipulation that before attempting to make rockets, the Swedes would have to undertake their own

FIGURE 5.27
Sketch of a rocket press in the Swedish rocket factory at Marieberg, near Stockholm, in 1836. (S.I. 79–14180; courtesy Armémuseum, Stockholm)

experiments to determine the most suitable formula. Also, Oscar was to be personally instructed in the art of making rockets, but it is unknown if this condition was fulfilled. All others were, with the result that on 28 December 1832 the Swedish *Konglig Raket Corpset* ("Royal Rocket Corps") was created. A rocket factory was soon built at Marieberg, near Stockholm.[58]

The *Corpset* consisted of a rocket battery and an artificer company that was responsible for making the weapons. Lieutenant Johan Wilhelm Westerling was appointed commander, probably because he had worked closely with Westermayr. The battery was composed of eight firing stands transported by rocket wagons. In addition to the commander, there were two wing chiefs, two staff sergeants, a bugler, two first fireworkers, two second fireworkers, sixty regular fireworkers or privates, an ironworker, and a wood worker, making a total of seventy-four men and thirty-four horses. On wartime footing, the firing stands could be doubled to sixteen and additional men added. Uniforms were dark blue with yellow cords (gold for officers) for decorations such as epaulets. Cuffs were a medium blue while breeches were dark blue with medium-blue stripes. Dress helmets had high plumes with the words *Raket Corpset* standing out above the peaks. These uniforms resembled those of regular Swedish artillerymen of the period with a few changes; for example, the rocketeers wore blue rather than yellow stripes on the breeches.[59]

Different types of rockets were made, including experimental ones with delta wings, by the French pyrotechnist Vaillant of Boulogne, but the standard Swedish model was the 2-inch (56 mm), weighing 7.5 pounds (3.4 kg) without its guidestick. Its range was 2,000–3,000 feet (600–1,000 m). There was also a

2.5-inch (6.3 cm) model with a 12-pound (5.4 kg) shell and a 3-inch (7.6 cm) model that weighed 18 pounds (8 kg) without its guidestick that had about the same range. These were also called the 12- and 18-pounders. The eight launchers could fire six rockets in 3 minutes.[60]

Yet the *Corpset* never saw battle. From 1814 to the present, Sweden has never been involved in armed conflict. The *Corpset* was short-lived—not because of this, ironically, but due to a recommendation by Westerling. Since he was well versed in pyrotechnics, on 19 March 1845 Westerling was ordered to Denmark and Prussia to make a complete study of "explosive caps, inflammation tubes" and other pyrotechnics, including rockets. He concluded that it was "fitting" that the Corps be reorganized into a *Konglig Fyrverkarkaren* ("Pyrotechnical Corps") as there was more need for the other devices and rockets also fit into this category. The recommendation was approved on 24 October 1845. The new organization made primings and other pyrotechnical devices for the Army until 1876. However, on 13 March 1846, a decree was issued ordering every artillery regiment to be furnished with two rocket stands and rockets. These arms were maintained by Swedish regiments until the 1860s when they, too, were abolished.[61]

Switzerland

The first serious attempt to induce Swiss military authorities to adopt Congreve-type rockets was made in 1828 by a young artillery lieutenant of

FIGURE 5.28

This curious sheet-iron, finned 2-inch (6 cm) caliber 7-pound (3 kg) model, with 3-pound (1.3 kg) shell, was made for the Swedes in 1821 by French pyrotechnist Vaillant of Boulogne. (S.I. 79–1418; courtesy Armémuseum, Stockholm)

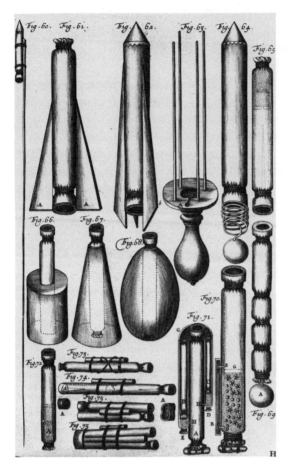

FIGURE 5.29
Finned rockets were not new,
as shown in this plate from
the Lithuanian Kazimierz
Siemienwicz's Artis Mag-
nae Artilleriae (Great
Art of Artillery), *1650.*
(S.I. AS206G)

Geneva, Adolphe Pictet, later an internationally known professor of esthetics and literature. Pictet paid for his experiments out of pocket. The experiments were conducted at the artillery school at Thun, Bern Canton. The Swiss Federal War Council gave "a very favorable report" and encouraged more experiments by alloting funds for them. By 1831, Pictet, now a captain, met "with more and more . . . success." His 6-pound (2.7 kg) rockets, fired at Thun, ranged up to 1,900 yards (1,740 m).[62]

In 1834, a commission headed by Engineer Colonel (later Chief of Staff) Guillaume Dufour was set up to assist Pictet. After a test firing of 200 rockets on the plain of Biere, Vaud Canton, Dufour wrote: "A commission of experts has testified to the excellence of the new rockets, and is making to the Upper Diet [legislative assembly] a detailed report in proposing their introduction in the Federal Army." Because of political and financial circumstances, however, the Diet postponed its decision, then put it off entirely.[63]

Much later, the year 1848 saw great revolutionary movements not only in Italy and Hungary but also in Switzerland. The Swiss civil war erupted and led to the foundation of the modern Swiss federal state. Consequently, the Army was reorganized. Previously, individual cantons alone raised and equipped armies for the Federation—a weak and inefficient arrangement. The national army had really been a militia, raised for defensive purposes only. Perhaps for the same reason, it had been difficult for the Diet to act on Dufour's recom-

FIGURE 5.30
Professor Adolphe Pictet
(1799–1875), a Swiss educator,
experimented with war
rockets in Switzerland in the
1830s and later in Sardinia,
Italy. (S.I. A5141D)

FIGURE 5.31
Detail of a Sardinian rocket launcher, made in Turin in the 1840s, showing transit for adjusting angle of firing. (S.I. A5259D; courtesy Museo Nazionale d'Artiglieria, Torino, Italy)

mendation. After the revolution, a more centralized army was created, but by this time Lieutenant-Colonel Pictet was in Turin, capital of the Kingdom of Sardinia, promoting his rockets there.[64]

Swiss military authorities and the government were now more receptive to adopting rocket arms. The ubiquitous William Hale came to Switzerland in 1849 and succeeded in selling a quantity of his stickless rockets. A hydraulic press was installed at the main arsenal in Zurich for making conventional Congreve stick rockets. The Swiss also turned to their neighbors, the Austrians. According to the well informed Konstantinov, "after a number of studies on the Austrian and English systems, it was the former that prevailed in Switzerland, in spite of . . . triumphant efforts . . . by Mr. Adolph Pictet."[65]

Interest in war rockets intensified when a former pyrotechnist from Wiener-Neustadt, who claimed to have commanded an Austrian *Raketenbatterie* before the uprising in his native Hungary, approached the Swiss government with an offer to sell first-hand information on the Austrian system; his name was Ladislaus Lukasky (or Lukaszy). He had successfully contacted the governments of Bavaria and Württemberg, and was prepared to manufacture rockets for those powers. The usual commission of artillery officers was assembled to examine his rockets, which were duly tested in February 1852 in Basel Canton. Headed by Major Hans Herzog, the commission found Lukasky's projectiles to be suitable and needing only a few modifications before Swiss Army acceptance. Herzog requested more trials to confirm the commission's assessment. After final tests at Thun, the Swiss signed the contract. The refugee Lukasky stayed with the Swiss several years, then moved on, probably to ply his precarious profession elsewhere.[66]

Meanwhile, elaborate plans were drawn up for the Swiss war rocket organization. Eight *Raketenbatterien* were established on 26 March 1853. Some served as *Auszug* ("Elite") or front-line troops. Remaining batteries were on reserve status. In effect, half the Swiss war rocket establishment existed only on paper. There were sixty-four men for each elite battery, or 252 in total. Reserve batteries each consisted of thirty-six men, or a total of 144, so that combined, the elite and reserve theoretically amounted to 396 men when fully activated. The elite section had forty-eight horses (forty of them were draught animals); thirty-five horses (twenty-eight draught) were assigned to the reserve section. Equipment included eight firing stands for the elite section, and four for the reserve; eight 12-pounder (5.4 kg) rockets for the elite, and four for the reserve; a 6-pounder (2.7 kg) wagon for the elite, the same for reserve; and a store wagon for each section. Store wagons also held signal rockets and provisions. The rockets followed the Austrian pattern. They were either 12- or 6-pounders (5.4 or 2.7 kg) ranging from 2,000–2,500 "paces" (1,830–2,290 m). Twelve-pounders were armed with 6- or 8-pound (2.7–3.6 kg) shells, shrapnel balls, or incendiaries. Smaller calibers were fitted with 3- or 5-pound (1.3 or 2.2 kg) shells. Regulations for the allotment of rockets for each battery and wagon were elaborate, as evidenced by the specially published *Verordnung Betreffend die Organization der Raketenbatterien (Vom. 26. Marz 1853)* (*Regulation Concerning the Organization of Rocket Batteries from March 26, 1853*). Elite and reserve batteries were to be stationed in each of the four cantons of Geneva, Argau, Bern, and Zurich.[67]

Switzerland was in much the same position as Sweden, maintaining strict neutrality after the close of the Napoleonic wars. After 1848, the Swiss still relied upon a militia force that could be raised on short notice if a war of self-defense should occur. According to this plan, qualified men received periodic training using prescribed materials. In practice, the government's responsibility was to provide instructors and schools and to make the munitions; cantons raised the troops. Overall centralization of the Swiss army was slow, and it was not until the new Federal Constitution of 1874 that a real national army could exist based upon universal conscription. Thus, the rocket organization was grossly encumbered by the Swiss bureacratic nightmare. For instance, the cost of the rockets had to be borne by each of the four participating cantons, while the rockets were obtained from Federal arsenals.[68]

Only during actual war could the system be put to a test. War almost did break out in 1856. Conflicting territorial claims between Switzerland and Prussia over Neufchatel Canton put the Swiss on a war footing in which the phantom reserve rocket troops on paper came to life. Prussia ordered mobilization as 30,000 Swiss troops were quickly raised and marched to the northern frontier. Among the materiel were twenty rocket wagons loaded with firing stands; it is not known how many rocketeers were available. Diplomatic pressure on the part of France and England averted hostilities. This was the last and only instance of Swiss rocket batteries being placed on such readiness. In 1859 they were nearly recalled again when Federal troops were raised in response to threats of violations against Swiss neutrality upon the outbreak of the war for Italian unification.[69]

By this time, progress in artillery development had affected Switzerland as it had other nations. These developments led to dialogues among the military as to whether the *Raketenbatterien* were really worth maintaining. The Federal Council recommended abolishment of the reserve batteries. Herzog, now chief of the Artillery, agreed but suggested reorganization of the elite batteries. These recommendations subsequently were approved by Herzog on 5 February 1862. As before, elaborate plans were drafted for the reorganization and apportionment of the stores. However, in a few years all this had vanished. Following the footsteps of the Austrians, who dissolved their own *Raketenbatterien* in 1867, the Swiss disbanded their rocket troops the same year. Existing Swiss rocket batteries were converted into mountain cannon batteries.[70]

Switzerland by no means completes the roster of nineteenth-century war rocket-armed nations in Europe. In addition to the major, well organized war-rocket organizations on the Continent, there were also numerous minor, and sometimes aborted, efforts to form rocket establishments.

CHAPTER 6

European Nations with Minor Rocket Establishments

By "minor" is meant small war rocket establishments or attempts to create such organizations. These efforts are presented chronologically from the beginning of these activities; in the first case, for ease of context, like geographical areas are grouped together.

Germany

Several German states were involved in the study of rockets; Prussia and Bavaria are the most prominent.

Prussia

Of all the Continental European nations, Prussia, with its reputation for an acute consciousness of the latest military technology, was the most likely to

123

initiate a strong program of rocketry research. Yet surprisingly little original work was done, though the Prussians had excellent opportunities to observe Congreve rockets when they first appeared. Bogue's rocket battery fought in Germany and in 1814 was attached for a brief time to Prussian General Friedrich Büllow's command. During a state visit to England in that year, Prussian Emperor Frederick William III watched Congreve personally demonstrate his rockets at Woolwich.[1]

The Emperor also witnessed a German rocket exercise a year earlier conducted by Captain Karl Dietrich of the Royal Saxony Artillery Corps on 23 August 1813. Emperor William bestowed upon the Saxon a gift of 300 thalers in order to encourage him to continue with the experiments. The war, however, made it an inauspicious time to do this. It was not until 1817, when he was on furlough in Prussia, that Dietrich, now a major, resumed his rocket research. The Prussians had succeeded in inducing him to remain in their country longer and to work for them. In November he was provided with workrooms in the *Feuerwerkslaboratorium* (Fireworks Laboratory) in the citadel of Spandau. Like Russia's St. Petersburg Rocket Institute, the Prussian lab was primarily responsible for producing royal fireworks and signal rockets. As an extra inducement to stay, Dietrich was made a major in the Royal Prussian Service. Old Saxony Army records show that his officer's commission was annulled in 1818 "because he did not return from his furlough, but had entered the Royal Prussian Service."[2]

Dietrich was assigned a detachment of two officers, four corporals, twelve grenadiers from the half-invalid company of infantry, and a permanent detachment of five to eight convicts to help him. This was less a rocket battery than a detachment of laborers and technicians. The organization soon became the *Geheime Brandraketen-Laboratorium* (Secret Fire Rocket Laboratory). Reminiscent of Danish and Austrian rocket establishments, the men swore an oath of secrecy—not even their superior officers were permitted to examine their labors. The laboratory was responsible only to the General Staff. In 1823 these works were placed under General Friedrich von Müffling, who expanded the facilities and initiated experimentation along Austrian lines. In 1826 he arranged a comparative trial between Prussian rockets and howitzers, but the latter proved to be superior in accuracy at short distances. Since both explosive and incendiary rockets came to be produced, in 1826 the facility's name was shortened to *Secret Rocket Laboratory*. Shortly, it was renamed again to *Raketen-Kommando* ("Rocket Detachment") but was still not a combat unit. On 18 February 1828 came another name change: *Feurwerks-Kompagnie* ("Fireworks Company"), and on 31 March 1831, the name was changed to *Königl.*

Feurwerks-Laboratorium ("Royal Fireworks Laboratory"). The manager was a Major König, while Dietrich was listed merely as a "member."[3]

Parachute, ricochet, and rocket guns and other rocket weapons were turned out at Spandau. Secrecy was still obligatory. Prussian artillerist Johann von Hoyer, who in 1827 wrote *System der Brandraketen nach Congreve und Anderen* (*System of Congreve Incendiary Rockets and Others*), said nothing of Prussian rocketry, though he did promote the formation of rocket troops.[4]

On 14 February 1837 the Prussians renamed the laboratory again. It was now a *Feurwerks-Abteilung* ("Fireworks Establishment"). Five years later, Dietrich retired. Ironically, after this the authorities finally placed the weapons in the hands of troops. The men were mustered only on a temporary basis when the Schleswig-Holstein (Prusso-Danish War) of 1848–50 broke out. The General Staff sent rocketeers to Swinemünde (now Swinoujscie, Poland) in June 1848. They were armed with 2-inch (5 cm) caliber rockets for defending the coast around the Gulf of Pomerania. A so-called "rocket train" was mobilized on 14 April 1849 and joined the army marching into Schleswig-Holstein. The war chronicles fail to define the "train," which may have been a

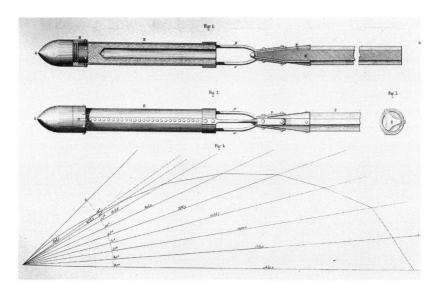

FIGURE 6.1

Prussian 2-inch (5 cm) war rocket, ca. 1863, featuring a novel guidestick attachment.

(*s.i. 83–287*)

field supply unit; nor is there any record of its participation in the fighting. Whatever it was, the Prussian rocket unit disappeared after the war. About the same time, William Hale took advantage of the war mood and persuaded the Prussians to hold a trial of his rotating rockets. This test was made on 17 October 1850 on the Tegeler Schiessplatz (Tegel Firing Range, now Jungfernheide) in Berlin. His rockets performed well but the Prussians refused to buy; anyway, it was too late to use them in the war.[5]

The Swiss Neufchatel Canton controversy of 1856 gave Prussia reason again to activate rocket troops. Pack-horses carrying rockets were prepared, as were reserve caissons for operations in the rugged Neufchatel mountains. Hale's hydraulic presses were installed at Spandau in anticipation of mass-scale production, but diplomacy resolved the crisis and war was averted.[6]

Though meant to be temporary, Prussian rocketeers remained on active status for an undetermined time. Perhaps they were armed with Hale's rockets beginning in 1859, when the Prussians finally purchased these projectiles and began making them at Spandau. They also retained standard 2-inch (5 cm) stick models. Yet almost as soon as they were adopted, in 1863 Hale and other war rockets were withdrawn and superseded by rifled guns. During the Franco-Prussian War (1870–71), however, Prussian *Raketeurs* were reactivated and attached to a "rocket train division." Interestingly, it appears that the Prussians fired rockets against French balloons during the siege of Paris in 1870, including one bearing the French Minister of War as he was about to depart from the capital. If so, these were surely the first anti-aircraft rockets, although the rockets may have been mere signal types. In any event, a so-called *Raketenstudienbüro* ("Rocket Research Branch") now existed. It was part of the Fireworks Establishment, which was divided into a section for producing experimental war rockets and another for making fuses and mines. This bureau ceased to exist in 1872, but the Fireworks Establishment lasted until late in the century making, among other products, lifesaving rockets, signal rockets, and occasionally experimental war rockets.[7]

Bavaria

In 1827, Bavarian King Ludwig I sent artillery officers on a rocket fact-finding mission to France, England, Sweden, and the Low Countries. Rocket-manufacturing secrets were purchased in England—from whom it is not known—and a *Raketenkommission* ("Rocket Commission") was set up in the arsenal at the Bavarian capital of Munich to begin rocket construction. Little progress was made. Then, in 1850, the itinerant Hungarian pyrotechnist Ladislaus Lukasky appeared and successfully demonstrated his own rockets, convincing the Bavarians to adopt the weapons permanently. According to the *Allgemein Militär-Zeitung* (*General Military Journal*) of 13 April 1850: "One hears that four rocket batteries of six [firing] stands each will be created to form an independent corps under the artillery command." In September the same journal reported that Major Hüss, "President of the Rocket Commission," had been sent to the nearby Austrian provinces of Tyrol and Vorarlberg to inspect rocket batteries there. However, the 16 August 1851 *Zeitung* announced: "The formerly discussed creation of rocket batteries will be discontinued. . . . The main reason for this appears to be that the [rocket] ammunition. . . cannot be stored without becoming entirely useless. Recent tests have shown that rockets manufactured eight or nine months ago and stored until now have failed to fire." The Bavarians tried again two years later, again without success, then gave up rockets altogether. As for Lukasky, he next promoted his rockets in the small German kingdom of Württemberg, but again the problem of deteriorating rockets frustrated progress."[8]

The experiences of Prussia and Bavaria underscore one of the major technological flaws of the nineteenth-century military powder rocket, namely its poor storage characteristics. This undoubtedly could be traced to improperly prepared propellant or inadequate propellant liners (cases for protecting the propellant). Dutch rocketry efforts were hindered by another technological drawback, the notorious inaccuracy of the rocket.

The Netherlands

In the Anglo-Dutch assault on Algiers in 1816, British Congreve rockets were given to Dutch sailors and in the same year, the Dutch themselves began to experiment. Three extensive series of firing trials were conducted at Staalduin, Waalsdorp, and Naarden by Lieutenant-Colonel Willem Petrus del Camp of the Netherlands Artillery. Probably constructed with the aid of the Netherlands Artillery, the rockets weighed 22–37 pounds (10–16.7 kg) with maximum calibers of 3 inches (7.6 cm). The largest reached 4,450 yards (4,172 m), but deviations were as much as 2,845 feet (889 m). Del Camp was so disheartened that he abandoned further experimentation.[9]

Captain Abraham Scheidius of the Netherlands Indies Artillery started his own investigations, probably in Java, where he was stationed. These became adopted by that service in 1821, but only on a trial basis. The sheet-steel projectiles were 2.7 inches (7 cm) in diameter, weighed 50.6 pounds (23 kg) with grenade warheads, and had ranges of about 2,650 yards (2,450 m). The Indies rocket unit was furnished with wooden trestle or tripod stands (usually set at 50° for firing). In 1824, when natives revolted in the Celebes (now part of Indonesia), the opportunity to try the weapons in combat presented itself, and trestles were supplied to companies of the 50th Field Artillery Battalion, which also bore normal field guns. The battalion tried incendiary "Dutch Congreves" against native fortifications made of felled trees near Campong Supra, but the results were disappointing. Demonstrations were made before Joseph Jacobus van Geen, Commanding General of the Celebes expedition, to determine the best firing angles for that terrain, and he believed the rockets could still be put to good use in coming battles.[10]

As it turned out, they saw little action and played no decisive role. Probably they did the most damage against native cavalry near Campong Mangara, Bombang, on 15 March 1825. Following the Celebes campaign, Captain Scheidius's rockets were withdrawn.[11]

In the Netherlands itself, Artillery Captain Dirk de Boer made his own rockets at Amersfoort from 1827 to 1829. In place of guidesticks he used metal vanes, though he was not the first to do so. Further trials, undertaken at Waalsdorp in 1830–31, were not entirely satisfactory.

At the same time, a J. Anderson came to the Netherlands to sell the secret of improved Congreves; he was probably James Anderson, "merchant" of London, who throughout the late 1820s and 1830s allegedly represented the proprietors of Congreve's private rocket factory at Bow. He attempted to sell the British Government the "exclusive right" to manufacture rockets and keep the "profound secret" of their manufacture from foreign governments. Anderson evidently did not keep his word, and launched 32-, 24-, 12-, 6-, and 3-pounders (14.5, 10.8, 5.4, 2.7, and 1.3 kg) on the bathing beach at Scheveninghen, just south of the Hague. Similar to the experiences of del Camp, dispersions were excessive. Anderson received a stipend, but his "secret" was not bought. De Boer's tests continued, but the final outcome was negative and the Dutch Army refused to adopt his rockets.[12]

Through agents in the Netherlands, William Hale was granted a Dutch patent (No. 192) for his original stickless rocket design of 1844, but this was for naught; the Dutch simply were not interested. Another foreigner tried; incredibly, it was "the false Dauphin," the alleged heir to the French throne, Louis XVII, who escaped execution during the French Revolution. He was living in Delft, Holland, under the name Karl Wilhelm Naundorff.[13]

In 1845 Naundorff was in desperate need of money and attempted to sell

FIGURE 6.2

Karl Naundorff (1785?–1845), claiming to be the lost heir to the French throne, almost sold the Dutch his war-rocket system. He died before negotiations were complete. (S.I. 83–4031)

his own knowledge of war rockets. He is said to have been a brilliant mechanic, inventor, and pyrotechnist and to have owned a pyrotechnical laboratory in England while he was exiled there. Naundorff first tried to interest the French in his ideas, possibly including his knowledge of rockets. He was turned down by them, mainly for sensitive political reasons, but shortly he succeeded in interesting the Dutch. After clandestine negotiations, a satisfactory trial of his rockets was made on 13 April 1845. The director of the Military Academy of Breda placed land at his disposal for further experiments, but the French police tried to intervene. On 20 July 1845, the Dutch Minister of War finally agreed to purchase his plans and guaranteed Naundorff 30,000 Dutch gulden (today about $7,800). But Naundorff was by then gravely ill, and a month later, on 10 August, he succumbed.[14]

The Naundorff affair was probably the closest the Dutch came to establishing a national war-rocket establishment. In 1859, a new pyrotechnic school was rebuilt out of the old arsenal in Delft. Illumination (flare) rockets were now made here, as well as war rockets for the garrison artillery for defensive purposes. At the same time, rifled guns were introduced for the field and coast artillery, immediately supplanting the need for war rockets. Remaining rockets were disposed of by firing them on Delft's firing range, ending Holland's colorful, though somewhat ill-fated, early attempts at military rocketry.[15]

Greece

Greece, too, has a curious history of attempts to use Congreve rockets. Congreve rocket warfare is intertwined with the history of Greece's fight for independence from the Ottoman Empire. Congreve rockets first appeared in Greek waters as early as 1808–09, when British Royal Navy vessels employed them at Cerigo and elsewhere to force the French out of the Ionian Islands. The Greeks quickly concluded that this mode of warfare, using inexpensive, portable artillery suitable for both mountain and coastal operations, was ideal for throwing off the Turkish yoke.[16]

England stood at the forefront of those nations that passionately supported the Greek cause, and the poet Lord Byron became the leading figure in that movement. On 18 March 1823, a Greek committee was founded in London to help raise arms and money. From the start, the two Greek representatives in London, Jean Orlandos and Andreas Luriottis, had sought rockets, but without success. Also attached to the committee was William Parry, allegedly an artillery engineer, whose background was questionable because he suffered from both alcoholism and boasting. He claimed to have served under Congreve at Woolwich and to have fought in rocket bombardments; others said he was no more than a ship's carpenter or caulker. Unfortunately, what appealed most to the committee most was Parry's claim that he could make rockets better than any man in England and that Congreve had unjustly received renumeration for improvements he (Parry) had suggested. The committee charged him with supplying the needed artillery and instructing the Greeks in how to make rockets for use in Byron's contemplated siege of Lepanto.[17]

Parry was expected to arrive at Missolonghi in January 1824 on the ship *Anne* with British artificers and all the materials for rocket-making. The *Anne* came on schedule, but neither rockets nor materials were aboard. Parry explained that the Committee was to blame, as they had not seen fit to send anything. Byron was very frustrated. "Where are the Congreve rockets, of which the Greeks who delight in that sort of weapon, have been told so much and have formed such high expectations?" he asked his artillery captain. Byron had no recourse but to abandon the siege.[18]

Apart from one or two other abortive attempts to try out Congreves, nothing is known of further Greek rocketry activities until well after Greece was finally free of the Turks. However, despite the country's hard-won independence in 1830, it found itself under new foreign masters. Due to major civil unrest, the European powers had imposed Otto I, a Bavarian, as Greece's first king, and he had brought a retinue of German advisers. Consequently, the new

FIGURE 6.3

The Greek rocket establishment, organized by Bavarian advisors in the 1840s, consisted of a battery with six mules for carrying six 6-pounder (2.7 kg) rockets. (s.i. 72–4973)

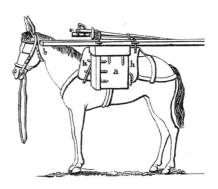

Greek Army, which included the nucleus of a Congreve rocket system, was started in the Bavarian capital of Munich. In 1836, Bavarian artillery captain Joseph Schmozl was dispatched to Nauplia, Peloponnesius, then the Greek capital, to continue to work. Here a rocket laboratory was established in an old building in a military park. There were the usual difficulties at first, but later firing trials on the Nauplia range were said to have been satisfactory. Soon, activities were shifted to the new capital in Athens.[19]

By June 1838, a small experimental company of *Rouketiston* ("Rocketeers") was organized and in 1840 they were placed on permanent status. The 24-man unit comprised a foot (infantry) section of eight firing stands for 12-pounder (5.4 kg) grenade rockets and mules for transporting the ammunition over Greece's rugged terrain; and a cavalry, or more properly, horse artillery section, with four stands for 6-pounder (2.7 kg) grenade rockets. The personnel almost exclusively were Greek nationals trained at Nauplia. Plans called for eventual expansion of the *Rouketiston* to 100 soldiers, but politics again intruded.[20]

Greeks resented domination by foreigners, which led to a bloodless coup in 1843 in which Otto was forced to dismiss his Bavarian advisers. The Bavarian-formed rocket establishment, partly staffed by Bavarians, also had to go, abruptly ending the Greek adventure with Congreve rockets.

Portugal

Portugal had a far longer and more active experience in war rocketry. As early as 1796, Sergeant-Major Jerónimo Nogueira de Andrade of the Portuguese artillery designed an incendiary rocket, though it never got beyond the design stage. However, Congreve rockets were used frequently in the country during the Peninsular War (1808–14).[21]

The British and their rockets returned during the Miguelist civil wars of 1832–34, when England sold arms and levied volunteers for the Liberal cause, determined to install Maria II as monarch. (Their opponents were the Miguelites, who favored Maria's uncle, Miguel, as king.)

Even before the hostilities, in 1831, British-born Italian soldier of fortune Colonel Francis Maceroni offered his own "naval compound rockets" to the Liberal forces, but his fee was too exorbitant, amounting to the command of a fleet, and he was refused.[22]

Standard British Congreve rockets were fitted on ships and distributed to British and Portuguese artillerymen for the 1832–33 siege of Oporto, the Miguelist stronghold. Rockets were fired from both sides during the siege. Miguelite rockets came from unknown sources, including an unnamed French engineer who, according to the London *Times* of 27 September 1832, "went mad soon after his arrival in Coimbra."[23]

In contrast, on the Liberal side, the Rocket Brigade commanded by British volunteer William Bollaert is well documented by his memoirs. A former chemist and mining engineer, Bollaert was selected for the Artillery because of his work with explosives. On 17 June 1833, he noted that Colonel Antonio de Padu da Costa, commander of the Liberal Artillery, "was about forming a rocket brigade, to be composed of '*rapazes inteligentes*' (intelligent lads), requesting me to be one of them . . . So at last I got into scientific soldiering."[24]

The Brigade was formed on 25 June, "but," wrote Bollaert, "as to the '*rapazes inteligentes*' . . . I never saw any of them to assist me, and had to draw upon our Portugese artillerymen. A Mr. Anderson had brought from England a large quantity of shell, shot, carcass, and Congreve rockets, 9-, 12-, 18-, and 24-pounders [4, 5.4, 8, and 10.8 kg]." Most likely this was James Anderson, who had attempted to sell rockets to the Dutch in 1830. At any rate, the Brigade and other British rocket units in this campaign saw extensive service.[25]

In the 1850s, Portuguese pyrotechnist and inventor Francisco Antonio Tavares began his own experiments with war rockets at Ribeira-do-Marchante, near Setubal, where there was a large testing range and artillery school. He also experimented at "Vendas No" (probably Vendas Novas, between Lisbon and Evora). Eventually, his rockets were appraised by commissions of Portuguese Marine and Army officers. Then, according to Tavares in his *Notice sur les Fusées de Guerre* (*Notice on War Rockets*) (Lisbon, 1869), the

Minister of Marine acquired some for "the expedition destined to operate on the banks of the Zambezie." By this he meant a punitive expedition in the Portuguese colony of Mozambique, southeast Africa.[26]

One Portuguese historian writes of the 1867 campaign that "Congreve rockets which were highly esteemed in Europe, were eminently fitting for the wars in the [African] countryside; and with some effect some were expedited to the command at Zambesie, for subjugating Bonga." It is unspecified in these accounts who made the rockets; as for Bonga, he was a notorious "half-caste rebel" of the region who followed a career of plunder and murder. The indigenous Portuguese force, carrying twenty 1-inch (3 cm) rockets, marched on Bonga's stockade of Massangano. But the Portuguese were slaughtered from behind as they approached the stockade, the rockets being of no avail.[27]

A second expedition, mounted in October 1867, included nineteen rockets and a launcher. This equipment, it was said, came from Lisbon. Again, Bonga triumphed. In the third expedition, in November 1868, one of the missiles caused a fire within the stockade, causing great confusion within. Bonga survived. Not until still further expeditions was a peace settlement signed in 1871. For the later expeditions, greater quantities and calibers of rockets were sent. These were of 3.5 inches (9 cm) and 4.5 inches (12 cm). Again, it is not known whether they were of Tavares's manufacture.[28]

Evidently, Portugal retained Congreve-type rockets until quite late. The *Army and Navy Journal* (New York) of 10 February 1877 said that "Hale rockets have been recently adopted by the government of Portugal in lieu of the Congreve." This is the last known reference to the use of the old powder war rocket in Portugal.[29]

Italy

The history of rocketry in Italy in the Congreve era centers in the Kingdom of Sardinia, the most powerful state in the patchwork of principalities that, in 1870, became a united Italy. The Kingdom started its own rocket investigations in 1814, but details are wanting. On 8 January 1823, as part of the reorganization of its artillery, Sardinia established a *Compagnia Artificierri* ("Artificer's Company"). This unit appears to have served a function similar to that of the Swedish Fireworks Corps in making fuses, experimental war rockets, and other military pyrotechnics.

On 25 November 1830, King Carlo Felice issued the following decree: "As has been told to us, the war rockets, after experimenting with them for many years, are now good enough to be employed in our army." But the King did not live to see his decree carried out. He died on 27 April 1831, and Carlo Alberto assumed the throne.[30]

The new monarch expanded the rocket program, in the same year specifying that each field artillery battery be apportioned 200 rockets of 3-inch (7.6 cm) caliber with grenades or incendiaries. Mountain batteries were provisioned with the same number of 2.5-inch (6.3 cm) caliber rockets. Defensive fortresses were apportioned 180 rockets. The respective batteries were also assigned rocket caissons, each vehicle holding sixty rounds. The King thus wished to integrate rockets into the artillery rather than set up a single, specialized unit. His decree also authorized rocket construction in the Royal Laboratory at Turin and outlined how artillerymen were to be instructed. It also authorized the director of the Royal Laboratory to personally inspect every rocket for possible defects and to recommend improvements. Further, rocket workmen, who were placed under the immediate supervision of a chief *Razziere* ("Rocketman"), were to be highly paid with wages graded according to ability.[31]

This system remained in force for several years. Then, about 1845, Lieutenant-Colonel Pictet of the Swiss Artillery visited Turin and was cordially received by the King. Carlo Alberto willingly agreed to appoint a commission to evaluate his rockets as possible improvements over those already in Sardinian service.[32]

The first trials were carried out in 1847–48 at the spacious parks of Venaria Reale, outside Turin. Pictet published the results as *Essai sur les Propriétés et la Tactique des Fusées de Guerre (Essay on the Properties and Tactics of War Rockets)* (Turin, 1848). In its final pages Pictet was compelled to add the following: "During the writing of this memoir, the war between Italy and Austria suddenly flared up . . . this was to have been an excellent occasion for proving our rockets. Unfortunately, the experiments had hardly been completed. There existed neither equipment nor personnel nor sufficient provisions. . . . Consequently, our rockets were not put into play."[33]

The Turin rocket plant temporarily suspended production upon the outbreak of hostilities. The factory apparently flourished after the revolution, as later descriptions can be found of different calibers of Sardinian rockets and ancillary equipment. It is also known that in 1850 Major Giovanni Cavalli, director of the Turin laboratory, witnessed trials of Hale rockets at Woolwich and Shoeburyness and saw hydraulic presses, but this equipment was not put to use.[34]

Sardinia was a participant in the Crimean War, but there is no evidence that its rockets were used. Not until 1860, during the final wars of the *Risorgimento* (Resurgence) for Italian national unification, can references to battle employment of Sardinian rockets be found. In late September of that year, during the naval bombardment of Ancona, incendiary rockets were fired against the forces of Francis II of the Kingdom of the Two Sicilies, who opposed unification, but their effect was not significant. Likewise, late in 1860 to early 1861, Sardinian rockets were sent against Gaeta, the fall of which was one more step toward a united Italy and the beginning of the modern Italian armed forces.[35]

Consequently, Sardinian war rockets were incorporated into the country's munition stores. But in 1873 the government of a now united Italy suppressed the further use of war rockets, which had been outmoded by the rifled and breech-loading gun. Signal and occasionally experimental war rockets continued to be made by the old Turin laboratory as late as 1899.[36]

Belgium

Rocketry experiments were conducted in the Low Countries, principally at Antwerp, even before Belgium won its independence from Holland in 1830. In the late 1830s, other rocketry experiments were carried out by the Under-Director of the Antwerp Arsenal, Saxon-born Karl Wilhelm Bormann, known in Belgium as Charles Guilliaume Bormann. However, though Bormann was a widely respected artillerist acclaimed for his improved Bormann cannon shell fuses, evidently he did not succeed with rockets.[37]

Nonetheless, Belgium produced interesting and innovative ideas in rocketry. For example, Captain Jean-Baptiste Splingard of the Belgian *École de Pyrotechnie* ("Pyrotechnic School") wrote a booklet in 1858 detailing new manufacturing techniques and describing a *fusée a âme annulaire* (rocket with an annular cavity). The annular (ring-shaped) cavity within the propellant apparently enlarged the burning area, increasing initial thrust, and hence, velocity and power.[38]

But like several other countries, Belgium only experimented with rockets and had no rocket troops. In 1859 Belgian artillery Lieutenant Alexandre-Guillaume Nicaise wrote in his *Considérations sur les Fusées de Guerre* (*Considerations of War Rockets*): "War rockets may be unquestionably used by the Belgian Army: (1) for fighting cavalry; (2) for replacing ordinary artillery in the polders [low land claimed from the sea], swampy [places] . . . where our campaign artillery will move with difficulty; (3) for the defense of low coasts and forts of the Scheldt . . .; and (4), for the defense of strong places." Belgian War Minister Baron Pierre Chazal was strongly in favor of Nicaise's plea for adopting war rockets for use in the country's unique terrain, and saw that Nicaise's booklet was well circulated. But the efforts were unavailing, probably because of progress in standard artillery.[39]

Spain

The history of military rocketry in Spain in the nineteenth century somewhat mirrors that of neighboring Portugal. Congreve rockets were introduced onto Spanish soil during the Peninsular War, and in the 1830s England provided volunteers and rockets to the Liberals (Isabellinos, after Isabella II) in the Miguelist Civil War. According to the now rare *Noticia sobre el Origen, Progresos y Estado Actual de los Cohetes de Guerra Llamados a la Congreve* (*Notice on the Origin, Progress, and Actual State of Rockets Called Congreve*) (Madrid, 1833) by Spanish artillery Captain Manuel Pezuela, Marquis of Viluma, there had been promising rocketry experiments in 1832–33 in Havana, capital of the Spanish colony of Cuba, initiated under the direction of the island's governor.[40]

At the outset of the civil war at home, *Noticia* came to the attention of Don Joaquin Navarro Sangra, Director General of War for the Northern Provinces. He immediately ordered similar experiments in Seville and dispatched an envoy, Lieutenant Colonel Don José Núñez Arenas, to London for the express purpose of procuring British rockets. England responded and sold 4,730

FIGURE 6.4
Spanish artillerymen fixing tripod rocket launcher during the first Carlist War of 1833–40. (S.I. 4356A)

rockets with carriages and 350 signal rockets to the Isabellinos. Part of the arrangement called for a volunteer English "Auxilliary Legion." Within the Legion, which arrived in Navarra in 1835, was a rocket battery under Captain J.B. Backhouse, Royal Artillery. Congreve rockets were also distributed to the forces of the future regent of the country, General Baldermero Espartero, who wanted them because of a shortage of regular ammunition. Rocketeers were hastily organized and fought principally in the mountainous Basque provinces, around Bilbao, in 1836. There was also a rocket battery in the army of Brigadier Don Joaquín Ponte y Araujo, which saw action in the vicinity of the castle of Ulizarra, near Ojascastro, Logroño, as well as in Vendejo, Santander, and other points.[41]

The Miguelist civil wars terminated in 1840 and the rocket troops were soon dissolved. Modest experimentation continued and in 1844, artillery Lieutenant Don Macario Arnaiz proposed the formation of standing rocket troops, but he was turned down due to lack of funds. Not until the opening of the Moroccan War of 1859–60 were Spanish rocket troops again activated. A private British fireworks company offered for sale rockets suitable for war. Spain agreed and integrated them within a specially formed *Compañia* or *Batería de Cohetes* ("Rocket Company" or "Battery") placed under the command of Captain Don Miguel de Orús y Barcaiztegui. Spanish novelist-politician Pedro Antonio de Alarcón, author of *The Three Cornered Hat,* was a soldier in this war and described the rockets in his *Diario de un Testigo de la Guerra de Africa* (*Diary of an Eye-Witness to the African War*) as "frightening monsters" and "terrifying projectiles."[42]

The "terrifying projectiles" were 3.5 inches (9 cm) in diameter. The total number of rockets transported by the *Batería* was 432, along with eight tripods carried by mules. Additional rockets and tripods, fabricated at the Spanish Navy works at Cadiz, were given to the Spanish fleet. Despite a limited training session of only four days, Orús's men fired their new weapons "with good direction" at Aduana on 23 January 1860, according to their captain. At Wad-Ras (or Uadrás), on 23 March, Orús' *Batería* helped to reinforce the Spanish avant guard. Alarcón remarked that it contributed to "a new and glorious triumph" in Spanish military annals. Rockets played no small part in the defeat of the Moroccans at Tetuán. Peace was shortly declared, and the *Batería de Cohetes* was disbanded.[43]

The Spanish high command was convinced of the value of rockets and in 1861 ordered the extensive *Pirotecnia Militar* ("Military Pyrotechnical Works") of Seville to commence mass production of the weapon; previously, the factory made only paper cartridges and the like. The state of the art still had far to go however, and explosions were common. As a result, the director of the *Pirotecnia,* Lieutenant-Colonel Salvador de Castro y Ruiz del Arco, was sent to Russia to consult with Konstantinov. Yet in Spain, too, war rockets were outmoded by other artillery, and were soon phased out. As late as 1895, however, Lieutenant-Colonel Gabriel Vidal y Ruby advocated their adoption for employment against insurgents in Cuba. They were suited for the Cuban terrain, he remarked, which was mountainous and full of thickets and jungles impenetrable by field artillery. "We must either carry and use rockets," wrote Vidal y Ruby, "or deprive ourselves of the valuable assistance of artillery and suppress it absolutely." He recommended either Hale's rockets or the French central-stick pattern. One interesting feature he suggested was carrying a weathercock on the end of a pole, which could be placed in a position to tell which direction the wind was blowing. "If it is not wished to manufacture rockets in Spain," he concluded, "they might be bought in England." Neither the Spanish nor British took him up on this, thus ending Spanish attempts at continuing the employment of these weapons.[44]

Hungary

Another small war rocket establishment briefly existed in Hungary, as a tool to help attain independence from Austria.

During the Hungarian revolution of 1848–49, Hungarians entered negotiations with several parties for obtaining war rockets, including Hale rockets, but none of the arrangements materialized. In the meantime, Hungarian-born Sandar Mozer, a former noncommissioned officer of the Austrian *Raketenbatterien,* set about producing his own rockets. By October 1848, after six weeks of experiments, he had finished. In December Mozer's hand-pressed rockets were fired before a Hungarian military commission. The small, 3- and 6-pound (1.3 and 2.7 kg) rockets had a maximum range of 1,800 yards (1,650 m). Upon the commission's recommendations, they were accepted, and the Minister of War promoted Mozer to a lieutenant in charge of a newly created Hungarian Rocket Corps.[45]

Rocket production began in Pest (Budapest), but the city was soon occupied by the Austrians. The factory was relocated to Nagyvared during the final days of December 1848. Despite the interruption, organizational work was excellent and production progressed quickly under Josef Szkopal, a weapons expert. Szkopal designed and built his own rockets, possibly based on an examination of captured Austrian models. Szkopal rockets weighed 7 pounds (3 kg) and ranged 1,148 yards (1,050 m).[46]

The factory soon produced three launchers, the equivalent of an artillery half-battery. These, with a supply of rockets, were furnished to Hungarian forces in Transylvania, under the command of General Josef Bem, the Polish rocket pioneer who had volunteered his services in support of the Hungarian cause. Bem's Hungarian rocket troops played a part at the siege of Gyulafehervar and in minor engagements. Hungarian rockets were also used at the siege of Buda.

Meanwhile, gun founder Aron Gabor visited the Nagyvared plant in May 1849, then returned to the foundry he had set up at Kezdivasarhely in Transylvania where he turned out his own rockets. These were tested in June 1849, but a few weeks later Gabor was killed.

Throughout the revolution, the Nagyvared plant produced about fifty launchers and an unknown quantity of rockets, including 12-pound (5.4 kg) types. An Austrian launcher along with 100 rockets were captured at the battle of Iglo in February 1849. Altogether, the Hungarian army had twenty-eight launchers during the campaign (possibly counting the captured Austrian stand). In any case, the Russian Army intervened in the struggle, defeating the Hungarians at Vilagos, where they surrendered, and themselves captured a dozen Hungarian rocket stands and 158 rockets.[47]

After the suppression of the revolution, Hungarians at home and abroad made plans for a renewed armed revolt. Negotiations were renewed with Hale, mainly at the insistence of Lajos Kossuth, leader of the Hungarian exiles. These were not fruitful, though sample Hales were apparently bought.[48]

Congreve and Hale rocketry was by no means only a European phenomenon. Across the Atlantic, both the United States and Latin America saw their own share of rocket troops and experiments during the Age of Congreve.

CHAPTER 7

Rocketry in the Americas

Congreve and Hale rockets appeared in three major U.S. conflicts in the nineteenth century—the War of 1812, the Mexican War, and the Civil War. There was also an attempt to establish a peacetime rocket organization during the 1830s. Yet the U.S. never had any permanent rocket battery. Perhaps this was because, with the exception of the War of 1812, Americans had no close-at-hand opportunity of copying rockets, as had the Europeans. Another factor was that the U.S. peacetime standing army was restricted in size and expenditures. Various rocketry activities also took place south of the border, in Latin America, but outside of Brazil and perhaps Peru, they likewise seem to have lasted only during wartimes.

War of 1812—U.S. Experiments

British-born Thomas Cooper, a U.S. resident and close friend of President Madison, made the earliest known American suggestion to use war rockets.

Cooper, Professor of Chemistry at Carlisle College, Pennsylvania, wrote to Madison on 18 February 1813: "I understand some privateer has brought in, an English vessel laden with Congreve rockets . . . would it not be advisable to distribute a dozen for analysis and imitation, to a committee of two or three men of science in Boston, New York, and Philadelphia?" Cooper's request was soon granted, though the rockets came from quite a different source.[1]

Meanwhile, John Beath, a Boston instrument- and truss-maker, became the earliest known American to make his own war rockets, also in 1813, though he was probably unaware of Cooper's suggestions. Beath fashioned what he called a "spring rocket," with an iron body and conical head 12 inches (30.4 cm) long and filled with balls or incendiary. The spring, his own innovation, was attached to the head and meant for sticking onto enemy vessels. On 6 March, the inventor fired 6-pound (2.7 kg) versions with different powder strengths before a group that included two American naval heroes of the war, Captain Isaac Hull and Commodore John Rodgers. Though the rockets ranged 2,000 yards (1,828 m), Beath's friend, James Ellison, a Boston Bank clerk, afterwards certified that the spring rockets "may be of infinite importance in annoying the enemy's squadron in the Chesapeake . . . [and] may be made from one to 40 lb [0.4–18 kg] weight, with ranges from 1, 2, or 2.5 miles [1,610–4,020 m]." The *Boston Gazette,* reporting on Beath's endeavors, commented: "We wish him all that patronage and support from Government which this inventor justly merits."[2]

Simultaneously, another independent U.S. rocket experimenter appeared. By the end of March 1813, Ordnance Major George Bomford, stationed at Albany, New York, reported to Chief of Ordnance Colonel Decius Wadsworth: "I have bestowed much time and reflection on the rocket, and have every reason to believe that I have succeeded in making them range as far in proportion to their weights as any hitherto attempted. My first rocket bursted after which I covered them [with] two or three turnings of glued canvass. When dry I gave them a brush of rosin varnish to secure them from moisture."[3]

At this juncture, a Congreve specimen, or according to one account, "a piece of the composition," was picked up after the attack of 3 May 1813 on Havre-de-Grace, Maryland, and sent to Madison. The President recalled Cooper's earlier request and forwarded it to him. Soon, according to one paper, the professor "ascertained the constituent parts, and their proportion of this combustible substance." But no rockets seem to have been made by Cooper himself, who is said to have passed his findings to Beath.[4]

Beath's name thus came to the attention of the President. The rockets were not made use of, but in recognition of Beath's efforts, Madison appointed him Deputy Commissary of Ordnance, though the appointment became so bogged down in the bureaucracy that it was refused altogether. This prompted the *Gazette* of 28 July 1814 to indignantly point out that a Congreve rocket "was placed on public exhibit at No. 1, Scolley's Building, Treemont Street, Boston," but "falls short in some particulars, and in none is superior to his [Beath's]." Furthermore, the paper went on, the British Government "rewarded Colonel Congreve with rank and independence," while "the American government *refused* Mr. Beath the inconsiderable office of deputy commissary of ordnance." So far as can be determined, Beath's case was not redressed.[5]

As the war progressed, Americans acquired additional rocket specimens. During an action at St. Leonard's Creek, Maryland, on 8 June 1814, Commodore Joshua Barney informed U.S. Secretary of the Navy William Jones that the rocket he was sending had gone "into the ground and did not explode." While *Nile's Weekly Register* of 20 August 1814 reported that this specimen too had been analyzed, it did not specify who was involved nor what happened to it thereafter.[6]

By then, following the destruction of the U.S. Capitol earlier that month, American opinions of Congreve rockets were at their sharpest, whether against or for the use of these weapons. The *Baltimore Telegraph* of 27 August 1814 reported that "we have been informed that the Presidential Palace [i.e., the White House] was destroyed by a Congreve rocket and that all the public buildings have been levelled to the ground." *Nile's* decried the rockets as "unfair" and "cruel." The *Boston Gazette* for 22 September published a suggestion, also circulated in other papers, that the United States adopt the rocket and the Committee of Defense erect "a *Rocket Battery*" at either Fort Warren or Independence. "We understand," they added, "Mr. Beath has expressed a willingness not only to superintend the making of these rockets . . . but also to be stationed at the *Battery* in case of attack."[7]

A few days later, on 26 September, the *Gazette* announced a new contender, a former French officer who entered a military school at the age of nine: "M. De Fauvel [John B.G.D. Faurel], of Baltimore, Lt. Col. of Engineers, has offered his services in constructing mortars to throw three bombs at a time . . . they will also discharge 200 rockets, superior to Congreve's . . . De Fauvel offers the plans and instructions necessary for casting three engines of defense to the Comitee of Vigilance thro'out the United States." But despite such claims, none of the early projects were heard of again.[8]

Nevertheless, a few rockets *were* employed by the Americans against the

British; the question of their origin is still unanswered. They were used in September 1814 by the newly formed "Corps of Artillery" created in May 1814 and commanded by Brigadier General Alexander Macomb at Plattsburgh, New York. In his General Orders dated 5 September, Macomb's adjutant general, William R. Duncan, stated that "Mr. Paris, captain of artificers, will form a corps of rocketeers with his men—they will take the direction of the chief engineer." According to H. Lallemand's *A Treatise on Artillery* (New York, 1820), "an artificer is an artillery soldier who prepares the fuses of shells, &c. makes quick matches, port fires, and all sorts of military fireworks; his pay for this is high."[9]

As for Captain Paris, he cannot be properly identified, but there is other evidence of the existence of U.S. rocketeers at Plattsburgh in 1814. According to the *New York Military Magazine* for 4 September 1841, Macomb "had prepared a brigade of rocketeers, with Congreve rockets which the enemy believed to be his own exclusive possession."[10]

A more telling clue appeared some years later, when Lieutenant-Colonel George Talcott of the Ordnance Department recalled that: "Extensive trials were made in 1813 of rockets and Shrapnell which resulted in the adoption of the latter for our service, and some rockets were also sent to the Northern Frontiers but they were not extensively used although we succeeded in giving them ranges quite equal to British rockets of similar dimensions. The only serious difficulty met with in the trials of rockets was . . . inaccuracy."[11]

Plattsburgh, located in upstate New York, fits the "Northern Frontier" description and it logically seems the Ordnance Department was responsible for the rockets. Perhaps they came from Ordnance Major George Bomford, who undertook his experiments at Albany, about 150 miles (240 km) south of Plattsburgh, down the Hudson River.

Additional war rocketry experiments were carried out in New York at about the same time, although they were completed *after* the affair at Plattsburgh. Bomford gave his rockets to Captain Alden Partridge, instructor of engineering at the Military Academy at West Point. On 9 December 1814 Partridge told Bomford: "I at length have the pleasure to give you some account of the experiments with the 4, and 6 pound [1.8 and 2.7 kg] rockets that you sent me some time ago." Partridge fired the rockets vertically although this direction would have been hardly useful against enemy ranks. With the assistance of Professor Andrew Ellicott of the Academy, Partridge apparently attempted to gauge the power of the rockets by measuring their altitudes. Ellicott timed ascents and descents with a stopwatch. Flights from liftoffs to

FIGURE 7.1

In the United States, Captain Alden Partridge (1785–1854), Superintendant of the U.S. Military Academy, constructed rockets based on British Congreve rockets captured during the War of 1812. (S.I. 77–10208)

landings averaged 26 seconds. Partridge deduced that half of this, or 13 seconds, accounted for the descent, which "according to the laws of falling bodies gives an altitude of 2,718 $^{1}/_{10}$ feet [828 m]."[12]

At the end of the war, General Andrew Jackson wrote to Secretary of War James Monroe from his camp at New Orleans on 17 February 1815: "Some entire Congreve rockets have been found, and a rest from which they are fired, which is my intention to forward to the seat of government whenever a proper opportunity shall offer." It is not known whether or not General Jackson's intention was ever carried out. Thus ended American rocketry during the War of 1812.[13]

Between the Wars

On 15 April 1816, Englishman Thomas Williamson, who was in Paris trying to sell his rockets to the French, wrote a sixteen-page letter to Madison explaining that he was the true inventor of the Congreve rocket and describing in general terms the results (but not the "how") of his ingenuity. He offered to come to the U.S. should there be a position commensurate with his genius. The letter was forwarded by the U.S. legation in Paris, which recommended him highly and added that the French were eagerly bidding for his services. Williamson's offer was not accepted by either country.

Meanwhile, Bomford reported that 145 rockets had been made at ordnance arsenals in the year 1822. The 1835 report listed a Congreve rocket case at Fort Monroe and rocket carriage at Champlain Arsenal.[15]

Following this lull in U.S. activity with war rockets, Secretary of War Joel R. Poinsett advised the Board of Ordnance in October 1838 of his wish to introduce a rocket battery into the army. Perhaps the move was prompted by the experiments of Captain Benjamin Huger of the Ordnance. (On 1 September 1836 Huger had told Bomford: "I have made a few experiments with the Congreve rockets, with considerable success.") Whatever the reason, Poinsett asked the Board for an opinion on the battery's future jurisdiction. The response was that its proper command should be the Artillery. The Secretary concurred, but further experiments were needed.[16]

By early April 1839, instructions were given to the officer commanding the Washington Arsenal to "commence a series of experiments with rockets . . . three inches [7.6 cm] diameter and proceeding to those of larger dimensions, when the proper strength of cases and the compositions to give a suitable range shall have been found by trials."[17]

Colonel Talcott and the Secretary of War must have been negotiating with Alvin C. Goell at the time; for on 31 May 1839, a contract was signed by Talcott and approved by Secretary Poinsett to hire Goell, who may have been a former pyrotechnist at Austria's Wiener-Neustadt rocket works. He was to be paid $3.00 a day to be in charge of war-rocket manufacturing at the Washington Arsenal. The contract called for him to "furnish drawings of all machinery, tools, and fixtures for making war rockets . . . to have a separate shop or place for work with a sufficient number of men . . . to make 3-inch [7.6 cm] rockets to range 3,000 yards [2,743 m] or upwards, to fire them from a carriage through tubes." Goell began his duties the following day.[18]

An existing statement of the cost of the new American peacetime warrocket establishment shows that during Goell's employment from 1 June 1839 to 7 January 1841, the amount spent totaled $13,264.33. This money was for new rocket driving houses with new boring and driving machines, rocket stands, molds, accessories, rocket sticks, tin, sheet and hammered iron for the cases, composition, drawings, and compensation to Goell.[19]

Despite the large financial outlay, the Board was unhappy with Goell's services. The work proceeded very slowly, and not all contractual conditions were met. Two types of rockets were produced; one was a 2-inch (5 cm) rocket weighing 7 pounds (3 kg), the other a 3-inch (7.6 cm) model weighing 19–20 pounds (8.6–9 kg), with sticks. Only fifty 2-inch and eleven 3-inch models were made by 1 February 1841. Goell complained that "I have not had the war rocket laboratory in operation a sufficient time to instruct four men in the art of making war rockets." In addition, he failed to furnish the government with his compositions, arguing that the formulae "were valuable . . . and . . . I could not make known my compositions until I had made experiments in the presence of the Hon. Secretary of War to his satisfaction," that is, when his experiments were finished. But he reminded Board member Major Rufus L. Baker that he had "seen me show five war rockets that ranged a full 3,000 yards [2,740 m]—this is evidence that my compositions are what I stated them to be." Goell then added a complaint that some of the iron given to him for the cases was "full of flaws."[20]

Rocket making, whether in the nineteenth or twentieth century, is laborious and requires the best quality raw materials and sufficient manpower. Perhaps Goell was justified in his complaints. But the Board was unconvinced and declared, after witnessing firing trials, that "the rockets are not well made and the parts not well proportioned." The sticks were "not properly balanced," the 2-inch (5 cm) rockets were a "partial success," the 3-inch (7.6 cm) rockets "a total failure," and "it appears that Mr. Goell does not understand the composition or . . . is ignorant of the proper method of driving it." The Board concluded that it was "neither proper nor advantageous to continue the manufactory under charge of Mr. Goell" and they considered the new brass driving machine constructed by him the only worthwhile information gained from his employment. Plans for a permanent U.S. rocket battery thus dissipated. (Goell should, however, be credited with producing the earliest known rocket manufacturing patents, at least in the U.S. These were U.S. patent 1,986 of 18 February 1841 for a weight-operated (non-hydraulic) rocket press; and U.S. patent 2,009 of 18 March 1841 for a rocket boring machine.)[21]

In the interim of the Goell affair, throughout 1840, Ordnance officers Baker, Huger, Captain Alfred Mordecai, and Major William Wade (retired) were sent abroad as a military commission to study European methods of war. They went to England, France, Prussia, and Sweden. French rocket-firing trials at the Metz Arsenal particularly impressed them. "In all the countries visited," summed up Poinsett, "war rockets are made on a more or less limited scale. All nations make a secret of the details of their manufacture, but the secret appears to be known to all nations."[22]

Indeed, war rockets were known even in the hinterlands of America. A companion of the famous explorer John Charles Frémont, cartographer Charles Preuss, wrote in his diary on 5 September 1842, as the Frémont party were returning after exploring the Rockies and Oregon country: "Last night the young lieutenant [Frémont, then in the Topographical Corps] boasted again how he would fight against the Pawnees if they should try to interfere with us. To kill them all—kill, kill, nothing less. Next year he wants to march against them with bombs and Conyvelts [Congreve] rockets if the government will give its assent." The United States did in fact fire Congreve rockets against Indians. Some are known to have been taken along on an experimental basis in the second Seminole War of 1835–42 in Florida; they made a notable appearance in the battle of Lockahatchee on 15 January 1838. Another Indian tribe was mentioned as a possible target for rocket warfare. On 16 July 1855, Captain William Maynadier, Ordnance, inquired of Lieutenant G.T. Balch, St. Louis, about "the availability of war rockets for use by the Sioux Expedition." Maynadier may have been referring to Hale rockets left over from the Mexican War, then stored in the St. Louis and other arsenals. Whether any of the projectiles were actually issued for this campaign is unknown.[23]

The U.S.–Mexican War

Manufacture of Congreve-type rockets in small numbers continued at American arsenals. The chief objection to the projectiles was the same as encountered in other countries: their lack of accuracy. In January 1844, William Hale in England took out his first patent on the stickless or rotary rocket that, he claimed, solved the problem. In America, war against Mexico was declared in May 1846. That fall, Joshua Burrows Hyde, a Connecticut-born engineer who had met Hale in London, offered to sell Hale's rockets to the U.S. Government on behalf of the inventor. The time was propitious, and on 19 November the Ordnance Department asked General Winfield Scott's opinion of the possibility of a mountain howitzer battery and brigade of rocketeers joining his planned expedition to Vera Cruz and Mexico City. Scott, who vividly recalled Congreve rockets sent against his own forces at the battles of Chippewa and Lundy's Lane in 1814 during the War of 1812, approved of the idea. He left it to Chief of Ordnance Colonel Joseph G. Totten to work out the details.[24]

Final approval was contingent upon results of tests with Hale's new rockets. These went well before a joint Army-Navy board on 24 and 27 November at the Washington Arsenal. Thirteen each of Hale's and Congreve's

2.75-inch (7 cm) rockets were fired. The army officers were impressed, but the blustery chief of the Navy's Bureau of Ordnance, Commodore Lewis Warrington, expressed "strong objections" on account of "the danger of accidental ignition, by the inconvenience of transport, and the difficulty of giving them a right direction when a vessel is in motion." The majority of the board overruled Warrington and felt that the Hale rocket was "at least equal, and probably superior, to that of the ordinary Congreve rocket, with respect to facility, for use on board of armed vessels or boats."[25]

On 11 December, the Secretaries of War and the Navy jointly entered into an agreement with Hyde to purchase manufacturing rights and plans for $20,000, dependent upon another qualifying test. This was held at the Arsenal on 5 January and also went well. Talcott had already issued orders on 3 December for the organization of the rocketeers—asking for volunteers from the Ordnance Corps. When finally formed, the unit was called the Mountain Howitzer and Rocket Battery, U.S. Ordnance Corps.[26]

Meanwhile, Warrington was compelled by the Secretary of the Navy to initiate manufacture of the rockets for that branch. On 30 December 1846, he ordered Benjamin Franklin Coston, then a young Navy officer making signal rockets at the Washington Naval Laboratory, to assist. Coston afterwards became internationally known for his development of hand-held Coston pyrotechnic signals for mariners. Another inventor, John Adolphus Dahlgren, later known for the Dahlgren gun and other naval ordnance advances, was assigned ordnance duty in January 1847 as a lieutenant in charge of the Navy's preliminary investigation of Hale's rockets and their application for naval service. (Actually, Dahlgren was no stranger to rockets. From 1838 to 1842, while on sick leave in France, he took the opportunity to study French war rockets first-hand and afterwards wrote a report on them.) At first, Warrington's relationship with Dahlgren was strained, partly because the commodore resented the Hale rocket project, which had been forced upon him against his wishes. Then, as Dahlgren became involved with many other projects, Warrington came to soften his attitude out of respect for Dahlgren's competence in ordnance matters and probably also out of relief that Hale's rockets were given a lower priority. In fact, it turned out the Navy never did use Hale rockets in the war.[27]

First-Lieutenant George Henry Talcott (no relation to the Colonel George Talcott mentioned above) was given command of the 105-man strong Howitzer and Rocket Battery on 28 December 1846. His subordinate officers were Second-Lieutenants Franklin D. Callendar and Jesse Lee Reno. Reno, after whom the city of Reno, Nevada, was named, normally commanded the

FIGURE 7.2

Hale rockets were first used in battle during the U.S.-Mexican War of 1846–47 in which Captain (later General) Jesse L. Reno (1823– 62) commanded the Mountain Howitzer and Rocket Battery on the American side. (S.I. A5364A)

battery. Armed with six 12-pounder (5.4 kg) mountain howitzers and an initial supply of fifty 2-inch (5 cm) Hale rockets, an unknown number of Congreves, and other ammunition, Talcott's men sailed for Mexico from Fort Monroe, Virginia, on 1 February 1847. The battery was adjoined to the Regiment of Voltigeurs and Foot Riflemen, a conglomerate of calvary, infantry, and artillery. The regiment was among the first wave of American forces of Scott's army that touched Mexican soil on 9 March at Sacrificios Island, about 3 miles (5 km) from Veracruz.[28]

On the whole, the American rocket battery did well in the war. In some skirmishes, the strange sight of rockets and their hissing noise sent Mexican horses flying. Mexican troops more familiar with standard, stick-stabilized rockets had never seen Hale rockets before and called them generically *"cohetes á la Congreve."* Talcott, in his dispatch of 26 October 1847, says that at Veracruz at "about 12 p.m. on the 25th, from the same place [Fort San Iago], I threw ten of Hale's rockets into the city, but drew no fire from the forts." Elsewhere he observed: "We threw about 40 rockets of the old kind [Congreves?] into the city." In the same engagement, Engineer Lieutenant George B. McClellan, later the Union's top general in the Civil War, noted in his diary that "at about 11:30 [p.m. on 25 March] the discharge of a few of our rocketeers caused a stampede amongst the Mexicans." And according to a Mexican historian, "both the enemy and the city now [28 March] threw Congreve rockets, and in a second there were numerous victims."[29]

American rocketeers also fought at Cerro Gordo, where Reno was mentioned in dispatches; Contreras, Cherubusco; and in the assault on Chapultepec castle, Mexico City, where Reno was again praised in Scott's dispatches. During the storming of the city Reno was wounded, his position taken over by Pierre G.T. Beauregard, another future Civil War general.[30]

At the conclusion of the Mexican campaign, the Rocket Battery had shrunk to sixty-nine men, a loss of thirty-six. The total number of rockets expended in the war is unrecorded, but remaining rounds were fired in practice. When the Voltigeurs mustered out on 25 August 1848, the battery too was deactivated. However, Hale rockets appear in standard ordnance manuals from 1850 to the Civil War. Hale's had thus become *de facto* regulation U.S. war rockets, which was further encouraged by the Hale family. For example, William Hale, Jr., came to America in 1851 with an improved firing stand and new rocket cases and was paid $770, while in 1855, his brother Robert followed with additional improvements. It is important to note that some of the rockets were sent to Baton Rouge, Louisiana, and New Mexico to test the effects of their storage when "exposed to the vicissitudes of the climate." Subsequent firing results in 1857 showed the New Mexico rockets did poorly after long-term storage in a hot climate; those kept at Baton Rouge and Washington performed satisfactorily.[31]

The U.S. Civil War

The Civil War seemed an ideal opportunity for the re-establishment of rocket troops, but mentions of war rockets are meager in the voluminous literature pertaining to this conflict. Civil War rocketry may be characterized as makeshift, both technically and organizationally.

Upon the outbreak of the war, William Hale offered to come to America and make rockets for the Union, but was refused. Other plans were soon set afoot by fellow-Englishman Thomas William Lion. Under his original name, Lyon, he claimed to have served as an officer in the British Army, where he learned to make Congreve rockets. This is not confirmed by *Hart's (Royal) Army List* for the pertinent years; *Hart's* shows a Thomas Lyon only as a captain of the 17th Regiment of Light Dragoons, a mounted infantry unit that was neither a Rocket Troop nor made rockets. Lion's Civil War pension records

FIGURE 7.3
During the U.S. Civil War,
both sides used Hale rockets;
Congreve rockets may have
also been used. These
central-stick types, now in
the U.S. Army Military
Academy Museum, West
Point, N.Y., may date
from that war or earlier.
(S.I. A2001; courtesy U.S.
Army Military Academy)

nonetheless reveal that in 1849 he sailed to America for the Gold Rush. En route, he stopped in Peru and decided to settle there. He joined the Peruvian Army and tried to promote the formation of a rocket battery; later, he did the same in Ecuador. Just prior to the outbreak of the U.S. Civil War, he left South America and went to New York. There, Lion entered into an agreement with fellow Englishman and pyrotechnist Joseph G. Edge of Jersey City, New Jersey. Then, on 1 October 1861, Lion wrote to Secretary of War Simon Cameron: "I hereby offer the U.S. Government my services in any Rocket Brigade or Corps that are already formed, or may be now forming. Or to raise a Volunteers Corps or Brigade to use Congreve rockets at which I have had considerable experience. Jos. G. Edge . . . will guarantee to manufacture under my directions Rockets 42 (Forth two) pounds weight that can be used in the Field with excellent results (either as shot or shell) with a range of Three Thousand five hundred yards! for which the British Government paid the sum of Fifty Thousand pounds sterling!"[32]

Lion's claims were false, but they were made in more gullible times, and at this critical juncture in the war Secretary Cameron's main concern was to get as many desperately needed arms as quickly as possible. Besides, the Union had no rocket unit and the idea seemed appealing. Consequently, in just a week the rocket brigade was approved and men were assigned to it. Lion was summoned to Washington to discuss details with the commander-in-chief, Major General George McClellan, who as a lieutenant had witnessed Hale's rockets fired against Veracruz 14 years earlier. However, it was decided that the new rockets would come not from the private sector but from the Washington Arsenal. Logistics and recruitment were the responsibility of the new Chief of Artillery of the Army of the Potomac, Brigadier General William Barry of New York. The unit, consisting of 160 men from Niagara, Warren, Wyoming, and other counties in upstate New York, was hence named the "New York (General Barry's) Rocket Battalion." Lion was detailed to Albany where its troops were mustered on 6–7 December 1861 for 3 years of service. Lion was appointed a major and the commanding officer. A and B companies of the battalion were commanded by Captains Alfred Ransom and Jay E. Lee, respectively.[33]

News of the regiment and its promised wonderful weapons created a sensation. The *Scientific American* for 23 November 1861 reported that "a very formidable weapon is, we understand, about to be introduced into our army on the Potomac. It is an improved Congreve rocket . . . one of the most fearfully destructive weapons ever devised by man. This terrible instrument of war, we presume, will also be employed to protect the coast, and for other purposes, on board the iron-clad ships and floating batteries of the United States." (Hyperbole aside, the rockets were never deployed on iron-clads, nor

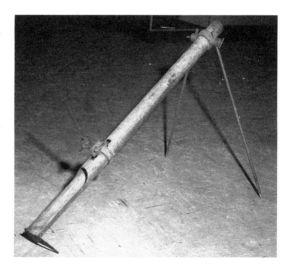

FIGURE 7.4
A Hale launcher at the West Point Museum; there is a similar one in the Fort Ward Museum, Arlington, Virginia. It could have been used by either side, since each captured the other's rockets. (S.I. A2002; courtesy U.S. Army Military Academy)

FIGURE 7.5

Thomas W. Lion (1829–94), British-born commander of the New York Rocket Battalion of the Civil War. He also attempted to promote rockets in Peru and Ecuador. (S.I. 74–5054; courtesy Mrs. L.T. Callahan, Rockville, Md.)

any ship, so far as is known.) *The Daily National Intelligencer*, Washington, D.C., of 11 December 1861, reported that the Battalion was "on its way to the a newly invented rocket gun, the peculiarity of which consists in its being breech-loading." The battalion arrived in Washington 10 December 1861 and was temporarily quartered at Camp Duncan on Capitol Hill, about a mile east of the unfinished Capitol building. Fittingly, its bivouac was christened "Camp Congreve."[34]

For four months, until April 1862, the battalion was stationed at Camp Congreve without its much-advertised rocket guns. Neither had it received horses.[35]

In the meantime, tests went forward at the Arsenal with two calibers of "rocket guns" that were really open-ended drawn iron tubes mounted on tripods. Protruding from the tubes were three spiral rods bound by metal bands. These rods were to impart additional rotary motion to the rocket to increase its speed; the rods also made the tube lighter. Both launchers were tested with old (possibly Mexican War vintage) Hale rockets, aimed across the Potomac River; General Barry and Ordnance officers present reported that some of the 3-inch (7.6 cm) rounds "went magnificently."[36]

The finished "guns" delivered to the Battalion differed from those in the initial tests and dispensed with the spiral rods, which were probably found to be too flimsy for combat use. Instead, the launchers were tougher wrought-iron tubes perforated with 1-inch (2.5 cm) diameter holes along the entire lengths at equidistant intervals. The holes allowed the exhaust gases to escape as the rocket was fired, helping to prevent the tube from becoming overheated, and also lightened it. Hale's rockets were used rather than Lion's. In trials with the new launchers, the rockets did not live up to expectations. Some tests were made against an army blanket, though it is said that the projectiles boomer-anged, presumably against the ground or other hard obstruction.[37]

Since Major General Ambrose Burnside was organizing an expedition for the Maryland campaign and had an urgent need for light artillery, the rockets and launchers were quickly exchanged for 6-pounder (2.7 kg) rifled cannons. However, the New York Rocket Battalion was not phased out. Bearing this designation but minus its rockets, it departed from Camp Congreve on 25 April 1862 and fought using conventional warfare, mainly in North Carolina throughout the remainder of the war.[38]

It was not until 11 February 1863 that the Battalion's name was correctly changed to the 23rd and 24th Independent Batteries of Light Artillery, New York Volunteers.[39]

There was still a considerable supply of rockets and tubes in the Washington Arsenal. On 14 April 1862, McClellan requested some for his planned siege of Yorktown, Virginia, during the Peninsula Campaign, but there is no record of any being deployed here, though rockets were briefly attached to his Army—then captured by the Confederates at Gaines Mill, Virginia, on 27 June 1862, only to be recaptured on 2 December, near Franklin, Virginia.[40]

Actually, many Union soldiers and sailors were receptive to using rockets, but it was difficult to procure good, servicable ones in time. One such request came in 1862 from Captain Charles Wilkes, commanding the James River flotilla, who wanted "barbed rockets. . . . If we had some Congreve rockets they would prove effective in driving the sharpshooters out of the woods."[41]

In the same year, Joshua Burrows Hyde, Hale's Mexican War agent, reappeared with an allegedly improved Hale rocket and managed to gain an audience with the President. Lincoln, with Secretary of State William Seward,

Secretary of the Treasury Salmon P. Chase, and Chief of the Navy Bureau of Ordnance Captain John Dahlgren, witnessed a trial of this rocket at the Washington Navy Yard on 15 November 1862.[42]

The fuse was lit. Suddenly, there was a tremendous explosion accompanied by great billows of smoke. In the words of Civil War historian Robert V. Bruce: "When the smoke drifted away, Dahlgren, who must have been white with horror, saw that a miracle had spared President Lincoln and the two ranking members of his cabinet." The rocket had exploded in its tube.[43]

Despite the near catastrophe, the test was deemed inconclusive and a second experiment was made on 17 November of that year, this time without the presence of the same eminent observers. Hyde's missile now took an erratic course, skipping off the roof of a nearby blacksmith's shop. No more was heard of Mr. Hyde or his experiments.[44]

Not until 1864 did Union war rockets again appear upon the battlefield. By April of that year, Prussian-born Brigadier General Alexander Schimmelfennig obtained both Hale and Congreve rockets and requested as many as 3,000 of the 2.75-inch (5.7 cm) Hales of the old (Mexican War) design. He also asked for 1,000 of the 3.75-inch (8.2 cm) models with ten stands, claiming rockets were easy to transport over the swamp marshes where he was stationed and indispensable for driving off Confederate picket boats or land troops from positions unapproachable with ordinary artillery. Schimmelfennig began testing Hales at his command post on Folly Island, South Carolina, and distributed rounds to several units in his forces. An improvised rocket battery was set up on the island commanded by another German, Captain Jacob Jungblut, 74th Pennsylvania Infantry, who deployed it on several small raids and reconnaissance missions, for instance at Legareville on 25 July and 6 August 1864, and on Kiawah Island at the same time. Company D, 127th New York Infantry, was also armed with rockets, as was the 41st New York Volunteers, commanded by German-born Colonel Leopold von Gilsa. Company D tried out some rockets against Ft. Sumter from a small boat, but the first one misfired and the rest were tossed overboard. In another instance, in an expedition up the Stono River, some of the men got ashore and sent a few rockets toward an enemy picket line, but they did nothing more than scare off a Rebel officer's horse. Von Gilsa used his Hales and rocket troughs (not tripods) for the defense of Folly Island, Cole's Island, and Long Island. Steps were taken toward organizing a "boat rocket battery" that apparently was not completed. In short, Schimmelfennig's hundreds of rockets did not accomplish much, but he always maintained an enthusiasm for them.[45]

Also in 1864, the U.S. Consul at Aix-la-Chapelle, France, informed the Secretary of War that Congreve rockets were available for purchase. But the response by Chief of Ordnance, General George D. Ramsey, seemed to mark the end of Union rocketry in the Civil War and sums up official opinions of its overall effect: "Experience with rocket men and horses can produce more effect with the improved cannon and projectiles now used. Rockets have but little range and accuracy compared to rifled projectiles, and are liable at time to premature explosions and great eccentricity of flight. . . . I cannot, therefore, recommend their purchase."[46]

The Confederate side likewise was characterized by abortive attempts to form rocket units, misfired rockets, and a few meager successes. They too had access to these weapons since arsenals with Hale rockets fell into their hands. They had adopted U.S. Army regulations, which specified Hales. Finally, there were men within the Confederacy who were experienced with rockets or capable of making them, even though the technology was always wanting.[47]

The first Confederate suggestion for the formation of a rocket battery came from General Pierre Beauregard, "the fiery Creole" who had briefly commanded the Mountain Howitzer and Rocket Battery at the storming of Mexico City in 1848. On 27 August 1861, following the battle of Bull Run, Beauregard wrote to his Chief of Ordnance, Captain Edward Porter Alexander: "I desire that you should call upon the [Confederate] President. . . . I have but thirty-five pieces of light artillery for thirty-five regiments of infantry, or one piece per regiment. Should we not be able to have additional light batteries, we must then supply their places with rocket batteries for the purpose of frightening the untamed horses of the enemy." Accompanied by Major Josiah Gorgas, Chief of Confederate Ordnance, Alexander called upon President Jefferson Davis; but Davis was not available. Instead, Adjutant Inspector General Samuel Cooper approved Beauregard's plan and Gorgas proceeded to carry it out. Confident in this authorization, Beauregard began enlisting the necessary men. On 4 September 1861, he told Colonel William Porcher Miles: "I hope the rockets (war) will . . . be forthcoming. I place much reliance upon them, for the purpose of running off the field McClellan's bipeds and quadrupeds." Upon Alexander's recommendation, First Lieutenant Edmund H. Cummins was chosen to head the battery.[48]

Meanwhile, rocketry experiments were begun in Richmond by Lieutenant George N. Duffey, an ordnance officer on Gorgas's staff. Although well known to Alexander, who praised his work, Duffey's experiments do not appear to have been connected at all with Beauregard's plans. Duffey was working on his own version of a stickless rotary rocket. One experiment, witnessed at the Richmond Ordnance Yard on 29 October by Robert G.H. Kean of the Confederate Department of War, ended in an explosion, although Kean still thought that the invention showed promise.[49]

Nine days earlier, probably unknown to Duffey and Kean, Acting Secretary of War Judah P. Benjamin had struck a blow against Beauregard's rocket battery scheme. Benjamin charged that Beauregard had exceeded his legal authority in forming the unit. It was inferred that Cooper's signature was not enough, and that Beauregard should have gone through the proper channels. He had committed, said Benjamin, an act "without warrant in law" but should "go unpunished" because his motive was good although his judgment was poor. Beauregard, furious and shocked, dashed off his own response, going over Benjamin's head and directly to President Davis. He was "utterly at a loss," he wrote, "to understand Benjamin's language and explanation. . . . The Secretary seems to be unaware, evidently, that a rocket company is but a field artillery company, nothing more, and not . . . a special corps or arm of the service . . . requiring congressional enactments." The Acting Secretary, he concluded, was an interfering "high public functionary."[50]

President Davis reacted tactfully. On 25 October 1861, he expressed admiration and high personal regard for Beauregard, but made it clear that he was "unquestionably wrong in the order to recruit a company for the Provisional Army. . . . "Now, my dear sir," added Davis, "let me entreat you to dismiss this small matter from your mind; in the hostile masses before you, you have a subject more worthy of your contemplation." But the matter would not drop, and it became so exacerbated that a serious rift developed between the President and his general that never healed. In a letter of 10 November 1861, Davis told him coldly, "You surely did not intend to inform me that your army and yourself are outside the limits of the law."[51]

The upshot was that Beauregard never received the rocket battery. Furthermore, from late 1861 until the war's end, Beauregard, an able but tempestuous officer, was given only unimportant commands and his promotions were restricted. In retrospect, his "paper" rocket battery inflicted more damage to the Confederacy than any real battery.[52]

Meanwhile, Duffey struggled with his own rocket plans. On 14 February 1862, Colonel J. Lucius Davis, Confederate Ordnance, recommended him for a promotion: "I have known . . . George Duffey for years as a faithful and able officer of [Virginia] volunteer Artillery. He . . . is now actively engaged in getting up a rocket corps & is indeed worthy of the said appointment."

But what happened to Duffey's own contemplated rocket corps is a mystery, as there is no further record of it. We can surmise that it, too, never materialized.[53]

The first Confederates actually armed with rockets may have been soldiers who captured them from Union troops on 27 June 1862 at Gaines Mill, Virginia. When the rockets were turned back against the Federals is uncertain; but on the morning of 3 July, during the Peninsula campaign, General James E.B. "Jeb" Stuart shelled union troops on the banks of the James River from Evelington Heights, Virginia. According to one Federal officer on the receiving end, Lieutenant John C. Tidball of Battery A, 2nd U.S. Artillery, "they also threw with great precision a score or so of war rockets." Another Federal officer, Colonel James T. Kirk, 10th Pennsylvania Reserves, confirmed the shelling when he wrote: "On Thursday, the 3d instant, while standing in line of battle, I had one man wounded by a missile from a rocket from a rebel battery."[54]

Yet it is also a possibility that the rockets were of Confederate origin. One of Stuart's officers, Lieutenant Colonel William C. Blackford, provides the following clues: "Stuart opened on them with a Congreve rocket battery, the first and last time the latter ever appeared in action with us. It had been gotten up by some foreign chap who managed it on this occasion. They were huge rockets, fired from a sort of gun carriage, with a shell at the end which exploded in due time, scattering 'liquid damnation' . . . Their course was erratic." A few Federal tents were set ablaze, he added, but otherwise "the rocket proved to be of little value."[55]

Perhaps the "foreign chap" was Hungarian-born Lieutenant Sigismund Zulavsky, a photographer by profession, who was called "Count Zulavsky." He had originally been assigned to Stuart's 1st Virginia Cavalry, then was temporarily discharged due to illness. On 19 May 1862, as a private citizen, he submitted a petition to the city of Richmond requesting funds to purchase horses for a "Rocket Corps," but got nowhere. When readmitted to the Army, Zulavsky was at least partly successful, for by 1863 he commanded a small "Rocket Battery" of about twenty-four men and three tripod launchers carried by mules. But because so many Confederate records were destroyed, especially during the burning of Richmond (1865), it is difficult to trace Zulavsky's movements precisely, though we do encounter him later.[56]

Other war rockets were available to the Confederates. For operations south of the James River, General Daniel H. Hill requested some from General Lee himself. Lee responded on 2 August 1862: "I do not know whether we have any of the rockets you mention, but if there are they shall be sent too." Perhaps these rounds also were captured from the Federals.[57]

It is known that captured Union rockets were issued to Captain Samuel T. Wright's Halifax (Virginia Heavy) Artillery. Captain Edward Graham's Virginia Battery (the horse artillery company attached to Wright's unit) also received rockets. As both of these units were stationed at Petersburg, Virginia, they were sometimes incorrectly called the Petersburg Rocket Battery. (Graham's unit was officially the "Petersburg Artillery.") In early October 1862, these troops saw action at Franklin, Virginia, where, according to the Petersburg *Daily Express* of 7 October, "Captain Wright's rocket gun[s] are said to have played havoc with the Yankee cavalry . . . unhorsing many a Yankee equestrain [sic]." A different picture is painted on the Union side. Major General John J. Peck admitted "shell, grape, and rockets were fired in great profusion," but there was "little or no damage to our well posted troops."[58]

While on a foraging expedition early in the morning of 1 December 1862 in the vicinity of Franklin, by the Blackwater River, Wright's rocket section unexpectedly encountered the 11th Pennsylvania Cavalry having breakfast. An advance guard charged the Confederate column and was followed by the remainder of the Pennsylvanians. In the surprise skirmish, twenty or thirty Confederate prisoners were taken, together with two rocket launchers and seventy 12- and 15-pounder (5.4 and 6.8 kg) rockets. From then on, the rockets recaptured by the Federals were made a part of their defense of Franklin and the river crossing.[59]

On 22 July 1863, Lieutenant Colonel Hypolite Oladowski, Ordnance officer for the Army of the Tennessee, wrote to Gorgas that Zulavsky had suggested war rockets to Major General "Fighting Joe" Wheeler and told him of the "efficiency of those rockets in the cavalry of Gen Stewart." (Probably this was "Jeb" Stuart because cavalry was mentioned.) Wheeler wanted some, too, and requested that Zulavsky be assigned to him. Gorgas answered him as follows: "Rockets have failed to give satisfactory result, and have been little used, either by General Stewart [sic] or anyone else . . . however we will send what we have."

On 26 July, Zulavsky himself informed Oladowski: "We arrived yesterday at this place [Gadsen, Alabama, then Wheeler's headquarters] and the first question General Wheeler asked me was 'Will you have the Rocket Battery?' " It seems that Zulavsky had no rockets with him due to the general having failed to make the proper requisition. Zulavsky thus found himself fighting the bureaucracy rather than the enemy. The problem was compounded when his launchers later became misplaced while being forwarded to him.

By December 1864, he was in Georgia and had made no headway with the rockets. Finally, out of exasperation, he gave them up. He requested of Wheeler to give him "permission to raise a company or battalion of scouts or other cavalry service." Next to his signature appears the title "Lt. R.A.C.V. Comdg Rockets" (Rocket Artillery Confederate Volunteers); Zulavsky was probably the only man in the Confederate Army to hold that position, which was filled apparently only for a brief time.[60]

One final Confederate effort to equip a rocket battery was made in Texas, late in 1863. Another "foreign chap," acting Ordnance Officer G.H. Schroeder of Major General John B. Magruder's staff, was responsible. Schroeder claimed to have been a lieutenant in an Austrian rocket battery at the battle of Comorn during the revolution of 1848. He said he had learned the secrets of "blending [propellants] and construction" of rockets and now wished to put them to the advantage of his adopted country. His superior, Major Getulius Kellersberger, afterwards recalled that he allowed him "a small expense account" and "gave him a few men and some materials, and it was not long until he had a three-foot [0.9 m] rocket stand completed and a half dozen small rockets with grenade heads."[61]

This equipment was made in Schroeder's rocket factory, set up in Galveston by 11 January 1864. Captain John S. Greer's battery of light artillery was to be furnished with the rockets and coverted into a rocket battery. But in a now familiar pattern, red tape and bad rockets thwarted the plans. As summed up by Major Kellersberger, "so ended the first and last rocket battery in Texas." It was probably also the last nineteenth-century U.S. rocket battery.[62]

Following the Civil War, the U.S. Army again shrank considerably in size, and except for Indian campaigns on the frontiers, it did not see any major conflict until the brief Spanish-American War in 1898. This period was one of great technological advances in artillery development. During the Civil War itself there were significant developments in large rifled cannons by such pioneers as Dahlgren, Thomas J. Rodman, and Robert P. Parrott. Rodman was also the first to compress gunpowder into perforated disks that fit into gun bores, thus producing tailor-made "progressive burning" propellant charges. Nitrocellulose-based smokeless powder was introduced in 1863, and by 1890 it had almost universally replaced gunpowder as an ordnance propellant. The once fearsome powder war rocket therefore had no chance to compete as viable armament in the U.S. after the Civil War and indeed, later war rocket entrepreneurs—including the short-lived War and Life-Saving

Rocket Company, started in 1877 by associates of William Hale, Jr.—were singularly unsuccessful in selling their wares in this country. Thus, by the Civil War, the Congreve-Hale era in America had virtually ended.[63]

Rocketry in Latin America

The situation was not so clear-cut in Latin America. Much of the history of early rocketry in Latin America remains sketchy and awaits further research by scholars. Congreve and Hale rockets are known to have been used in as many as seven nations in this region—Brazil, Chile, Peru, Argentina, Cuba, Mexico, and Paraguay—and in some cases were in service until the 1870s–80s. Probably the powder rocket lingered longer in South America because of a lack of industrial and financial capacity to produce more advanced artillery developments. Also, rockets were cheaper to acquire and produce than guns, and the tropical or semitropical terrains of most of these countries did not hinder the transport and use of the rockets, although the climate did. As may be expected, these weapons were in demand for the innumerable revolutions of the region.

Brazil

Congreve rockets were probably introduced into Latin America by Congreve's friend, Commodore William Sydney Smith, when he attempted to use them near Rio de Janeiro, Brazil, in 1809 during British intervention in local affairs. In the same year, apparently, a few were demonstrated in Rio before King John VI of Portugal, who had fled to the large Portuguese colony upon Napoleon's invasion of his country.[64]

In May 1850, William Hale, Jr., travelled to Rio to sell his father's spin-stabilized rockets, which the Brazilians bought. The *Laboratório Pyrotechnico do Campinho* (Pyrotechnical Laboratory of Campinho) was created in 1852 and made war rockets on a modest scale. The same year, a Brazilian rocket battery of four firing tubes and 160 men, commanded by Captain Antonio José do Amaral, was formed and played a part in the famous battle of Monte Caseros in Argentina on 3 February 1852 against the forces of Argentine dictator Juan Manual de Rosas.

Years later, in 1879, do Amaral, then a professor in the *Escola Militar* (Military School) in Rio, described both Congreves and Hales in his *Nomenclatura Explicada de Artilharia e Guia do Fogueteiro de Guerra (Instruction for the*

Artillery and War Rocketeer's Guide). It is thus possible that the battery at Monte Caseros was armed with both Congreves and Hales. It is known that in the same engagement, Major Joaquim Gonzalves Fontes commanded a *bateria de foguetes à Congrève*.[65]

Brazil's experience in the Rosas wars prompted it to improve arms production. Consequently, an *Officina de Foguetes* ("Rocket Department") was attached to the *Laboratório* in 1860, though rocket production remained low. However, rockets made here were used extensively in the bloody War of the Triple Alliance of 1865–70 in which Brazil was allied with Argentina and Uruguay against Paraguay. At the end of 1867, central-stick rockets were started at Campinho, indicating that Brazilian-made Congreves up until then were of the old side-stick design. The new rockets were known as being either of "the English system" or "the French system," which showed their possible origins. However, the *Relatório da Repartiçaó dos Negócios da Guerra* (*Report of War Department Transactions*), which annually listed Brazilian munitions production, shows that in 1867 there were 1,262 "Austrian rockets" in addition to 110 English stick models. There were also 150 Hales built at the *Laboratório* that year with more made annually thereafter until the year 1869, when no more were made. During the Triple Alliance, Brazilian war rockets were also fabricated by a naval engineer named Baptista at a pyrotechnic laboratory at Penta da Armadzao, in the city of Nicteroy, opposite Rio. After the war, Brazilians continued improving their rockets and in 1872, the *Laboratório's* director, Captain Augusto Fausto de Souza, made a new launcher for central-stick rockets.[66]

By the late 1870s, as in the Old World, the popularity of war rockets waned, and by the mid-1880s all war rockets disappear entirely from the annual production lists, so we can assume that this marked the end of Brazilian activities with the old powder rocket.[67]

Chile and Peru

The history of Congreve rockets in Chile and Peru is interrelated and dates from their joint liberation from Spain. In 1819, the English seaman-adventurer Thomas Cochrane, appointed commander of the Chilean Navy, decided to use Congreve rockets to burn the Spanish fleet at the Peruvian port of Callao. Rather than transport rockets all the way from England, and for economy's sake, 1,000 were to be made in Chile from available raw materials. For superintending the manufacture, Cochrane hired Stephen Goldsack, who worked

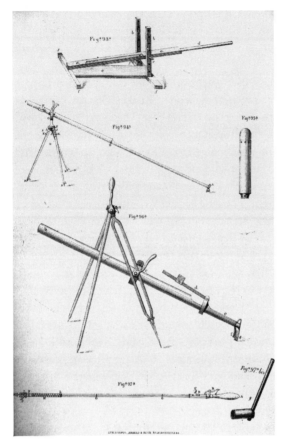

FIGURE 7.6

Brazilian launchers included one (Fig. 93) of wood and iron; weighing a prohibitive 198 pounds (90 kg), it was soon discarded. More practical was another one (Fig. 94) weighing 70 pounds (32 kg). Fig. 95 is a Hale rocket, and Fig. 97 is a friction igniter using fulminating powder. (S.I. 75–684)

under Congreve in 1809 in Woolwich as a foreman. To further cut expenses, Spanish prisoners were enlisted for rocket-making at Santiago.[68]

Early in October 1819, all was ready before Callao. "Great expectations were formed . . . as to the effect to be produced by these destructive missiles," wrote Cochrane in his memoirs, "but they were doomed to disappointment, the rockets turning out utterly useless. Some, in consequence of the badness of the solder used, bursting . . . before the . . . [rocket] raft, and setting fire to others." One of these rafts was blown up, severely burning its captain and thirteen men, while other rockets "took a wrong direction in consequence of the sticks not having been formed of proper wood, whilst the greater portion would not ignite at all from a cause . . . discovered when too late . . . The filling of the tubes was . . . entrusted to Spanish prisoners, who . . . had embraced every opportunity of inserting handfuls of sand, sawdust, and even manure, at intervals in the tubes, thus impeding the progress of combustion."[69]

Four decades later, Peruvians acquired their own European *cohetes á la Congreve*. Details are lacking, but the trend was clear in the annual *Memoria presentada al Congreso Estraordinario* (*Memorial Presented to the Extraordinary Congress*) by the Peruvian Minister of War and Marine. The *Memoria* for 1851 observed that "another species of light artillery is known, by the name of Congreve rockets . . . that at all costs should be introduced." The *Memoria* for 1858 shows that the Peruvian Congress took action: "Europe was asked for an amount of rockets of the Congreve type . . . they are easy to transport and simple handling makes them very appropriate for our country." Then in 1860, the *Memoria* says: "There is also in service two siege batteries and a sufficient number of Congreve rockets."[70]

There was a curious private proposal to introduce Congreve rockets into Peru by Thomas William Lion. As mentioned earlier, Lion left England in 1849 for the Gold Rush in California. En route, he stopped and settled in Peru, joining the Peruvian Army. Upon the death of his Peruvian wife some years later, Lion resigned his commission and on 2 March 1860 he wrote from Callao to an unnamed high-ranking officer in Lima: "Being at present without employment . . . I desire to offer my services to your Excellency for the defense of our country. I find myself capable of giving instruction to the Artillery in the use of Congreve rockets; also their operation and method of manufacture in Peru." An affirmative answer was sent on 17 March 1860, but a demonstration of Lion's rockets would first have to be made.[71]

Evidently, Lion was not able to fulfill the obligation; on 1 October 1860, he was at Guayaquil, Ecuador, making the same offer to the head of that country, Juan José Flores. Results did not pan out here either. Exactly a year later, he had much better luck in the U.S.[72]

Argentina

Cochrane, who had faced disaster with rockets in Chile, also introduced them into Argentina while trying to liberate that country from Spain in 1823. He encountered no sabotage and was able to use a few rockets, though sparingly. By 1826, rocket launchers reportedly were fitted on the Argentine naval vessel

San Martin; perhaps this equipment was leftover from Cochrane's operations.[73]

Congreve rockets reappeared in Argentina in 1845 when British seamen used them against Juan de Rosas at San Lorenzo. But Rosas procured his own and used them in the Argentine revolution of 1852 against his rival, Justo José de Urquiza. At Monte Caseros, Argentina, as well as in Brazil, fielded rocketeers. The Argentinians had four tube launchers and the rocketeers were commanded by Colonel José Maria Pirán. Nothing is known of Argentine rocket activities after this. But since Argentine troops and equipment supported the Uruguayan Manuel Oribe during his siege of Montevideo from 1843 to 1857, in which Congreve rocket tubes were among Oribe's armament, it is possible that those rockets were Argentinian.[74]

Cuba

Not surprisingly, Cuba's first efforts to produce war rockets were made by Spanish military authorities. Upon his installation as Governor of the island in 1832, Captain General Francisco Dionisio Vives ordered rocketry experiments at Havana's military works. The experiments were placed under Brigadier General Fernando Cacho and a Colonel Calleja who made a special search for the right propellant formulae suitable to Cuba's excessively dry climate. Cacho and Calleja's formulae were essentially similar to those in Europe, but contained more moisture than usual to prevent cracking, which could lead to explosions. The rockets were light, 7 pounds (3 kg) in weight loaded, and had short ranges, about 1,400 feet (424 m), but the prime objective was to determine the feasibility of these projectiles in the Cuban climate. The problems were never fully solved, perhaps one reason why nothing further is heard of the project.[75]

Spanish authorities in Cuba also expressed an interest in Hale's rockets beginning in the early 1850s, but there is no evidence that any were sent. Standard stick-guided models may have been reintroduced to the island during the Cuban insurrection period, beginning in 1895. Spanish newspapers variously reported that either 5,000 or 500 rockets invented by a French military officer named Couspiérre were carried by insurrection leader Enrique Collazo y Tejada in one of his expeditions that departed from Florida. One unusual feature of the rockets was that they were said to have been made of aluminum for minimizing weight, which is quite possible since the metal had just become commercially available. Couspiérre was also said to have chosen heavier iron for the warheads in order to inflict maximum damage, and the weapons were made more lethal with the addition of dynamite set off by a lead-fulminate impact-detonating fuse. But the name Couspiérre is not on the 1895 list of French officers. There is, however, a Jean Baptiste Couspeire, a reserve lieutenant in the chasseurs (engineers) who, interestingly, was born in Cuba; perhaps he was the inventor. Anyway, Collazo's expeditions failed, so the alleged rockets would not have had any effect.[76]

Mexico

The picture of nineteenth-century rocketry in Mexico is even more unclear because of innumerable revolutions, guerrilla armies, and lack of adequate records. It is known that rockets were obtained by the Mexicans by the Mexican-American war of 1846–48 as George B. McClellan noted in his diary for 20 May 1847 at the siege of Veracruz: "They [the Mexicans] fired rockets ect. at us during the early part of the night." While Colonel Albert C. Ramsey, U.S. Ordnance, reported: "The [Mexican] rockets were of very little service." Americans captured thirty-six Congreve rockets in the war, though there are no records as to their origin. War rockets were also among the ammunition of General (later President) Porfiro Diaz during the "War of Reform" in 1857–60, but their use was insignificant.[77]

Paraguay

The first use of war rockets in tiny Paraguay perhaps dates to 1865–70 during the War of the Triple Alliance. They came from different sources, mainly because Paraguay's dictator, Francisco Solano Lopez, relied upon foreigners to supply his small army. One of them was Prussian master armorer Wilhelm Wagener. Lopez's resourceful if impoverished government eagerly presented the Prussian with a contract, and he began working at the Asunción arsenal in 1864. In a short time, Guellermo Wagener, as he was called, had developed a novel multiple, triple-tube Congreve rocket launcher. It must have been very effective; one historian says it "sobered Brazilian inspectors for its advanced design and efficiency." Another reported that the Historical Museum (presumably in Rio) conserved a captured specimen with the inscription: "Invented and made by Wagener—Asunción—1864."[78]

At the battle of Humaitá, in 1866, another type of rocket appeared among the "motley armature of the Paraguayans," according to English observer

Captain Richard F. Burton. "By the side of . . . self-rifling shells and balls," he wrote, "were found . . . Hall's [Hale's] rotating rockets." Perhaps they were captured from Brazil, or were old rounds leftover from a minor and abortive U.S. "Paraguayan expedition" commanded by William B. Shubrick in 1858 in which Hales were taken.[79]

Other rockets came into the hands of the Paraguayans through John and Alfred Blyth, boiler and iron and brass founders of London. In September 1864, they sent "articles for the rocket factory" on the steamship *Ygurey,* and later there was additional shipments of rockets and rocket equipment. After this campaign, however, there is no further evidence of military rocketry in Paraguay. Still, it is interesting to speculate on the number of other private rocket entrepreneurs, like the Blyths or Wageners, who must have similarly plied their businesses (which, for a period, must have been quite lucrative) elsewhere in Latin America.

CHAPTER 8

Rocketry in India, China, and the Middle East

Native Indian and Chinese rockets continued to be used into the nineteenth century, but eventually were supplanted by Congreve-Hale projectiles. As may be expected, this technology was spread largely as a result of British colonialism. This technology meant not only the use of Congreve-Hale rockets by British colonial forces, but also the start of manufacturing on European patterns. The latter also applied to the Middle East. As such, these were the beginnings of modern rocketry in these regions. Moreover, the story of nineteenth-century rocketry in India in particular is linked directly to Congreve.

India

War rockets did not disappear in India after the fall of Serringapatam in 1799. Mahrattas continued using them up to the last of the Mahratta wars, ending in 1818.[1]

European (i.e., Congreve) rocketry began in India in 1815. According to Captain E. Buckle, Bengal Artillery historian, in that year the colonial government in India decided that "it would be advantageous to beat our Indian enemies at their own weapons [by] . . . adding a rocket troop to the Bengal Artillery." The following year, the first consignments of Congreve rockets were sent to India by the Commander-in-Chief of British forces stationed there, the Earl of Moira. After successful tests at Dum Dum and Byculla, the Bengal Rocket Troop was established in November, followed by the Madras Rocket Troop in December. These organizations were patterned after rocket troops in the homeland, but with local characteristics. The Bengal Troop, the largest of the two, was commanded by Captain William S. Wish, and had a staff of two lieutenants, a lieutenant fireworker, eighty gunners, sixty-five *sepoys* (native soldiers), five *sirdars* (officers), and sixty *surwans* (native bearers). One uniquely Indian aspect of the troop was the mode of transportation for the rocketeers: seventy camels. There were also twenty-six horses and twenty *bouches à feu,* or firing stands, with 960 rockets allotted. Each rocketeer carried eight rounds on his camel. For good reason, the Bengal Troop was sometimes

FIGURE 8.1

Congreve rockets carried by camels of the Bengal Rocket Troop in 1817. The rocket sticks are to the right of the first camel. (S.I. 73–4317)

called the "Camel Rocket Corps." Later, bullock-drawn transport carriages were added.[2]

In 1817, Congreve established his private "Congreve Rocket & Ordnance Stores Manufactory" at 14 London Street, Bow, West Ham, Essex, expressly for supplying his rockets to the East India Company. The same year, the Bengal Troop assisted in the siege of Hattrass in the war against a local Indian prince, the Zemindar of Hattrass. The Madras Rocket Troop first fought in the Pindari or Third Mahratta War of 1817–18, distinguishing itself under its captain, Samuel Rudyard. In the latter year, the Bengal Troop became known as the 7th Bengal Horse Artillery, or, incorrectly, as the "7th Rocket Troop." A redesignation also came for the Madras Troop; but it was a near fatal one.[3]

"The Madras Rocket Troop has been found . . . to be of little or no use on service," reads the minutes of Major General Sir Thomas Munro, Governor of Madras, on 20 November 1821, "as the rockets are more dangerous to our own troops than to those of the enemy, as well from their uncertain flight, as from their being liable to explode the moment they are let off. As the defect of the rocket seems to be owing to the decomposition of its powder by the heat of the climate, and as no means have been found to remedy it, I have long thought that the maintenance of the Rocket Troop was an idle waste of the public money." The governor's remedy was to convert this organization into a reserve unit of artillery, but the measure turned out to be only a temporary one.[4]

In 1822, the Bengal Rocket Troop had its camels replaced by horses, allowing greater mobility. The same year the Madras Rocket Troop was resuscitated. Then, Captain H. Nicholson of the 11th Bengal Native Infantry, earlier appointed "Superintendent of Rockets in India," was ordered to Madras by Lord Moira to investigate Congreve's "new rocket system," which featured projectiles capable of withstanding the Indian heat. Unfortunately, no technical details of this improvement have been found, but we may surmise that the gunpowder propellant was essentially the same but contained more moisture and was not rammed as hard (to prevent cracking). Special propellant liners may have also been added to seal in the propellant.

Sir Archibald Campbell, Commander-in-Chief of British forces in Madras, was convinced of Congreve's claims. "It is difficult to express to you the gratification from the exhibition of the rocket practice yesterday evening at Saint Thomas's Mount," he told Nicholson on 7 December 1822. "The great improvements affected by Sir William Congreve, in the composition and construction of this powerful and destructive implement of war, has entirely removed the strong prejudice . . . against it in this army. . . . I shall take an early opportunity of recommending to this government the re-establishment of a rocket troop." Thus was reborn a small Madras rocket establishment in May 1823.[5]

Meanwhile, Captain Samuel Parlby, 3rd Bengal Troop of Horse Artillery, was designing his own war rockets and as early as 1814 proposed them to Lord Moira, who responded that Congreve's were already on order. In 1824, Parlby again approached the government, this time asking for comparative trials of his rockets against those of Congreve. The request was approved and the trials were held on the Dum Dum artillery grounds on 31 May 1824. Parlby managed his own rockets and Captain Charles Graham, then commander of the Bengal Rocket Troop, fired the Congreves. Seventeen Congreve rockets went through the target while Parlby's struck twenty-two times. "The general result," summed up the *India Gazette* for 3 June 1824, "was highly favorable to Cap. Parlby's rockets, which hit the object aimed at with greater precision than Sir W. Congreve's; but with less velocity and force." However, it was noted that Parlby's rockets were fresh while Congreve's were three years old. Parlby's rockets received much publicity at the time in the Indian popular and military press, but they were not adopted. Much of the attention was generated by Parlby himself, who for years thereafter expressed grievances that his rockets were judged superior to Congreve's by everybody who saw them, yet the East India Company never fairly compensated him, much less adopted them.[6]

Congreve expressed his own grievances against the Company over alleged fraudulent use and sale of his manufacturing secrets. He complained that while his factory at Bow initially supplied the Company, his rockets were still manufactured in India without his consent and compensation. Congreve sued but no settlement was made in his lifetime. His pamphlet, *An Appeal to the East India Company on the Manufacture of the Congreve Rocket in India* (London, 1824), states his side. The Bow factory long survived these grievances and existed up to the 1870s, but it is not known how long it produced its wares for the East India Company Army.[7]

Graham's Bengal Troops successfully used Congreve rockets in the Burmese War of 1824–26 (see Chapter 3). But on 13 June 1828, special orders were issued from the governmental seat of British India in Fort William, Calcutta, ending all rocket troops in the country. The Governor-General decreed that war rockets were no longer to "be attached to any one particular troop of Artillery" but "distributed to field batteries of horse-artillery in such proportions as the commander-in-chief sees fit." The Madras and Bengal rocket troops were converted into gun batteries. Thus, as in England, the war rocket service in India became very flexible and in effect was expanded at the same time the original specially formed rocket troops were abolished. This flexibility added longevity to the Indian rocket service, with the result that India was perhaps the second most prominent location of British colonial rocket actions outside Africa. When Hale rockets superseded Congreve's, they came to be used in India too. Hale rocket engagements are known to have taken place in India well into the 1880s and perhaps the 1890s.[8]

China

In China, old-style rockets were used as late as the 1860s. They appeared to be relics of another age, differing little from those depicted in the *Wu Pei Chi* of two previous centuries. Compared with their European counterparts, they were small and primitive. Perhaps with some justification, British accounts tended to deride them. During the first Opium War, for example, the *Annual Register* (London) of 1841, noted that the average native Chinese war rocket was "so trifling is its projectile force" that it was reduced to "a simple means of annoyance, instead of destruction." There was also an understandable European bias toward Congreve rockets used in China. "Great," said the *Register,* "must have been the consternation of the celestial nation at such a visitation of their native and familiar plaything, with its [the Congreve rocket's] appalling roar, and to them, new and gigantic dimensions and powers of destruction."[9]

Indeed, many British battle accounts of Chinese war rockets show them to have been ineffective. One English sailor recounted that during a naval attack off Canton in May 1841, the Chinese threw "showers of rockets . . . beautiful in appearance, but as harmless as they are beautiful." He also described Chinese rockets "filled with arrows and dust" and "curious rocket arrows, by which two men were slightly hit." No incendiary seems to have been carried in the warheads.[10]

The Chinese themselves were confident in their rocket weapons. When Chinese troops poured into Chao-Pao-Shan in March 1842, according to Chinese historian Wei Yuan, they "were strictly enjoined not to use fire or rockets, lest they should set fire to the town." Probably exhaust flames, and not the contents of the warheads, were apt to cause conflagration. Chinese government troops frequently used rockets against bandits, such as against the Nien at Shench'iu, Honan Province, in 1853. Chinese junks also were armed with them.[11]

When the British captured Amoy in 1841, they seized, among other stores,

Chinese rockets that were brought to London and exhibited in the London Adelaide Gallery and other museums. The specimens were found to be little more than skyrockets adapted for war but were said to have been capable of killing a man at 200 yards (180 m). The American magazine *Harper's Weekly* for 7 March 1857 thought that the rocket resembled "the 'fiery darts' of biblical parlance. A feathered arrow, six feet [1.8 m] long, with a long flat steel or copper head, has a rocket attached; it cleaves the air with an irregular motion, and a red hot steel head inflicts a painful and dangerous wound, the rocket continuing to hiss and seeth and spit out fire after it has fastened on its poor victim." Native Chinese war rockets may thus be classed as antipersonnel weapons and were not capable of bombardment, as were the Congreve types.[12]

As innocuous or lethal as these rockets were portrayed, the Chinese eventually came to realize how inferior they were when compared with English or French models (also used during the 1857–60 war). Hong Kong, acquired as a British colony in the Opium Wars, became a major British naval supply depot for thousands of Congreve rockets by the 1850s. How did the Chinese come to adopt these arms for their own arsenals? In 1867, when a pattern of Congreves was declared obsolete, according to War Office Minute 21,177 of 15 February of that year, it was decided that "the rockets will be disposed of to the Chinese Government." Probably the transferrence was executed through Hong Kong. The Chinese, with European help, soon began manufacturing these armaments themselves. The *Siam Repository* of April 1870 reports that the Shanghai Imperial Arsenal then had a 40-foot (12 m) shop for making Congreve rocket tubes to which was attached a blacksmith's shop "with six forges for making rockets." By 1873, Hale rockets and firing troughs were being made at the Nanking Arsenal. However, during his visit to Nanking in 1874, Captain B.W. Bax, R.N., was informed by a Dr. MacCartney, the Arsenal's Superintendent, that "the Chinese preferred Congreve rockets" over Hale's because of their greater range and lower trajectory. The Chinese maintained this preference for quite some time.[13]

As late as 1900, during the siege of the Peking legations in the Boxer Rebellion, the French discovered that the Chinese were still using a Congreve-type (possibly Boxer's pattern) and tripod launcher and had "brusquely abandoned the armament so dear to their ancestors to adopt that of the 'Barbarians of the West,' even to fight with them with their own weapon." The rocket launcher was 3.5 feet (1 m) long with a 3-inch (8 cm) tube. The rocket itself was a 17.5-inch (45 cm) iron cartridge, 1.9 inches (5 cm) in diameter, with a 6.5-foot (2 m) wooden (apparently bamboo) guidestick. The rocket weighed 5.5–11 pounds (2.5–5 kg) and had a range of 985–1,310 feet (3,400 m) with a "not very

FIGURE 8.2

The Chinese, probable originators of the rocket, adopted both Congreve and Hale rockets, seen here at left with a trough launcher in the Nanking Arsenal, 1873. (S.I. 80–14962)

great speed." This was undoubtedly the last time the Chinese carried the Congreves that had supplanted their own venerable rockets, conceived centuries before.[14]

The Middle East

Congreve rocketry also penetrated the far-flung reaches of the Ottoman Empire, which stretched from southeastern Europe to the Middle East. Tiny Albania, then under suzerainty of the Ottomans (Turks) and governed by quasi-independent princes, was one of the first countries to deploy Congreve rockets in battle. One of her rulers, the despot Ali Pasha of Janina, received aid, including Congreve rockets, from England in gratitude for help in negotiating the treaty of peace between Turkey and Napoleonic France. In February 1809, Captain William Martin Leake, Royal Artillery, instructed Ali's men in the use of the rockets. But instead of firing them against the French as was intended, Ali used them in his conquest of the south-central Albanian town of Berat in 1810.[15]

The Ottoman Empire itself sought Congreve rockets for the modernization of its army along European lines. Experiments were first conducted by Swedish diplomat-soldier Baron Carl af Wetterstedt (or Witterschett) on 2 March 1822 for the Ottoman Viceroy of Egypt, Mohammed Ali, but they failed. The Turks were eventually forced to purchase Congreve rockets from an Englishman for the Turco-Egyptian army during the Russo-Turkish War. Russian rocket pioneer Konstantinov believed this was probably Robert Forsyth Wade, former manager and, from 1822, proprietor of Congreve's Bow factory. A loosely organized rocket battery was hastily formed, but it failed miserably and barely managed to materialize to usable strength.[16]

British rockets making up part of the Turco-Egyptian "militia," as it was sometimes called, were subsequently placed at the disposal of the Egyptians. In contrast to their weak Turkish masters, the Egyptians possessed a well organized, disciplined fighting force whose soldiers were trained mostly by European officers. As a result of favorable tests of Congreve rockets up to 32-

FIGURE 8.3

The Chinese favored conventional stick rockets until as late as 1900. This one, used in the Boxer Rebellion, had both Western and Oriental features; the tripod is Western (with rose-shaped holes for lightness) but the guidestick is a length of Chinese bamboo. (S.I. 73–3231)

pounders (14.5 kg) at Cairo in 1830–31, the Egyptians created their own rocket brigade. Meanwhile, Pasha Mohammed Ali elevated himself to a position of virtual independence and made war on his suzerains, the Ottoman sultans. In 1830 he attacked Algeria, with his new rocket brigade among his forces. Some 800 rockets were equally divided for land and naval use. One historian says the Egyptian rocketeers made "a serviceable detachment against the cavalry of the Barbaries."[17]

Ali's son, Ibrahim Pasha, successfully deployed his own rocket-armed soldiers against Turkish cavalry and small towns in Syria in 1832–33. He ordered that rockets be discharged in great numbers against the Turkish-held bastion of Saint-Jean d'Acre in 1832. For this engagement, the Egyptians had two companies of rocketeers transported in two separate ships. Approximately twenty "gun-rocket boats," probably standard gunboats with portable rocket stands, also sailed with the Egyptian fleet. However, the rockets were not very effective. Their bursting fuses were made too short, causing them to explode prematurely instead of upon the fortress or enemy shipping.[18]

Ali further modernized his army after the Syrian War of the 1830s, and consequently, British 3- to 24-pounder (1–10.8 kg) rockets were tested in Cairo in 1838. But not until the rule of the Khedive or Turkish Viceroy, Ismael Pascha, from 1863 to 1879, were war rockets again supplied to Egyptian troops. They, too, may have been British in origin and were perhaps leftover or captured from an earlier expedition. Egyptians fired a few during the Egyptian nationalist uprising of 1881–82. As a result of her defeat, Egypt virtually became a British possession, though this did not end the employment of these weapons here.[19]

The revolutionist Mohammed Ahmed, styling himself "the Mahdi" (The Prophet), used rockets to rid his land of the infidels. In the summer of 1883, one of his lieutenants claimed: "We are coming with armies whose numbers can be counted only by the most high, and with arms which you [the English] possess not, including rockets and Remingtons." The English did of course possess rockets, but the Mahdi's own rockets saw unexceptional service.[20]

In Turkey itself, it seems that a small experimental laboratory featuring a hydraulic rocket press was operating in Constantinople by the late 1830s. The source for this technology is unknown, but the Ottomans had their own rocket pioneer in artillerist Brigadier-General Mahomet Emin-Pascha, who reported on his combination stick-rotating rocket in his *Mémoir sur un Nouveau Système de Confection des Fusées de Guerre* (*Memoir on a New System of War Rocket Manufacture*), published in Paris in 1840. As Emin-Pascha did not discuss Ottoman Army war rockets, perhaps his work was independent and experimental. For field use, Turks seem to have relied upon British equipment, as was evident during the siege of Acre in 1840 and in the Crimean War (1853–56). Colonel Atwell Lake noted that in Turkish foraging parties at Kars, during the latter campaign, "the use of [British] rockets [by the Turks] has been introduced with the greatest success as a support for these light troops, and they scarcely ever make movement, even in small bodies, without a detachment of rocketeers." After this, no other Turkish developments are known.[21]

Neighboring Persia (now Iran) developed its own war rocket establishment by the 1840s. It seems to have been started by Prime Minister Hadji-Mirza-Agassi who founded an arsenal in Teheran. In less than eight years there allegedly were 20,000 Congreve rockets of different calibers made here under his orders. The Persian rocket establishment still existed at the time of the Crimean War, the rockets transported by carriages and the men furnished with horses and camels. In 1856, it was reported that each of the eight horse artillery batteries, in addition to the three reserve batteries, in the Persian army had a rocket cart. There was, therefore, no elite Persian rocket brigade, but rockets were widely distributed among the artillery. This system lasted until as late as the 1870s. Since the rockets were then called "Congreve," they must have been still of the stick configuration.[22]

As with the Turks, information on the conclusion of Persian rocketry developments is wanting. It is assumed that like so many other countries around the globe that once embraced Congreve rocket weapons, these nations too phased them out in lieu of superior conventional artillery introduced in the West, whose military technology they fervently emulated.

CHAPTER 9

The Persistent Mr. Hale

William Hale's invention of the stickless, or rotary, rocket amounted to more than just a dispensing of the cumbersome and inefficient wooden stabilizing sticks of the Congreve rocket. His overall improvements represented the difference between the first crude, largely handmade, sheet-steel and canvas-covered rockets of the Congreve era, and the finely machined, all-metal stickless rockets produced at the height of the Industrial Revolution. Ultimately, these improvements resulted in lengthening the lifespan of the old military powder rocket by 40 to 50 years, also increasing the possibilities for further, nonmilitary applications.

Hale's primary rocketry invention consisted of stabilizing the rocket by causing it to rotate by means of canted exhaust holes. The method of rotation gradually evolved through different models from 1844 until 1865 (see Chapter 11), and entailed a large expenditure of money and effort to produce and promote internationally. At the same time, Hale developed new manufacturing techniques and refined the hydraulic rocket press, which he preferred over the muscle-operated, inefficient and dangerous pile-driver press of the Con-

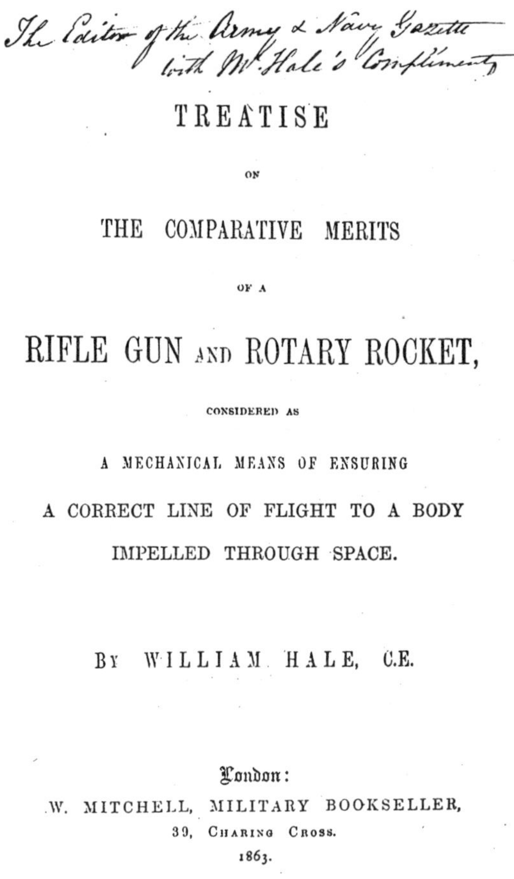

The Editor of the Army & Navy Gazette
with Mr Hale's Compliments

TREATISE

ON

THE COMPARATIVE MERITS

OF A

RIFLE GUN AND ROTARY ROCKET,

CONSIDERED AS

A MECHANICAL MEANS OF ENSURING

A CORRECT LINE OF FLIGHT TO A BODY

IMPELLED THROUGH SPACE.

BY WILLIAM HALE, C.E.

London:

W. MITCHELL, MILITARY BOOKSELLER,
39, CHARING CROSS.
1863.

FIGURE 9.1
In 1843 British engineer William Hale developed his stickless, or spin-stabilized, rocket, greatly improving the accuracy of rockets and dispensing with the cumbersome wooden guidestick.
(S.I. 79–8998)

greve era. Although Hale's improvements did not completely solve the problem of rocket instability, primarily because of the inherent weakness of gunpowder, they still represented revolutionary strides in early rocket technology and Hale is thus considered a major pioneer.

Early Life

Though sometimes mistakenly called an American, William Hale actually was born in Colchester, Essex, England, on 21 October 1797. It is believed he may have been descended from the great seventeenth-century Lord Chief Justice of England, Sir Matthew Hale, though his own circumstances were more modest. William's father was a baker; his maternal grandfather, William Cole, was a versatile educator and writer on diverse subjects from his own theories on comets to algebra. It is likely that Cole was Hale's first teacher, though Hale appears to have been largely self-educated.[1]

He showed a penchant for mechanics, especially concerning ships. Colchester is situated close to the port of Greenwich, and it is possible that Hale served before the mast in his youth. His first patent, taken out in 1827 for "improvements in propelling vessels," reflects a good working knowledge of ships and was supposedly the first English design for an internal-screw vessel. Significantly, the ship utilized a crude form of "jet propulsion" based upon the 2,000-year-old principle of the Archimedean screw. Water was sucked into the vessel by the steam-powered screw, then discharged in order to drive the ship forward. The inventor showed an early insight into jet propulsion, later correctly describing it in terms of Newton's Third Law of Motion: "For every action there is an opposite and equal reaction."[2]

By 1832, a paper about the internal-screw vessel was read before the Royal Society in London. A clockwork model was built and tested before the King and Queen. Hale won the first class Gold Medal of the Royal Society of Arts in Paris. Hale afterward submitted his invention to the Admiralty. Then, by his own admission, Hale lost interest in the project. In 1842, he began to pursue "ordnance matters."[3]

About 1828, Hale married Eliza Rouse, of Colchester, and had two daughters, Emma and Mary Ann, and two sons, William, Jr., and Robert. His sons, who both became rocket pioneers in their own right, were born in Colchester on 28 September 1829 and 28 May 1831, respectively. In about 1835, the elder Hale settled in Greenwich, presumably to be close to Royal Navy officialdom. More of his patents appeared. In addition to further patents on steam power, there was an improved windmill, a rotary engine, and a method of producing gas in "aerated liquors." The last specification was taken out in partnership with George Purt, a soda-water manufacturer in Saint Mary-at-Hill, London. Perhaps Hale's early preoccupation with spinning mechanisms, and even his study of soda-water *gas* production (and presumably, *flow*), played roles in his thinking toward the solution of rocket stability by gases causing the spinning.[4]

Hale Discovers Rockets

In 1839 or 1840, Hale pulled up his roots again and moved near the Royal Arsenal in Woolwich. Here he collaborated with Edward Dell, a local wine merchant who had apparently formerly worked in the arsenal's Royal Carriage

Department. Dell had acquired enough generalized knowledge to consider himself an ordnance expert, and he soon talked Hale into what proved to be a deceptive partnership in an improved gunpowder case. In 1841 and 1842 they jointly took out patents for this invention in England and France. It was soon disclosed that Dell had privately made a contract with someone in the arsenal to purchase "Dell's Patent Powder Case." Although Hale lost £500 by taking out the patent, it turned out that he did gain some valuable knowledge. The gunpowder case was an improvement over an idea worked out many years before by William Congreve; Hale became fully aware of Congreve's other achievements, especially in rocketry, and immediately sought to make his own improvements.[5]

Hale first set about locating suitable testing grounds. He complained of trouble finding "an extent of ground over which to fire, quite free from buildings and cattle." It is not known how much livestock he stampeded, nor how many landlords he startled, but he later admitted that his experiments forced him to move on no fewer than ten occasions. By 1843, he made sufficient progress, he later wrote, that when the "use of the stick of the rocket could be dispensed with, I addressed the Board of Ordnance. . . . That was in September." Other stickless rockets had been tried without success, both in England and abroad. The British Government ordered trials to be made at Hale's expense.[6]

This arrangement persisted for many years, as Hale rockets went from one modification to another until the British finally agreed to purchase the invention. Hale perennially complained that the government had treated him unfairly by using his rockets in several campaigns without properly compensating him. These grievances were perhaps justified; it was not until 1867, some 26 years after he had first introduced the rocket, that the government officially purchased Hale's invention for £8,000. In the interim, Hale, his sons, and agents negotiated sales with many nations. Like Dell, some of his partners were neither trustworthy nor competent; Hale faced additional worry from competitors who claimed priority. He was granted his first rocket patent on 11 January 1844 (incorrectly cited by some writers as 1846). He also obtained Dutch patent rights, and later applied for French and Swiss rights. Hale began developing a hydraulic press for his rockets as well (see Chapter 11).[7]

In December 1846, Hale made the first sale of his rockets to a foreign government when, through his agent Joshua Hyde, the United States purchased manufacturing rights for $20,000 in preparation for the Mexican War. Also in 1846, Hale presented a firing demonstration at Vincennes, France, before General Baron Gaspard and the Duke de Montpensier, who had shared

Napoleon's exile in St. Helena. While the French were highly pleased with the rockets and agreed to pay for further tests, the inventor's price of 200,000 francs for the secret was considered to be too high.[8]

In 1848, Hale found time to devise "an entirely new percussion shell," which he tested before the Artillery Select Committee at Woolwich. It was found to be technically satisfactory, but was not adopted. Upon the flare-up of the Hungarian revolution in August of that year, Prime Minister Lajos Batthyany began making inquiries of the British Foreign Secretary, Viscount Palmerston, about the possibility of detailing to Hungary a British officer knowledgeable about rockets. Apparently, no officer was sent, because Hungary's independence was not recognized by Great Britain; but the Batthyany government learned of Hale's private rocket factory. A special delegate, Fedor Karacsay, was ordered to London to open talks with Hale. These negotiations, which continued until the abdication of Batthyany and the assumption of Lajos Kossuth, did not prove to be fruitful. The main problem seems to have been the high cost of Hale's services and a lack of money on the part of the revolutionary Hungarian government. The Hungarians, however, fully recognized the value of Hale's rockets. One Hungarian negotiator who spoke with Hale, K. Stolzman, reported to the unofficial leader of the Hungarian mission in London, Ferenc Pulszky, that the rocket was "the most important, the most formidable and the most efficient" project; but he regretted that Hale's priority was money, not political principles. Hale was then opening negotiations with the Russian ambassador for the sale of rockets despite his previously anti-Russian sentiments. Hale clandestinely continued his negotiations with the Hungarians long after the revolution collapsed in 1849. It later proved to be almost his undoing.[9]

Perhaps because of his failure to secure a sale to the Russians, first through the ambassador in London and then through Matthew Nottingham, whom he sent to St. Petersburg, Hale again began to act as his own agent. In 1849, he went to Switzerland where, according to one military writer of the period, his rockets were "narrowly investigated" by a military committee in Zurich. Passing through Schaffhausen, a few kilometers north, while on his way to the German principalities, Hale visited Johann Conrad Fischer's reknowned iron and steel foundry. There, the Swiss industrialist invited him, mistakenly recalling him as Captain Hale, to witness the fusing and casting of pig-iron and steel. This experience led Hale to seek stronger steel for his rockets and to patent several improvements in methods of rolling iron and steel. By 1850, he had reached Berlin. According to one account, the Prussian artillery committee was "astonished" by the steadiness of the rockets, despite a strong wind, and by the range and "immense power which the engine seemed to possess." The committee also was impressed with the finale—the launching of a single rocket composed of seven individual Hale rockets "inclosed in an iron cylinder." The committee agreed that the large projectile was ideal for sieges "and even in sea fights, by carrying a barrel of powder into a fort or ship." A detailed report was sent to the king, but still the Prussians refused to buy, probably because of the great expense involved.[10]

Hale returned to England the same year and enjoyed a minor triumph. Queen Victoria's consort, Prince Albert, "was pleased," in Hale's words, "to have an experiment made before him at Osborne, when I fired twenty 10-pounder [4.5 kg] rockets at my own cost." The London *Times* reported that Albert personally examined the rockets and asked Hale about the nature of them. The government still did not adopt the projectiles, but Hale persevered and improved upon the design. His sons then began taking up the rocket business actively. By 1851, 22-year-old William, Jr., went to South America to open negotiations for rocket sales, while at about the same time Robert, age 20, sailed to Washington, D.C., to try to interest the Americans in improved models and launchers.[11]

At home, the elder Hale now received private and governmental orders from Canada, Denmark, and the free city of Hamburg; an offer also came from Cuba. However, he made another gross misjudgment in choosing his associates, one that was to threaten everything he had built and reverberate throughout all Europe.

The Kossuth Affair

In September 1852, through his contacts with the Hungarians, William Hale, Sr., hired a "destitute" former Hungarian artillery major named August Usever, or Usener. Prussian army lists for 1844 show Usever as a 2nd lieutenant in the Prussian 8th Artillery Regiment. He later joined the Hungarian service, probably during the revolution of 1848, for he claimed to have been a political refugee who had come to England from Hungary after the revolution failed. In the summer of 1852, finding himself penniless, Usever sought help from the former leader of the Hungarian revolution, Lajos Kossuth, who was living in exile in London following the abortive revolution. To many millions, particularly Hungarians, Kossuth was a patriot-hero and the legitimate ruler of his land; to others, he was a fallen tyrant, anguishing for any opportunity to regain the power he had briefly held. In his own time, he was, above all, a rallying point and counselor for his people in exile.[12]

Kossuth found Usever a job as an artificer in Hale's Rotherhithe rocket factory, on the banks of the Thames near Woolwich (see Figure 9.2). Hale employed other "foreign refugees" through Kossuth. By this time, Hale's link with Kossuth seems to have been strong; István Gyorgy Nagy, the historian of nineteenth-century rocketry in Hungary, contends that there is evidence of a "silent partnership" between the two that was especially valued for the years 1848–52, which were financially difficult for Hale, who filed for bankruptcy on at least two occasions (1849 and 1850). Even when Kossuth visited America before moving to England, he is known to have written to Hale through his London emissary, Colonel Mikles Kiss, regarding a remittance of money.

Usever worked at the Rotherhithe factory for only three months; illness forced him to resign. He then returned to Kossuth, asserting that the exiled leader "was bound to support all Hungarians in distress." Apparently, Kossuth was unable to provide further assistance to Usever, who then stormed out, warning Kossuth before he left that he would "regret it." This, at least, is Usever's later account of what happened.[13]

As events unfolded, Hale, rather than Kossuth, turned out to be the real victim of Usever's wrath and machinations. Usever notified the British gov-

FIGURE 9.2

Hale's rocket factory at Rotherhithe, London, was investigated in 1853 by the Thames Police for reportedly making rockets for the exiled Hungarian revolutionary Lajos Kossuth. (S.I. 71–62–2)

ernment that Hale's Rotherhithe factory was a secret place for producing war munitions "on a large scale" for the "revolutionary designs of the secret committees of Italian and Hungarian exiles," and that the building was either owned by or rented to Kossuth himself through a third party. (According to Nagy, Usever was really a paid informer of the Imperial Austrian Secret Police, who aimed to discredit and ruin the cause of Kossuth and Hungarian refugees in England.) Nagy claims that Usever "wormed himself into Kossuth's confidence," and Kossuth then recommended him to Hale.[14]

Acting on Usever's tip, the police sent detective sergeant John Saunders to spy on the factory, each day wearing a different disguise. On the morning of 13 April 1853, Saunders and Superintendent of Thames Police James C. Evans presented a search warrant to the occupant for illegal manufacture of gunpowder within 3 miles (4.8 km) of London city limits. Neither Hale nor his sons were on the premises, but James Boylin, a worker who was filling some rockets, sent for them. The police seized all the gunpowder casks and cartons of rockets and took them by barge to Woolwich Arsenal. There they were ostensibly stored for safekeeping.[15]

While awaiting trial, the scandal implicating Kossuth exploded in the world press. There were charges of a grand conspiracy in which Hale, in league with Kossuth, was making his rockets "for use against a sovereign with whom England was at peace." No other than Karl Marx, then a London correspondent for the *New York Herald Tribune,* was among the reporters who further complicated the plot by attempting to connect the Rotherhithe affair with another revolutionary case, known as the "Calabrian hat conspiracy." Another paper said that "electric telegraph brought intelligence of similar seizures in Rome, Genoa, etc." and that the "Rotherhithe Case" or "Kossuth Plot" would have dire effect "upon the Court of Vienna." Indeed, because of the revolutionary implications, notes were exchanged between embassies in London and Vienna, though no formal diplomatic steps were taken. The case was hotly debated in Parliament, one member of the House of Commons calling it "The Rotherhithe and Kossuth Mare's nest." Viscount Palmerston, Home Secretary and soon to be Prime Minister, also spoke out against the affair, but called for moderation and truth. Kossuth reacted with a letter he had read in Parliament declaring that while he did know Hale, "all the accusations in the *Times* of today about a house in my occupation having been searched, and a store of war materials belonging to me been discovered and seized, are entirely unfounded."[16]

The trial was held in the Bow Street Police Court, which was reportedly "crowded to excess on the occasion." The crowds in the galleries, eager to hear

FIGURE 9.3

The so-called "Rotherhithe case" created a worldwide sensation at the time. This woodcut shows the packed Bow Street Court House, with the "Hungarian witness" August Usever on the stand. (s.i. 71–62–3)

of any sedition and further intrigue, were not disappointed. Though only a misdemeanor, the nature of the proceedings brought many witnesses for both defendant and plaintiff. Hale's former employees were summoned, including Usever. He gave the most defamatory testimony. He told of secret talks in German between Kossuth and Hale and that the younger Hale (Robert) had warned all the workmen "not to talk at the public houses, or anywhere, about the factory, nor mention the name of Kossuth, nor even the word Hungarian, because this . . . would . . . betray our work."[17]

Hale's oldest son, William, Jr., wrote to the papers, pointing out that his father had spent an "outlay of upwards of 20,000 pounds" in developing the rocket, and that the government was "well aware of the existence of his manufactory . . . and further, that they [the rockets] were intended by him for the British government." He added that his father had "determined . . . [to take] legal proceedings against the government."[18]

The judge, Thomas Henry, thought all the conspiratorial allegations of the case to be irrelevant. This instantly dashed the plans of Usever and the Austrian Secret Police. No charges were ever made against Kossuth and he was not called as a witness. Judge Henry made only one demand: Were in fact the Hales guilty or innocent of illegally storing or making gunpowder within London city limits? William Hale pleaded guilty to the charge, but said he was ignorant of the law. He paid his fine—two shillings for every pound in excess of the legal amount of 200 pounds (90 kg) of gunpowder—and once more found himself financially ruined. Altogether there were several barrels of gunpowder and 1,500 loaded rockets. Further infractions of the law were found, dragging the case out further, but minus the political commotion it started with. Then, in May, on the eve of the Crimean War, the government dropped the charges. The impending war seems to have immediately altered the government's opinion of Hale, and certainly of the relative importance of the case. As for the Kossuth-Hale "partnership," Nagy finds that it did not entirely dissolve after the Rotherhithe affair. "We have every reason to suppose that Kossuth made up to Hale for his material damages in part or as a whole," he writes. In October 1853 Kossuth wrote a letter in which he expressed a desire to establish a new Hale rocket factory in Belgrade, near the old Hungarian border. The fate of these plans and of Hale's subsequent Hungarian connections is unknown.[19]

Back in Business

Hale saw the Crimean military and political developments as giving him a quick opportunity to recover his fortune. He settled his shattered affairs as best he could, collecting £870 in compensation for damages from the government. When the war began, he requested permission to sail to the front. Permission was granted, and he left his son Robert in charge of matters. In December 1853 the elder Hale arrived in Constantinople with rockets. From there he re-embarked for the Black Sea and joined the Allied fleet anchored in Kavarna Bay, just north of Varna, Bulgaria. The Admiralty shipped his rockets from Constantinople for experiments ordered by Admiral Sir James Deans Dundas. However, the tests were not conducted until the following August, just prior to the departure of the army and part of the fleet from Varna. While waiting for the tests to begin, Hale presented private exhibits at Scutari and elsewhere to several ship commanders. A grand display was held on the heights of Baldjik before all the captains and admirals of the fleet. The rockets flew well and the officers were unanimous in their praise of them. The projectiles were recommended for adoption by both the fleet admiral and commander-in-chief of the British Army in the Crimea, Lord Raglan. Raglan bought what rockets and machinery Hale had for £500. Several rounds were subsequently fired with great success at Balaklava, after the famous Charge of the Light Brigade, and against the Malakov fortress.[20]

Following the Baldjik experiment, Hale was asked to return to England to prepare more rocket stores for the war. By the close of 1854, it was decided to manufacture the rockets experimentally at Woolwich. A new shed was erected at the arsenal and hydraulic presses were installed. This marked the semi-official adoption of Hale's rockets by the British. They were intended to be made at least for the duration of the war. Following the Crimean conflict, Hale continued to give demonstrations of his improved rockets, both on the Woolwich firing ranges and from aboard the test ship *Excellent*. The British government made occasional requests for more rockets, but only on a piecemeal basis. The inventor continued to press for more compensation.[21]

In 1855, Robert returned to America and sold newer rocket models to Secretary of War Jefferson Davis. By 1857, William Hale, Sr., started negotiations with the Austrians. William, Jr., went to Vienna in 1858 and met with such "an extraordinary success" that the Austrians purchased the secret; Emperor Franz Joseph and Archduke William personally thanked the younger Hale after witnessing tests. (The Austrians subsequently modified the invention and "Halle" rockets, as they called them, were employed in later campaigns, such as at the island of Lissa, in 1866, against Italian insurrectionists during the *Risorgimento* wars.) By 1859, the elder Hale had renewed talks with the Prussians; in 1860 they, too, decided to adopt his rockets. Hale rocket experiments were also carried out in 1860 at Felixdorf, in the Kingdom of Saxony, perhaps by William Hale, Jr.[22]

Between 1849 and 1859, the French undertook their own intensive investigations of rotation rockets as a way to overcome instability. These efforts, carried out by Colonel Auguste Goupil, Captain Dominique Munier, and other artillery officers, proved to be unsatisfactory. Ellipsoid wings, rifled launching tubes, and other means were tried. In about 1859, soon after unsuccessful tests were made at the Metz pyrotechnic school with "inclined spiral canals in the baseplate (similar to Hale rockets)," Hale received "an urgent invitation" from Emperor Napoleon III "to exhibit his inventions." William Hale, Jr., presented the exhibit. The Russian rocket pioneer Konstantinov, writing in 1869, remarked that the younger Hale was now acting independently of his father, and had brought an entirely new rocket design featuring curved vanes ("three elbow-shaped canals") located in the path of the exhaust. This may have been the "intermediary design," patented in 1862.[23]

"Now it turns out," Konstantinov also observed, "that when speaking of Hale's rockets, it is necessary to differentiate two systems of rotationally guided, tailless rockets. One belongs to Hale, the senior, and the other to his son [William, Jr.] . These two inventors broke up and each went his own way . . . as regards the commercial exploitation [of rocketry]." It may be that William Hale, Jr., and not his father, was responsible for the curved-vane feature of Hale's rockets. An examination shows that all Hale rocket patents issued before 1870 were taken out by the elder Hale; however, the father may have patented what was accomplished by his son. We may never know for certain, but based solely upon the patents, this major improvement must be ascribed to the senior Hale.[24]

Comparative tests of this model were held at La Fère, about 70 miles (110 km) north of Paris. Hale's rockets produced "marvels," though two of them exploded upon leaving the launcher. The mishaps were attributed to improper preparation. Konstantinov adds that in about 1861 William Hale, Sr., offered the French new rockets "based on an entirely new principle," but the French did not see fit to test them. Perhaps this was because they were as costly as those he tried to sell them 15 years before. The French turned down the Hales for the last time.[25]

Upon the outbreak of the American Civil War in 1861, William, Jr.'s, own agent, J. Walsh Crane, wrote to U.S. Secretary of War Simon Cameron that: "Mr. Hale offers to come with me to organize the [Rocket] Brigade and go immediately to the front . . . all he asks is the sum necessary *to make* 500 rockets. . . . We pay our own expenses and ask for nothing until your Honor is satisfied." Soon after, William, Jr., promised to deliver about 5,000 of the 12-pounder rockets "for carrying burning lava" himself, and to ship these, with other "vast stores," on the fastest steamer from Southampton or Liverpool. Evidently, Secretary Cameron turned down this ambitious offer. In the latter part of the war, however, in 1864, William, Jr., did go to Washington in order to make improved rockets in the Washington Arsenal.[26]

Sometime after 1862, the elder Hale initiated experiments in England to adapt his rocket for lifesaving by fitting a metal turnbuckle and chain to the base of the projectile. But this project, afterwards continued by William, Jr., and others through Hale's Rocket Co., Ltd. (incorporated in 1875), and a successor firm, did not succeed after years of trying (see Chapter 12). Hale's war rockets were far more viable commercially and technically, and the inven-

tor proudly received an honorable mention "for his exertions in the improvement of rockets" at the International Exhibition held in London in 1862. There,
he exhibited his 1860–62 model war rocket, in addition to "comet shells," a
launcher, and a "gun and rocket boat." Probably the latter was a model of a
vessel mounted both with guns and Hale rocket-launcher tubes.[27]

Final Success

In 1867, England officially purchased William Hale's rocket patents, superseding Boxer stick rockets (see Chapter 4), which had in turn replaced the earlier
Congreve rockets. Hale, then 70, turned away from the rockets upon which he
had incessantly labored.[28]

Resuming work on ships, his original preoccupation, Hale took out
another patent on ship propulsion. The following year he published a paper on
his earlier ideas. By then, his internal-screw vessel was considered to be
outmoded and his *Treatise on the Mechanical Means by Which Vessels are propelled
by Steam Power* was poorly received. In contrast, his rockets were praised at the
International Exhibition in Paris in 1867, where they were displayed by both
the British and the Austrians. The following year, starting with the Abyssinian War, Hale rockets began to appear frequently in England's numerous
colonial campaigns in Africa, right up to the turn of the century.[29]

William Hale was still trying to perfect his lifesaving rockets when, on 30
March 1870, he died in London of typhoid fever and was buried in the Old
Brompton Cemetery. A century later, the International Astronomical Union
chose his name to be shared with astronomer George Ellery Hale (the two men
were not related) to designate the Hale Crater on the Moon (90°E, 74°S) and to
honor him as a rocket pioneer.[30]

CHAPTER 10

Hale's Rockets

William Hale attempted to correct two major defects of the nineteenth-century powder rocket. One of his goals was to eliminate the cumbersome wooden stabilizer guidestick; the other was to improve the rocket's notorious inaccuracy. He sought the solution to both problems through the single feature of spin-stabilization. Hale's improvements were further strengthened by the incorporation of machined, all-metal construction and hydraulic propellant loading, which made the rocket's manufacture and performance more uniform. The irony of his achievements, however, was that concurrently with his labors on the rifled rocket came the rapid evolution of the rifled, breech-loaded gun. By the time of the Franco-Prussian War (1870–71), irregularities of rifling and breech-loading were overcome and the gun had surpassed the rocket so entirely as to make it obsolete. Only the British and Russians maintained their rocket services for colonial warfare, long after the rocket had become extinct everywhere else.

Designs

The idea of spinning an artillery projectile to obtain greater accuracy by offsetting any lateral forces in its path went back to as early as 1525, but for centuries there existed neither the skill to work the metals nor the machinery for boring and rifling with the required accuracy. Spinning, or rifled, rockets were not new either, and they often appeared in firework displays. However, these small pasteboard rockets wobbled rather than spinned, producing interesting visual effects but no greater stability. Whether or not Hale was aware of these developments in 1842 when he first took up "ordnance matters" is not known, but in any case it was quite a different matter in those years to create spinning in a metal artillery rocket, since the dynamics of rocket flight were so little understood and the machinery for producing this arrangement virtually nonexistent. Achieving optimum spin-stabilization was not without its own inherent problems, and Hale rockets passed through three major modifications between 1844 and 1865 before the final "classic" design was attained.

The first Hale model (British Patent No. 10,008, of 11 January 1844) generated spin by four equidistant tangential or oblique holes bored around the base. In the base's center was a larger hole, the central exhaust exit. As the powder burned, resulting gases were expelled through the exhaust, providing thrust, and also issued from the tangential holes, creating a pinwheel effect or spinning of the entire rocket around its longitudinal axis.[1]

These rockets had one peculiar drawback. They sometimes had a tendency to oscillate or wobble at the tail end after the propellant had been expended.

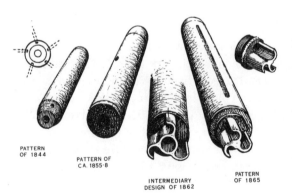

PATTERN
OF 1844

PATTERN OF
CA. 1855-8

INTERMEDIARY
DESIGN OF 1862

PATTERN
OF 1865

FIGURE 10.1

Hale's rockets evolved over the years through distinctive patterns. This drawing is based upon Hale's patents from 1844 to 1865. (S.I. 84–3463)

FIGURE 10.2

The first Hale rocket config-
uration of 1844, with wooden
dowels in the escape holes of
a 10- or 20-pounder (4.5 or
9 kg) rocket to show how spin
was produced as the pro-
pellant burned. (s.i. A1083)

Hale called this phenomenon the "after end orbit." It was behavior that negated the accuracy and stability the inventor was seeking. By 1855, he had eliminated the problem by shifting the tangential spinning vents to slightly

FIGURE 10.3

American Hale rockets had spin holes around the center of gravity of the rocket. Propellant for
the spin was separate from the main thrust propellant in the motor case. (s.i. A2000)

FIGURE 10.4

Another Hale variation, a 2-inch (5 cm) model, was found on the Civil War battlefield at Petersburg, Virginia. Now on exhibit in the National Air and Space Museum. (S.I. 76–6951)

beneath the warhead. The spinning motion was therefore centered around the rocket's center of gravity. Internally, there was a tandem arrangement in which a separate propellant cavity in the rocket's forepart contained a propellant charge to produce the spin while the rear charge provided forward thrust. Hale received a patent for this modification (No. 2497 of 8 November 1858), which was later adopted by the Austrians.[2]

The 1855–58 rocket may have been in service at the close of the Crimean War, and was used by both sides during the U.S. Civil War a few years later. The Prussians also were shown models and bought them. The problem with the new design was that the dual powder sections were redundant and

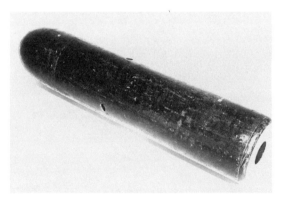

FIGURE 10.5

A British version of the 1855–58 Hale design, a rare 100-pounder (45 kg), also on display in the National Air and Space Museum. It carried a 13-pound (5.8 kg) charge of guncotton in the warhead. (S.I. A1082)

sacrificed the rocket's efficiency. Hale calculated that fully one third of the whole force of the available gas was expended to produce rotation, while only two thirds produced "onward motion."[3]

Between 1862 and 1865 either Hale or his elder son William, Jr., produced a third major modification. A return was made to a simple and efficient single propellant cavity, yet the full force of the exhaust gases and rotation was obtained; at the same time, oscillations were avoided. In this arrangement, the forward spin holes were eliminated entirely. The gases issued out of a single large hole in the center of a turbine-like tailpiece with three spiral vanes. This tailpiece was a single unit welded to the rear of the motor tube. The idea was that the "whole force of the gas" impelled the rocket forward via the central hole. At the same time, the gases in their compressed state were to "expand" toward the vanes, thus causing rotation. This "intermediary" design appeared as British Patent No. 1220 of 25 April 1862. However, it was quickly discovered that the gases from the single hole were only weakly spread out over the vanes, producing a correspondingly weak spin. Also, the welding process of the tailpiece was time-consuming and expensive.

The final or "classic" configuration, using the same principle, was patented on 20 April 1865 (No. 1103). In this design, the single large gas hole was eliminated. Instead, the gases issued from three smaller holes at the bases of each of the curved vanes. The gases thus equally impinged directly on each of the vanes, producing a steady, even rotation. Another alteration was that the tailpiece with its vanes was a single cast-iron unit and was made with threads so that it could easily be screwed into the rear of the rocket.[4]

FIGURE 10.6
Detail of the intermediate design of Hale's rockets, patented in 1862, showing the introduction of curved vanes to provide spin. (S.I. A1084)

FIGURE 10.7

The final model of Hale rocket. The two specimens at left show the threaded end closure that permitted the exhaust gases to operate simultaneously to produce thrust and spin-stabilization. They are contrasted with the first model, lower right. (s.i. A1129A)

Calibers

Despite the different configurations of Hale rockets over the years, calibers remained standard. Some were phased out, however, because they were considered too light, too heavy, or otherwise impractical. These were the 3-, 6-, and 12-pounder (1.3, 2.7, and 5.4 kg) models, and were withdrawn in 1870. The ponderous and largely experimental models of 100 pounds (45 kg) or more and 6 inches (15.2 cm) in diameter with guncotton heads were never issued for service. The so-called 6-pounder (2.7 kg) did not weigh what it was supposed to, and in 1867 was redesignated as the 9-pounder (4 kg). The 9- and 24-pounders (4 and 10.8 kg) survived and generally proved to be the most

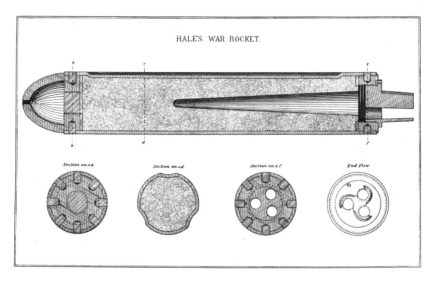

FIGURE 10.8
Internal view of the final Hale rocket, showing the retention of the centuries-old "soul" or conical cavity within the gunpowder propellant. (S.I. A4540B)

useful of the rockets in Britain's later "little military expeditions."[5]

In addition to calibers, there were also "Mark" numbers, reflecting slight design modifications made by the Royal Laboratory beginning in 1867, when England officially adopted the rockets. From 1867–77, Hale's rockets went through seven Mark numbers.[6]

FIGURE 10.9
Full-view of the final Hale pattern, a 24-pounder (10.8 kg), with longitudinal corrugations to crimp in the propellant so it would not displace during the rocket's rotating flight and result in cracking, which could lead to explosions. (S.I. A1085)

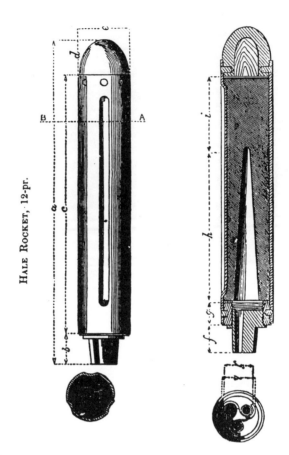

HALE ROCKET, ·12-pr.

—	3-pr.	6-pr.	12-pr.	24-pr.
a - - - - -	13 ins.± ·025	16·25 ins.± ·025	19·25 ins.± ·025	23·18 ins.± ·025
b - - - - -	1·24 in. ± ·01	1·56 in. ± ·01	1·95 in. ± ·01	2·43 ins.± ·01
c - - - - -	10·38 ins.± ·015	12·93 ins.± ·015	15·1 ins.± ·015	18·0 ins.± ·015
d - - - - -	1·4 in. ± ·02	1·76 in. ± ·02	2·2 ins.± ·02	2·75 ins.± ·02
e - - - - -	2 ins.± ·01	2·5 ins.± ·01	3 ins.± ·01	3·75 ins.± ·01
f - - - - -	1·18 in. ± ·01	1·48 in. ± ·01	1·85 in. ± ·01	2·305 ins.±·01
g - - - - -	·64 in. ± ·01	·8 in. ± ·01	1·0 in. ± ·01	1·25 in. ± ·01
h - - - - -	6·1 ins.	7·6 ins.	9·5 ins.	11·875 ins.
i - - - - -	3·1 ins.	3·85 ins.	3·75 ins.	3·813 ins.
j - - - - -	1·1 in.	1·4 in.	1·8 in.	2·2 ins.
k - - - - -	1·2 in.	1·5 in.	1·9 in.	2·4 ins.
Vents { No. of	3	3	3	3
{ diameter of	0·32 in.	0·4 in.	0·5 in.	0·625 ins.
Thickness of case, W.G. ·	12	12	11	10
Nitre - - -	68·75	68·75	70	70
Sulphur - - -	12·25	12·25	16	16
Charcoal - - -	18·75	18·75	23	23
Weight of composition -	1¼ lbs.	3 lbs.	5 lbs.	9 lbs. 6 ozs.
Total weight of rocket -	4 lbs. 8 ozs.	8 lbs. 6 ozs.	14 lbs. 2 ozs.	25 lbs. 12 ozs

FIGURE 10.10

Dimensions of Hale rockets, from the official British Army 1870 Treatise on Ammunition.

(*S.I. A5206D*)

Manufacture

Basic manufacturing procedures for Hale rockets consisted of: (1) preparing the rocket tube; (2) inserting a "false base" in one end; (3) placing the tube into a hydraulic press; (4) putting in preformed pellets of powder and hydraulically ramming them down the tube; (5) placing a millboard washer on top of the driven propellant; (6) fastening on the warhead with rivets; (7) removing the false base and drilling the conical propellant cavity; (8) attaching, with screws, the true base, the center of which was bored and tapped to receive the threaded tailpiece; and (9) painting, marking, and packing.[7]

Prior to 1870, Hale rocket cases were made from sheet-iron of the best charcoal iron or from ordinary rolled sheet-iron and steel. These tubes were rivetted together. But in 1865 Hale recommended lap-welding, and on 20 October in a trial between lap-welded and riveted rockets the "superiority" of lap-welded tubing for rockets was established. (Lap-welding had been tried years before with Congreve rockets, but failed because the metal was too thin and was further weakened by being cut against its "fibre" or grain.) In 1870, beginning with Mark II models, Hale rocket cases were made of a thick, but mild, steel called Atlas metal, produced by the Bessemer process (the Bessemer process of refining steel, one of great advances of the Industrial Revolution, was developed in 1855 by the Englishman Henry Bessemer). Whatever the metal used in Hale rocket production, care was taken that the raw sheets were cut in a lateral direction, where its greatest strength lay, ensuring maximum resistance against bursting from the hydraulic pressure of loading and firing. Lap-welding had become a standard procedure by this time and was performed once the metal had been rolled around cylindrical mandrils. However, it was found that the propellant was liable to be forced into hollow spots or defects in the joint during the propellant pressing and "might start a galvanic action" between the iron and spelter. Mark VII models obviated this, since the bodies were made of solid steel, and lap-welding was dispensed with altogether. The Army's annual *Ammunition* treatises for 1887–97 mention the "Weldless Steel Tube Company" as supplying the Royal Laboratory with ready, precut lengths of rocket tubing.[8]

Mark I–Mark V (1867–76) models of Hale 24-pounder (10.8 kg) rockets were laterally grooved or "corrugated" in three places. The idea was proposed by Royal Laboratory Comptroller Major-General Edward M. Boxer. He felt that the corrugations provided a better hold on the propellant, thereby preventing its separation from the body wall during the spinning flight of the rocket. But in fact the corrugations were found to weaken the case and in 1876 they were eliminated, though they returned with the Mark VI model.[9]

To ensure propellant integrity in a variety of climates, the British tried a number of propellant-case "inhibitors," as they are called today. Inhibitors avoided a direct contact between propellant and bare metal, thereby eliminating cracks and corrosion. The practice of painting interior coats was the earliest and simplest technique. Before 1870, three coats of "Brunswick Black" were applied to both the interior and exterior of the rocket. Other inhibitors tried include everything from tin and burnt-in oil and tallow preparations to shellac-coated calico with brown paper. Not all measures were successful. The brown paper was found to "ruck down" during the propellant pressing, and the tallow also tended to ride to the bottom. After much frustration, the Royal Laboratory of the later 1870s to 1880s found that to use no inhibitor at all was the most practical solution, so long as the interior of the chamber was roughened by scoring it spirally, ensuring a tight propellant fit, and by scouring the interior of the propellant case to remove all impurities and until thoroughly clean and dry. This practice was begun with Mark VII models and became standard procedure.[10]

Both Congreve and Hale rockets used gunpowder as the propellant, although the proportions of the ingredients changed from model to model. Burning rates were modified by increasing or decreasing the amount of saltpeter and/or charcoal. Propellant density was made more uniform by the hydraulic method. Rocket artisans of the day also felt that rocket performance was influenced by the relative fineness of their powder. Robert Hale noted in 1855 that he was particularly pleased with mixtures obtained from the Dupont de Nemours Company of Wilmington, Delaware, which he visited. By 1870, the British formula for Hale's 12- and 24-pounders (5.4 and 10.8 kg) was 70% saltpeter, 16% sulfur, and 23% charcoal of (alder) wood. For 3- and 9-pounders (1.3 and 4 kg) the proportions were 68.75%, 12.25%, and 18.75%, respectively. For the sake of convenience, the powder was pressed into individual pellets for loading.[11]

Congreve, William Moore, and probably others suggested steam-powered rocket presses many years before Hale did, and French naval lieutenant L.C.H. Le Chavallier successfully operated an experimental hydraulic press in 1834, but the subsequent history of the hydraulic rocket press is more obscure. Perhaps this is because it was a logical engineering progression whose history is taken for granted. Certainly, hydraulic presses came into their own by Hale's time, but his exact connection with this important development is still unknown, other than the fact that his rockets were always loaded this way. However, independent rocket-press development also seems to have taken place in England. Indeed, one design was a direct outgrowth of the famous

James Nasmyth, inventor of the steam ham-
mer, sketched his idea of the hammer adapted
to driving rockets as a hydraulic rocket press
in 1852. (S.I. 84–14743; Crown Copyright,
London)

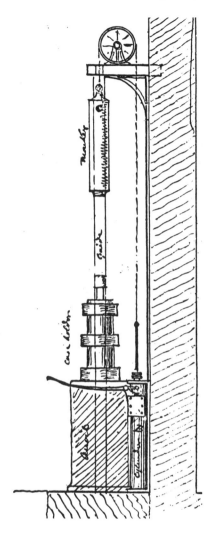

steam hammer, invented by Scottish engineer James Nasmyth in 1839 and built
in 1842; the hammer was a more efficient replacement for muscle-operated
heavy-duty forges in steel manufacture. Nasmyth himself, reluctantly at first,
played a role in adapting his invention to rocket-making.[12]

In 1848, Nasmyth's Bridgewater Foundry at Manchester supplied a 10-
horsepower steam engine to the Royal Laboratory in Woolwich. By 1852, the
engine became woefully inadequate because of the demands made upon it,

including some unspecified minor phases of rocket manufacture. The Lab's new Firemaster, Lieutenant Colonel John Tylden, wrote to Nasmyth on 7 September requesting cost estimates for an extra boiler and "the expense of supplying the necessary machinery for making, and driving rockets." Nasmyth subsequently inspected the "Rocket Department." He told Tylden he was satisfied that while the muscle-powered "monkey press" was "somewhat primitive," it still obtained a thoroughly "dense and compact charge." He concluded that "no satisfactory results would issue from the substitution of hydraulic power . . . in that department of rocket making I should incline to 'let well alone.'"[13]

Nasmyth did, however, offer proposals for improving the production of Congreve "rocket bottoms, namely that part into which the stick is screwed, and out of which the inflamed gases rush." For this improvement he designed a special lathe "having a hollow mandrill . . . for grasping the cases" and also recommended that "a small screwing lathe be employed for cutting the threads on rocket stick sockets."[14]

But Tylden was not persuaded that Nasmyth's assessment of a hydraulic press was sound, particularly from an economic viewpoint, although he appreciated the engineer's "*candid* opinion." The colonel persisted, requesting Nasmyth to review the matter and design a hydraulic system. With this prodding, Nasmyth responded more positively. On 1 November, he produced a "rough sketch" that was an "application of my patent steam hammer." If the Board of Ordnance were interested, Nasmyth added, he could deliver the press to the Lab for £155.[15]

Now armed with facts and figures, Tylden obliquely proposed Nasmyth's press to the Board. Savings of time and money would result with a new 22-horsepower steam engine as opposed to procuring a new boiler for the old one, he said. In addition, he said, "the present engine should be removed nearer to the sheds, for the purpose of driving rockets." Tylden continued, saying that "this arrangement, although startling in its outlay," would also save "large amounts, produce *more* work, and *diminish* the manual labor." Four men, he reasoned, were required for the manual press to make five 12-pounder (5.5 kg) Congreve rockets a day, in contrast to one for the hydraulic press that could produce 40 daily.[16]

Tylden followed-up his investigations by visiting mills and foundries, including Nasmyth's, to observe various steam engines firsthand and to determine if a better machine might be found for driving the rockets by steam.[17]

Unfortunately, there is no further documentation on this crucial phase of

WAR-ROCKET MAKING.—THE HYDROSTATIC-DRIVING PROCESS.

FIGURE IO.I2

Hale may have developed his hydraulic press independently. All of his rockets were made using it and the improved press ensured greater uniformity in manufacturing and safety. (S.I. A4671A)

the early history of rocket technology, so we cannot learn how Woolwich finally did adopt hydraulic machines. But it seems that Tylden's efforts went far in promoting the idea. It is also possible that Hale independently developed his own press. We know that at the height of the Crimean War, late in 1854, short-term manufacture of Hale rockets was sanctioned, and the necessary hydraulic presses installed in a new shed in the Lab. An article in the 22 April 1855 *London Illustrated News* on rocket manufacture at Woolwich also confirms this: "Amongst other improvements introduced by Mr. Hale, in the manufacture of rockets, not the least interesting is the adoption of hydrostatic pressure in place of ramming by mallets or monkeys."[18]

The same article mentioned a pressure of seven tons per square inch (4,786 kg/cm²) for the Hale press. Apparently, this was considered ideal, because three decades later the 1887 issue of the *Treatise on Ammunition* cites the same pressure for the 9-pounder (4 kg) Hale, while 24-pounders (10.8 kg) were pressed at 10 tons (6,837 kg/cm²). No figures are available for corresponding pressures for older monkey presses, but they were undoubtedly less than those produced by the hydrostatic method.[19]

To resume to Hale rocket manufacturing steps, following propellant ramming and removal of the "false base," a conical hole of 11.8 inches (30 cm), or two-thirds the length of the case, was drilled into the solid column of propellant, as had been the practice for hundreds of years. As noted, this space provided greater burning area and served as a combustion chamber. The real base piece, a thick cast-iron disc of 1.25 inches (3 cm) for the 24-pounder (10.8 kg) and 0.8 inches (2 cm) for the 9-pounder (4 kg), was next secured by "screw rivets." A soft lead wire washer and a millboard washer sealed the joint between the body and base piece, preventing gas seepage. In the center of the base piece was screwed the "tail piece" with its vanes. (Prior to the introduction of the curved vanes in 1862, exhaust exits were drilled directly into the rocket case.)[20]

Warheads for Hale's were fixed to the rocket cases by either eight or ten rivets, depending upon the Mark number. At first, British Hale rockets were exploding shell types. By 1867, shell heads were discontinued in favor of cast iron plugged with oak wood. The sheer force of the projectile, which was generally fired at short ranges, and its solid head caused sufficient damage against both "hard" targets and simple native fortifications of branches or sod. The rocket's incendiary value was also recognized, probably because the still burning propellant often caused a fire after the rocket fell, especially in bush country. Unlike the variety of warhead shapes for earlier Congreve rockets, Hale's warheads came in one basic style: cylindroconoidal (with rounded noses). (By contrast, the Austrians provided several types of warheads for their Hales, including explosive, shrapnel, and illumination models.) The Royal Laboratory occasionally experimented with other warheads, such as the 24-pounder (10.8 kg) with removable guncotton warheads, in 1877; in the same period incendiary types were tried, but never became standard issues.[21]

Mark VII Hale rockets included another fixture, a mild-steel (probably Atlas metal) semicylindrical safety cap screwed onto the baseplate. Earlier models were covered with canvas and tied with twine. Sometimes exits were protected only by paper.[22]

The entire body was protected by three coats of paint, generally a special formula called "Brunswick Black," on both the interiors and exteriors of the first Hale models, before 1870. In that year, red lead paint was introduced, but complaints were soon received from foreign stations (perhaps those in hot climates) that the paint came off "like chalk," leaving the iron bare. To remedy this, a new formula containing more oil was adopted in 1873, but the red color was retained with the result that all British Hale war rockets made after 1870 were a dull red, except those that were repainted black for display or other reasons.[23]

The final step in the process of manufacturing Hale rockets consisted of marking and packing. In 1878, the Commissary-General suggested that for land use three 24-pounders (10.8 kg) be packed per box "as is done for sea service," rather than continue with the usual six per box. This made the boxes easier to lift and store, since a crate of six rockets weighed 191 pounds (86.6 kg). A lighter box also lessened chances of its being dropped—the sort of accident that could prove catastrophic. "Rockets," the regulations cautioned, "should be carefully handled; accidents with new rockets or with those that have not been knocked about are very rare."[24]

A numeral, a letter, and the date were usually stamped on the bases, heads, and cases of the rockets for inventory and quality-control purposes. Numbers ran up to 1,000, after which the letter was changed. Finally, the letters A.M. (Atlas Metal) were stamped near the head, if applicable.[25]

Related to manufacturing was "quality control." Apart from trial launches, a random proportion of rocket tubing was hydrostatically tested for flaws. Rockets in storage were inspected quarterly; those showing the slightest sign of rust or corrosion at the seams or rivets were withdrawn and thoroughly cleaned with emery cloth or serge with fine dry sand and washed with turpentine.[26]

Hale rockets were usually requisitioned by the Army in lots of 100. A 24-pounder (10.8 kg) cost £1 18s. 6d. and each 9-pounder (4 kg) cost £1 3s. 9d.[27]

Launchers and Igniters

Hale found both tubes and troughs (also called "V's") to be eminently suitable for firing. Tubes were tried first, probably because they were used for launching Congreve rockets. Tubes were preferred for launching Hales from the bows of ships and boats, and troughs were preferred for land service. There were other Hale rocket launchers, but it is difficult to trace their evolution. One interesting development was a "hybrid" launcher, a half-tube resembling a gutter spout. Later models were mounted on wheels or featured multiple half-tubes. The former was a typical makeshift creation prevalent during the U.S.

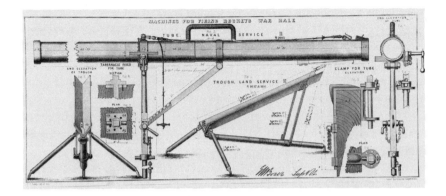

FIGURE 10.13

Hale rockets were fired from V-shaped troughs or tubes depending on whether they were intended for land or naval service, as depicted in this 1870 British specification. (S.I. 75–13980)

Civil War. Earlier, in 1851, William Hale, Jr., came to America to sell "an improved stand for firing Hale's rockets" and rocket cases. The design, probably a tube and not a trough, was a successful one, and the Secretary of War purchased it and the cases for $770.[28]

When Robert Hale came to Washington in 1855 with "important improvements in Hale's rockets," another new launcher was discussed and a mild controversy ensued when he accused an officer of the Spanish legation of making an "evil" pencil sketch of "Mr. Hale's Rocket stand." After irritating Ordnance Department personnel by forcing them to make unnecessary reprimands, the matter was tactfully dropped.[29]

Robert Hale's secrecy was perhaps unwarranted because descriptions of Hale launchers at the time show them to resemble standard Congreve tube launchers. Hale stands were on tripod legs and were elevated by set screws or sliding bars. The main difference was that Hale launchers in general were built closer to the ground due to the fact that the rockets were fired at lower elevations (around 15°) since their paths were on less parabolic and more horizontal planes. Hale's launchers were also shorter than Congreve's—8 feet (2.4 m) long on the average, compared to 15 feet (4.5 m) for those of Congreve—as Hale stands did not have to accommodate guidesticks.[30]

One clever design feature of some Hale tube launchers was a restraining lever that held back the rockets until they had built up sufficient thrust for launch. For a 9-pounder (4 kg), the "repressive" weight was 6 pounds (2.7 kg). Hale was taking advantage of what today is called the rocket's "thrust curve." By the time the rocket had traversed the length of an 8-foot (2.4 m) tube, it was already in its third or fourth rotation and well on its way to attaining stability. These launchers had appeared by 1852 and were still in use in 1865.[31]

Hale briefly mentioned trough launchers as early as 1844, in his first rocket patent, but the idea apparently did not fully mature until years later when it was described and depicted in his patent of 29 January 1860 for "Impelling Shells or Shot." Hale was working out a way to prevent his new "comet shell" and other ordnance from pitching or rolling when fired from vessels, and found that the V-trough solved the problem. The standard V-trough land-rocket launcher was originally formed of two pieces of plate-iron hinged together and supported by two short legs in the rear and one in the front. It was approved for service on 17 September 1867. In 1873, William Hale, Jr., took out Patent No. 2607 for a multiple-trough launcher mounted on carriage wheels; but despite much publicity, it apparently was never officially adopted.[32]

An improved version of the tube configuration was introduced as a custom-design for the Abyssinian expedition of 1868. The Abyssinian launcher was much shorter than standard tubes; it was only 3.5 feet (1 m) long and 2.8 inches (7 cm) in diameter for the 9-pounder (4 kg) Mark I Hale. The tube weighed 28 pounds (12.7 kg) and was well suited for transport by mules over

FIGURE 10.14
Rocket troughs were favored for use in the colonial campaigns because they were light and simple to operate. In 1877 a new Hale launcher-carriage was made, but it probably was never put to use. (S.I. A5222)

FIGURE 10.15
In 1873, a multiple-rocket launcher was proposed and patented by William Hale, Jr.
(S.I. A5222A)

rough African terrain. The tube's middle was wrapped with spun yarn "to allow of its being handled when heated by firing."[33]

At about the same time, the so-called "Congreve-Boxer tube launchers" were modified to fire Hale rockets as "sea service machines." The tubes were suspended from a stanchion fixed on the sides of boats by an "iron clutch" with clamping screws. Royal Navy Lieutenant J.A. Fisher's tube of similar construction was also adopted.[34]

Igniters for Hale's rockets were friction tubes with a trigger and lanyard arrangement fitted onto tube launchers, or a simple slow match and portfire. In experiments at Shoeburyness in the late 1870s, electric tubes with 200-yard (180 m) leads were also tried. This method could fire rockets as "ground missiles." Reminiscent of Congreve's formidable "ground volleys," the rockets were laid down with their heads slightly elevated on a slope. The technique, which may have become operational, was ideal against cavalry because the rockets flew low to the ground.[35]

Performance

Hale's successful elimination of the guidestick is irrefutable, but it is difficult to judge the true performance of Hale vs. Congreve rockets in terms of stability and accuracy because of the crudity of testing equipment and poor knowledge of rocket ballistics in those years. Nevertheless, Hale's rockets apparently were better made because there are fewer reports of his rockets exploding on launchers or sputtering dangerously in the first moments of flight. An occasional Hale rocket did burst. In 1878, the Admiralty received a report from the captain of the *Téméraire:* "whilst firing rockets, one burst in the tube, tearing it open and blowing off two feet [0.6 m] of the outer end. . . . The rocket was Mark III manufacture 23.12.71. Three men and one officer were singed by the explosion, and two of them contused from fragments." The Admiralty matter-of-factly replied that while there was no assignable reason for the burst, there would be nothing gained by withdrawing rockets of early date, "as rockets with every care will sometimes fail."[36]

Some military realists did recognize that only against large, vulnerable targets was any worthwhile effect achieved. "Hale rockets," wrote one artilleryman, "are employed, both in the land and naval services, for bombarding towns, in order to set fire to the houses, shipping, etc. It is difficult with rockets to obtain anything like accuracy of fire, and they can therefore be used only against objects covering a considerable extent of ground."[37]

Range, the only real criteria that meant anything to early rocketeers and tacticians, actually showed a decrease compared with Congreve's projectiles. One *Treatise of Ammunition* reported of Hale's: "Much has been sacrificed for convenience in carriage . . . and the question of the effect of the rocket after graze or impact at long ranges appears to have been treated as a secondary one."[38]

While ranges were never identical from round to round, the following guides were determined for a 9-pounder (4 kg) Hale: range at 5°25' was 1,000 yards (914 m); 8°40', 1,500 yards (2.5 m); 12°20', 2,000 yards (1,828 m); and at 16°32', 2,500 yards (2,286 m). The greatest range was 3,400 yards (10,200 m) from a firing elevation of 2°44'. However, the average range for a Mark VII 9-pounder (4 kg) was 1,200 yards (1,100 m); for a Mark VII 24-pounder (10.8 kg), it was 1,200 yards (1,100 m). Deviations were 40–50 yards (36–45 m) for both types, unthinkable margins of error today. Times of burning were "about" 10 seconds for 24-pounders (10.8 kg) and 8 seconds for 9-pounders (4 kg).[39]

It appears that the Woolwich artillerists did not measure burn times on static stands, but on the firing range, while the rockets flew. Like Congreve rockets, velocities were never computed, but using known flight times and ranges, speeds were approximately 200 miles per hour (90 km/hr) maximum for both calibers. Thrust measurements were made on rare occasions. On 15 October 1879, the Royal Laboratory measured the "pressure" exerted by the heads of 24-pounder (10.8 kg) Hale rockets on a piston as 280–320 pounds (127–145 kg). Again, the artillerists took much for granted and failed to realize that the propulsive force was not constant. In another test, using a spring scale, a more realistic value of 325 pounds (170 kg) for 1.75 seconds was recorded. Both Hale and Congreve rocket thrust curves must have described Rock-of-Gibraltar-like profiles, with maximum thrust peaks lasting but a second or so after ignition, then abruptly tapering off. Assuming a specific impulse of 80 pounds per second for gunpowder and the above burning times, the average thrust was probably more like 50 pounds (22 kg) for the small rocket and 100 pounds (45 kg) for the larger one. Thus it appears that Congreve and Hale rockets were comparable in range, but that Hales had greater initial thrust and uniformity of burning due to hydraulic propellant loading, and less drag because of the absence of guidesticks.[40]

In assessing performance, we must also look at the state of gunnery at the time. In the early 1840s, when Hale created his first rotating rocket, dramatic changes also took place in the technology of other firearms. Flintlocks gave way to percussion locks, which simplified the firing process. In 1846, as Hale rockets were making their battlefield debut, Major Giovanni Cavalli in Italy and Baron Mattias von Wahrendorff in Germany independently produced successful rifled breech-loaded cannons. Rifled guns had spiralled grooves inside the barrel, which made the projectile spin on an axis parallel to the straight barrel instead of indiscriminately flying out. This greatly sharpened the accuracy of the projectiles and increased their velocity as well as range. Rifled ammunition, which had become long instead of spherical, also became more streamlined and therefore had added speed and greater striking energy compared to round shot. In breech-loading, ammunition is loaded in the back of the barrel. This greatly increased the rate of fire, since the pieces did not have to be sponged with each round. However, as with any new development, it took time to iron out the imperfections in rifling and breech-loading. For example, early models of rifled guns were subject to fouling by powder, while the first breech-loading mechanisms were complicated, expensive, and suffered from gas leakages in their breech-blocks. But by the time of the Crimean War and the U.S. Civil War (mid-1850s to 1860s), many of the problems were already being solved. These and other technological improvements were completely revolutionizing artillery. The Franco-Prussian War (1870–71) was a real turning point for artillery development. The French introduced their *mitrailleuse* machine gun with its incredible rate of fire, while breech-loading, rifled guns; hydraulic recoil-absorbing mechanisms; and mechanical fuse-setters were used by both sides. Hence, when the final version of the Hale rocket was adopted by England in 1867, the more advanced nations had either switched, or were on the verge of switching, to the new artillery systems.[41]

In comparing Hale rockets to guns of the period, however, it should be noted that Congreves were often employed side-by-side with cannons in all kinds of terrain and actions, whereas Hale rockets, as used by the British, were limited to African or Indian bush or mountain country. Even the light, steel rifled guns developed for "mountain artillery" could not compare to rockets in portability, for example. In 1879 the British introduced the 7-pounder (3 kg) R.M.L. (Rifled Muzzle-Loader), which was considered the best mountain gun in the world and saw service beyond the Boer War (1899–1902), but the jointed steel gun still required five mules for its transport of 400 pounds (180 kg); its projectile weighed 7 pounds. The rifle was, of course, also used in colonial warfare, though it was used as an infantry, antipersonnel weapon for picking off one man at a time, whereas the rocket was considered to be light artillery and could be used against groups of individuals, cavalry, or structures. Machine guns were also taken in colonial campaigns, but despite their rapid rate of fire, they sometimes jammed and were not always reliable until Hiram Maxim's improvements in the early 1880s.[42]

By then, "smokeless," or double-base powders (with nitrocellulose-nitroglycerine bases), had been stabilized enough for use as more powerful propellants for guns, replacing centuries-old gunpowder. (Nitrocellulose was discovered in 1846, but burned too rapidly then for use in guns.) In England, the smokeless, double-base propellant known as Cordite was officially adopted in 1890, yet no moves were made to adapt it for use as a rocket propellant. In retrospect, this was quite short-sighted, as double-base propellants would have given rockets a nearly twofold leap in power and performance. However, practical smokeless powders appeared too late, when Hale rockets were already on the wane. (Not until the late 1930s did the British finally apply Cordite as a rocket propellant, and in World War II virtually all solid-fuel rockets used double-base propellants, making them incontestably superior in range to their Congreve and Hale ancestors.)

The use of Cordite in conventional artillery vastly increased the velocity and range of guns. At the start of the Boer War (1899–1902) the British were armed with a 15-pounder (6.8 kg) recoilless gun that lobbed its projectile 4,100 yards (3,750 m) and soon adopted the much-improved German Erhardt 15-pounder Quick-Firing (Q.F.) that had a range of 6,400 yards (5,550 m). In addition, the Field Artillery was equipped with a 5-inch (12.7 cm) breech-loading howitzer that threw a 50-pound (22.7 kg) Lyddite shell 4,800 yards (4,390 m). Lyddite was a new explosive introduced in 1898. Far greater ranges and heavier projectiles were also possible with medium and heavy artillery. The medium 4.75-inch (12 cm) Q.F. piece fired a 45-pound (20.4 kg) H.E. (High Explosive) or shrapnel shell some 10,000 yards (9,145 m).[43]

In the final analysis, Hale rockets survived as long as they did because in colonial Africa and India they still enjoyed a few advantages, as did their predecessors, Congreve rockets. They were portable and thus more manageable than field guns for guerrilla campaigning in difficult terrains; and they were capable of devastating psychological effects against ill-armed adversaries. However, their singular disadvantage—unpredictability—resurfaced from time to time. Major General Garnet Wolseley, immortalized as W.S. Gilbert's "modern major general" in the opera *Pirates of Penzance,* epitomized this situation in recalling his own experiences with Congreves and Hales in the second Burmese and Ashanti wars of 1852 and 1879, respectively: "In a thick bush country like Burma or Ashanti [South Africa], rockets are likely to be as demoralizing to your own men as to the enemy, owing to the eccentricity of their flight when they strike trees. This is not the case if you are in open, and especially a level, district from which you can discharge your rockets into thickets or large patches of wood, which you wish to clear of an enemy. Hale's rockets, with shell attached, can be used in tolerably level and open countries with good effect, especially against horsemen."[44]

Yet, inexorably, the spiralling revolution in weapons technology and the overwhelming superiority of guns in range, firepower, and precision caught up with Hale's rocket even in the wilds of Africa, and by the time of Boer War, it had finally become outmoded.

CHAPTER 11

Hale Rockets in Combat

A closer look at Hale rockets in action shows that they were generally quite effective, primarily because very often the opposition simply had nothing comparable, sometimes fighting only with spears and shields. At the infamous battle of Isandhlwana, however, the sheer number of men in the opposing native armies and fierce guerrilla strategy fought on their home grounds turned the tide, despite unmatched British firepower. This chapter provides examples of the nature of late nineteenth-century British rocket troops, the problems they encountered, and the eventual decline and demise of the old powder rocket.

Major Campaigns

Hale rockets made their debut in battle during the Mexican War of 1846–48. The British fired a few rounds at the opening of the Crimean War in 1853, but

FIGURE 11.1

Hale's rockets finally superseded Congreve-type rockets in 1867 and were immediately used in the Abyssinian War where they were demonstrated to Prince Kassai, a British ally.
(*S.I. A4540*)

the first major conflict in which they were employed by British troops was the Abyssinian War of 1868, a year after their official adoption.

In response to Abyssinian King Theodore II's injustices to British subjects, Queen Victoria's Government ordered Lieutenant General Sir Robert Napier's army to the Abyssinian capital of Magdala. Among Napier's hand-picked troops was a Naval Rocket Brigade under Commander Thomas H.B. Fellowes, H.M.S. *Dryad*. Fellowes's unit, which arrived at Anneley Bay on 7 January, had eighty-three men with a dozen 12-pounder (5.4 kg), or according to some accounts, 6-pounder (2.7 kg) Hale rocket launchers borne by six mules. The confusion may have arisen due to the fact that 6-pounder Hale rockets were apportioned to each Royal Artillery battery. There was, in addition, a mule-load of rockets for each of Napier's six subdivisions. The rockets were contained in panniers (leather pouches) that fit on the backs of the mules. Both the panniers and launchers were custom-designed for the

Abyssinian expedition. In contrast to earlier naval rocket units that were mere detachments, Fellowes's Brigade was a specially organized rocket force.[1]

On 7 April, en route to Magdala, Napier's army reached the plateau of Dalanta, on Fallah Mountain. According to historian G.A. Henty, "there was an exclamation of pleasure as the Naval Rocket Brigade was seen advancing up the valley." The enemy meant to capture the brigade and were scattered all over the plain from the nearby fortress of Aroghee; but the rocketeers were quick to react. Said Henty: "It took the sailors but an instant to unload the rocket tubes and ammunition, and in less than a minute from the first mules arriving on the crest, a rocket whizzed out over the plain. It was the first answer to the fire which the guns of the fortress had kept up, and was greeted by a cheer by the troops. The race had been won; we had been saved from disaster. . . . Rocket after rocket rushed out in rapid succession. Astonished at the roar of these novel missiles, the enemy paused in dismay; the horses plunged wildly and many in spite of their riders, careened across the plain."[2]

Magdala was reached on 10 April. Hale's rockets again saved the day. Theodore himself watched the fight from the summit of Fallah. "When the British fire opened upon Fallah," reads the War Office's official account, "the rockets ranged to the place where Theodore was standing, and one killed a horse close behind him. He exclaimed, 'What a terrible weapon—who can fight against it?' Then he covered himself with his shield, and watched the battle in silence." Napier's dispatches say that "the rockets were then turned on the summit of Fallah. They were well directed, and . . . produced a very great effect. A part of the enemy attempted to pass round the sides of Affijo to turn our right, but were checked by a few rockets." After Theodore's defeat at Arogee, in which rockets played a conspicuous role, he committed suicide. Napier's forces, however, still needed to free British prisoners at Magdala.[3]

On the 13th (Good Friday), Magdala was successfully stormed. Two hundred and four rockets were expended by the Brigade and an additional fifteen were expended by a mountain battery that was also equipped with a 7-pounder (3 kg) steel gun.[4]

In retrospect, the Abyssinian War was important in the history of early rocketry because it established a good reputation for the efficacy of Hale rockets in Africa. Had the rockets not succeeded here as well as they did, they might have been withdrawn from service entirely. There was enough confidence in them that in 1873 about 1,000 9-pounder (4 kg) Hales were taken in the Second Ashanti War, on the Gold Coast, West Africa. In this campaign they were distributed throughout the army of Major General Wolseley, and many were supplied to British vessels. The town of Elmina was the primary target, and it was set afire by land rockets as well as by rockets from the steam cutters *Simoom* and *Colonial,* the *Argus,* and boats of the *Rattlesnake* and *Barracouta.* One rocket hero during what proved to be a drawn-out and difficult campaign was Lieutenant Frederick Eardley-Wilmot, Royal Artillery. Later in the year, at Iscabio, according to one history of the war, "Lt. Wilmot went to the front with his rockets, and was almost immediately . . . very severely wounded . . . yet in spite of this, he continued in acting with the utmost gallantry until about an hour later he was shot through the heart. . . . One rocket was reported to have fallen into a group of chiefs and captains, and killed or wounded six among their number. But the success was very dearly purchased."[5]

Earlier, Eardley-Wilmot and his captain, Arthur Rait, had drilled gunners of the allied Houssar tribe in the firing of Hale rockets. The Houssars became very proficient and fired rockets quite successfully by against the enemy for the remainder of the war, which ended on 4 February. Rait's rocketeers also assisted in conquering the Ashanti capital of Coomasie.[6]

By contrast, the Zulu War, fought against the South African chieftain Cetewayo, proved that Hale rockets and rifles did not necessarily make the British invincible in the face of overwhelming numbers of bold native war-

FIGURE 11.2
Hale rocket hero: Brevet Major Francis B. Russell (1842–79) commanded British rocket troops in the Zulu War of 1879, and lost his life fighting thousands of Zulus.
(S.I. 78–10187)

riors. In January 1879, General Frederick Thesiger, Lord Chelmsford, was sent to Zululand with an army in which rockets were distributed among several batteries, amounting to about fifty rounds and one trough per battery with an additional fifty rockets carried in an ox-wagon. Within the center column was a small rocket detachment of eight or ten men led by Brevet Major Francis B. Russell, Royal Artillery, that had two or three 9-pounder (4 kg) Hale rocket troughs. This unit soon counted itself among those immortalized at the famous battle of Isandhlwana hill.[7]

Russell's battery was attached to Colonel Anthony Durnford's column, encamped at the foot of the hill. On the morning of 22 January, Durnford was ordered to "move up to Isandhlwana camp at once with all your mounted men and rocket battery. Take command of it." He left with Russell's troops to execute the orders, but as he approached the camp he saw Zulus heading toward Lord Chelmsford. Durnford was obliged to leave his post and intercept the enemy. At the foot of Isandhlwana a fierce battle ensued. Unexpectedly, an "immense force" of Zulus suddenly swept down from adjacent hills and almost completely massacred 6,000 British. Later, the remains of five men of the little rocket battery were found, including Russell's. Prior to being overrun, Russell had managed to discharge three rockets with some effect. The Zulus were temporarily stopped, then fired a volley. The mules carrying the rockets panicked, and the Zulus immediately took advantage of the confusion and charged down the hill, quickly engaging in hand-to-hand combat. It was then that Russell and his men were killed and a rocket trough and rockets captured; afterwards these were found at Cetewayo's arsenal at Mayizekane.[8]

The disastrous affair at Isandhlwana, a major defeat for the British, prompted a special Court of Enquiry in which the movements of Russell's rocket battery are cited extensively. But despite the blow to British arms and prestige, Chelmsford's remaining columns later rallied and finally broke Cetewayo's power at the battle of Ghingilvo, in which Royal Marine rocketeers from H.M.S. *Shah* made part of the relief force.[9]

The last major conflict in which Hale rockets saw service was the First Boer War in the Transvaal, South Africa, fought against Boer colonists demanding self-government. The war began in January 1881 with a march upon the Boer concentration at Laing's Nek. A naval outfit of about 120 men armed with two 24-pounder (10.8 kg) Hale launchers and Gatling guns accompanied the British army. This was the brigade of the *Boadicea,* commanded by Commodore Frederick W. Richards. A party of Boers who had positioned themselves in a bush-covered donga, or ravine, were driven out at Laing's Nek, according to one observer, by "some splendid rocket practice of the Naval

Brigade." This action was typical of the rocket skirmishes that followed, especially when reinforcements arrived from India on H.M.S. *Dido* with another naval brigade carrying two 24-pounder (10.8 kg) rocket troughs. However, at the battle of Majuba Hill, on 27 February, neither guns nor rockets were present, and Majuba was a defeat. One historian commented: "Before the Boers could have got out of their wagons and tents, we could have slaughtered a quarter of their number with rockets—if we had those weapons." Shortly, on 6 March, an armistice was signed ending the Boer uprising.[10]

Minor Campaigns

The Boer War was by no means the last instance of the use of Hale rockets in combat. The history of British colonial warfare in the late nineteenth century is replete with scores of minor rocket actions, not all of them in Africa. Following are a few examples.

In 1873, Chinese pirates were driven off the Perak coast in the Straits of Malacca, Malaysia, near the Larut River, with the aid of Hale rockets. Difficulties persisted here, however, and in November 1875 rockets helped supress insurgent tribes along the Perak River. A punitive expedition was sent to raid the Malaysian stockade of Passir Salak, just north of Quallah Biah, but rocket-fire was poor, mainly because the rockets launched by a naval detachment were obsolete 9-pounders (4 kg) fired from wooden troughs. The only means of discharging them was to insert paper primers in the vents and light them with matches; the rockets had apparently been withdrawn from long-term storage. Another problem was that the rockets sometimes flew through Malaysian thatched native huts without igniting them. Newer rockets were soon dispatched, including 24-pounder (10.8 kg) tubes that were fitted onto native boats for use on the Perak River. These rockets were more effective and evidently contributed toward the fall of Passir Salak, Kampong Psiang, and other enemy stockades.[11]

Hale rockets also saw extensive use in the Kaffir War of 1877–81 in South Africa. For example, a Navy brigade from the ship *Active* with two guns and two 24-pounder (10.8 kg) rocket tubes attacked the fort of Ibeka. As Kaffirs emerged, the tubes opened fire and did "terrible execution," according to one observer. The enemy, on horseback, were completely dispersed by the flights of the rockets, which were "altogether beyond their comprehension."[12]

The Royal Artillery likewise employed rockets in the punitive expedition to Naga, on the northwest frontier of India, from November 1879 to January

1880. The rockets, 100 9-pounders (4 kg), came from Calcutta on the backs of elephants, but one of the animals fell over a cliff and some of the rockets were damaged. The unfortunate creature apparently perished, but the ammunition was sorely needed and retrieved for use. According to Lieutenant Alfred Mansel, the rocket commander in the expedition, at the final battle of Khonoma, 22 November 1879, "one of the rockets from the Mozema Hill, at an early stage of the engagement, set part of the village on fire; but, as a rule, they acted very irregularly, which may be attributed to the severe shaking they received *en route*."[13]

Beginning in the 1880s, the entire African continent was the most conspicuous scene of Hale rocket warfare. In Egypt, the rockets were used frequently as the British gained control over that country and occasionally had to suppress uprisings. For example, rocket tubes were fitted onto the *Monarch* and other vessels that bombarded Alexandria during July 1882, damaging buildings. In 1884–85, in adjacent eastern Sudan, General Sir George Graham used rockets frequently against slave traders. In 1894, the Royal Navy employed

FIGURE 11.3

Large tubes for naval use were attached to the bows of ships, as in this scene of Hale rockets being used against rebels in Alexandria, Egypt, in 1882. (S.I. 72–4976)

FIGURE 11.4
Hale rocket launchers in action at Gonjora, Zanzibar, British East Africa, in 1895.
(S.I. 81–7540)

war rockets against rebellious Arabs in the British territory of Zanzibar, East Africa, and in Gambia, West Africa, against the Sofa tribe in reprisal for atrocities committed against British residents.[14]

In 1897, a rocket battery was formed from Royal Artillery gunners and drivers with mules stationed in India "at the express wish" of General Sir William Lockhart to stem the Afridi uprising in Tirah, Afghanistan. Royal Artillery historian Major-General Headlam noted that "the rockets proved ineffective, however, as well as dangerous, and the battery was sent back from Tirah." In another account, it was observed the Afridis showed contempt for the rockets by slapping their posteriors.[15]

In 1897–98, rocket warfare returned to Egypt when the Moslem Dervish sect came to dominate the area as far as the Sudan. British gunboats patrolling the Nile between the fourth and sixth cataracts were armed with rocket tubes, firing them at Um Tuir, near the mouth of the Atbara River, and at other points. Rocket ammunition was issued to the Anglo-Egyptian army of General Lord Horatio Kitchener. Rockets, Kitchener believed, were ideal for setting fire to the Dervish grass huts. Kitchener's tactics worked, helping the British defeat the rebels and push towards Omdurman and Khartoum for the reconquest of the Sudan.[16]

One Royal Naval rocket detachment in the 1898 Sudan campaign is especially noteworthy as it was in the charge of Lieutenant David Beatty. For his services, Beatty was made a commander and subsequently received rapid promotions, eventually becoming Admiral of the Fleet. The future Earl Beatty, who accepted German surrender to the British during World War I, recalled one engagement along the banks of the Atabara: "I with the rocket tube first occupied a position on the left of the [British] Artillery . . . where I was able to get within 300 yards [274 m], but was ordered back to 400 yards [365 m]. Here we did a certain amount of execution, firing the village in four places." Beatty's 24-pounder (10.8 kg) Hale rockets had been carried on the backs of camels.[17]

Another future figure in world history also served in the Sudan. He was Winston Churchill, who wrote about his experiences in *The River War, an Historical Account of the Reconquest of the Soudan* (London, 1899). Then a lieutenant in the 4th Hussars and a war correspondent, Churchill told of one artillery action at Atabara on 8 April 1898 in which "the cannonade grew loud and continuous. The rocket detachment began to fire, and the strange projectiles hissed and screamed as they left the troughs and jerked erratically towards the *zeriba* [enemy camp]."[18]

The date on which the last Hale war rocket was fired in battle is unknown. Perhaps it was discharged by Royal Navy Lieutenant V. Buckland in Sierra Leone, West Africa, in a campaign that lasted from February to May 1899. No mention of the use of Hale rockets appears in the voluminous annals of the Boer War of 1899–1902 nor in World War I, although the rockets were certainly "on the books" until that conflict. They are included in the 1915 *Treatise on Ammunition* and described and listed in the War Office's *Priced Vocabulary of Stores Issued in His Majesty's Service,* published the same year.[19]

Decline of Hale's Rockets

The decline of the Hale era actually started long before, probably in August 1872, when a Royal Army circular stated that war rockets would no longer form any portion of stores of fortresses and were confined to siege trains and field operations "as occasions and circumstances demanded." In September 1884, a further order declared: "The use of war rockets will be discontinued for land and sea service, except when required for special purposes by Her Majesty's ships on the following stations." These were Sydney, Simons Town (Niger, West Africa), Ascension (South Atlantic), Hong Kong, Bombay, and Trincomalee (Ceylon), and represented a large expanse of the British Empire. On the average, 200 rockets and four trough launchers were allotted to each station, except for Hong Kong, which was assigned 600 rounds and a dozen launchers. On the surface, this order seems to have perpetuated and even expanded the rocket service. In fact, it restricted rockets to mostly naval engagements in which requests for rockets had to be approved by the senior naval officer at each station. Then, in 1886, Royal Artillery Order No. 49 changed the term "rocket battery" to "rocket unit," a rating decrease that could have meant a handful of troops or a detachment. Further whittling down of the distribution of Hale rockets within the Army may have taken place at the same time. The Admiralty also asked for the return, "for examination and disposal," of rockets at stations not affected by the order. Moreover, each station was obliged to test fire 10 percent of its rockets each year. Then, apparently also during the late 1880s or 1890s, according to Major General Headlam, the idea of employing rockets at all, "except possibly in small wars—was definitely abandoned."[20]

With the settling of Britain's colonial holdings and the advent of lightweight rifled field howitzers and machine guns, Hale war rockets became an anachronism even in the jungles of Africa and Indian frontiers. However, not until 11 September 1919 were Mark VII 9- and 24-pounder (4 and 5.4 kg) Hale rockets finally declared obsolete. This late declaration of obsolescence must have been a bureaucratic oversight and could not have reflected reality; by the final year of the nineteenth century, the British Hale war rocket had already ceased to be used, closing nearly a century of the first Golden Age of Rocketry.[21]

CHAPTER 12

Other Applications

As in the present Space Age, the Congreve-Hale eras witnessed an impressive variety of nonmilitary applications and scientific inquiries derived from basic rocket technology. An examination of these helps to provide a better understanding of the impact of Congreve-Hale rocketry during the Industrial Revolution and also offers a wider perspective of the early history of rocket technology in general.

Scientific Inquiry

"How does the rocket move?" was a perennial question posed long before Congreve by "natural philosophers" (e.g., scientists) and pyrotechnists alike. In 1666, Sir Isaac Newton provided a solution in his Third Law of Motion—"For every action there is an equal and opposite reaction"—but its connection

225

to the rocket was difficult to grasp and it was thus paradoxically absent in discussions of rocketry for more than two centuries. Instead, a more understandable, though erroneous, explanation of rocket motion became popularly accepted. It was perhaps first expressed in 1686 by French physicist Edmé Mariotte in his *Traité du Mouvement des Eaux* (*Treatise on the Movement of Water*), in which he declared: "A rocket rises by the impulse of the flame against the air." Other nonmathematical hypotheses about rocket motion appeared, but it was not until the Congreve-Hale era that these theories were analyzed mathematically and tested.[1]

However, nineteenth-century artillerists lacked adequate testing equipment and knowledge of interior rocket ballistics, while the general public clung stubbornly to the "air pushing" school. Nonetheless, several pioneers of the nascent science of rocket ballistics appeared; they were mainly military men, inspired by Congreve rockets.

Congreve adjoined a "Speculation as to the Principles of the Flight of Rockets" to the 1807 edition of his *Concise Account of . . . the Rocket System,* but this was merely an explanation of the shifting center of gravity in rockets and how wings or spiral vanes might counteract instability. Congreve's contemporary, William Moore, a Royal Military Academy mathematics instructor, was a bonafide rocket ballistics pioneer, though he admitted that his results were theoretical and invalid until proven by experiment. Moore produced his *Treatise on the Motion of Rockets* in 1813, but his initial findings had already appeared in *Nicholson's Journal of Natural Philosophy* from 1810 to 1812. Using known physical principles, Moore found that thrust ("lifting power") is related to acceleration, and he identified exhaust velocity, specific impulse, and other parameters of rocket dynamics. In the absence of experimental data, Moore could only assume numerical values, such as thrust equalling 1,000 times the pressure of one atmosphere.[2]

Yet in demonstrating theoretical optimum velocity and range with air resistance and in a vacuum, he came close to postulating a spacecraft. Using the known dimensions and firing duration of a 24-pounder (10.8 kg) Congreve rocket, he calculated that if unchecked by air resistance it would reach a speed of 2,896.9895 feet per second (883 m/sec) at burnout and "never return, but continue to move forever, or fly off to an infinite distance" (within the solar system). Moore suggested that true values of "lifting force" and other factors could only be ascertained on a ballistic pendulum of his design. The instrument was never built, but the idea anticipated Konstantinov's rocket ballistic pendulum by more than three decades.[3]

Austria was perhaps second after England to undertake theoretical studies. In 1818–19, Major von Hauser of the Engineers and Lieutenant Moritz Meyer, Horse Artillery, each published theories of rocket ascent. Later, a more substantial work appeared, artillery captain Anton von Sonnenfeld's *Ballistik der Kriegs Rakete* ("Ballistics of War Rockets"), dedicated in 1850 to General von Augustin, but it remained unpublished.[4]

In Italy, Paolo Ruffini, a famous physician and mathematics professor, wrote "*Osservazioni intorno al Moto dei Razzi alla Congreve*" ("Observation of the Movement of Congreve Rockets"), presented to the Royal Academy of Modena in 1822. Ruffini appeared not to have had a military readership in mind, but as he taught near the school of artillery and engineering, it is probable that this work, too, was meant for the army. Ruffini also used standard principles of mechanics and hydraulics as the basis for his calculations.[5]

Other noteworthy studies include "*Théorie du Mouvement et du Tir des Fusées*" ("Theory of the Movement and Firing of Rockets"), published in 1830 by French artillery Captain Dominique-Nicholas Munier; "*Üeber die Berechnung der Steighoe der Raketen*" ("Calculation of the Height of Rockets"), published in 1859 by Lieutenant Emil Kahl, Royal Saxony Artillery; and "*Trajectories des Fusées Volantes dans le Vide*" ("Trajectories of Skyrockets in a Vacuum"), published in 1873 by Belgian Major General Casimir-Erasmé Coquilhat. From a military point of view, these treatises attempted to show that certain performances could be achieved and to arrive at useful data for determining the best trajectories to use for aiming rockets against targets, especially in wind.[6]

In France, dynamotors were being used to obtain thrust values by the 1840s, and the Russian Konstantinov's electric ballistic pendulum, introduced in 1849, was a remarkable achievement with which he arrived at several fundamental laws of rocket dynamics. Nonetheless, gunpowder artillery rockets were then small and weak, and therefore very susceptible to wind and other unknown variables. In practice, actual performances of powder war rockets could not be predicted with any precision; the early mathematical treatises are thus of historical interest only.

In the 1880s, an obscure Russian mathematics teacher named Konstantin Tsiolkovsky finally grasped the significance of Newton's Law and began laying the theoretical foundations of rocket propulsion in the vacuum of space. (Of paramount importance, he recognized that reaction motion functions both in air and in a vacuum.) This great theoretician, however, was influenced more by Jules Verne's space fantasies than Russian Congreve-type rockets.[7]

Lifesaving Rockets

Of all applications of the nineteenth-century rocket, none was so useful and humane as lifesaving. By the close of the eighteenth century, guns were adapted for throwing lines to or from stranded ships; but guns were heavy and difficult to maneuver. Unlucky were those vessels out of the reach of lifesaving gun stations on shore. During the same period, Italian pyrotechnist Petroni Ruggieri thought of a more portable means. This he called a *fusée á secourse* (rescue rocket). It was a modified firework skyrocket carrying a line almost 2,000 feet (600 m) long, but Ruggieri did not follow-up the idea.[8]

A.M. Ducarne-Blangy, an 80-year old "gentleman of Picardy," France, was probably the first to construct and fire a *fusée á secourse*. He may have started experiments at Fere in 1791; tests were conducted at Meudon in the summer of 1799 before high-ranking naval officers. Ducarne-Blangy's rockets were 1.3, 1.7, and 1.9 inches (32, 42, and 48 mm) in caliber, then standard for large skyrockets. Motor cases were made of traditional pasteboard with wooden guidesticks. The lifelines were not rope but 0.13-inch (3.4 mm) gauge wire, 540–630 feet (165–192 m) long, secured to the end of the stabilizer stick. Nothing came of these or subsequent tests, which were favorably reported on in the press.[9]

Then, on the terrible day of 29 December 1807, the British frigate *Anson* foundered off Loe Bar, near Land's End, Helston, Cornwall, England. The *Anson* crew of 100 lost their lives in a futile attempt to swim the short distance to the shore amidst crashing waves while Helston's horror-stricken villagers stood on Mount Bay's rocky cliffs and watched helplessly. One witness was Henry Trengrouse, a Helston cabinetmaker. Disasters of this sort were not new to Trengrouse, who had already applied his skills to fashion a better lifesaving boat.[10]

Working in secrecy over the next decade, the Cornishman spent about £3,000 of his inheritance money developing a reliable, practical, lifesaving apparatus that included, in addition to the rocket, a pulley line and hawser; cork life vest and bosun's chair, to be hove over the line; rocket launcher; a modified military musket; lifeline; and a wooden sea chest for carrying it all. The apparatus was portable enough for conveyance to any part of the coast and equally adaptable for ship to shore or vice versa.[11]

After long negotiations between Helston and London, Trengrouse was granted permission to exhibit his apparatus before Army and Navy officers at Woolwich Arsenal on 28 April 1818. The demonstration went satisfactorily. Naturally, Congreve was interested; but his interest was to Trengrouse's detriment. The previous month, Congreve had disputed Trengrouse's claim to the invention. The Cornishman produced evidence to support his side, but for unknown technical or political reasons, the Lords of the Admiralty did not adopt the Trengrouse apparatus. Instead, they directed Congreve to produce his own lifesaving system. For his labors, Trengrouse received a governmental order for only twenty sets of his apparatus, a monetary prize, a silver medal from the Society of Arts, and a testimonial with accompanying diamond ring from Russia's Tsar Alexander.[12]

Independently, Captain William Ricketts, Royal Navy, suggested the lifesaving rocket concept in an 1809 article that was published in the *Naval Chronicle;* but, like Ruggieri's, his suggestions never went beyond the idea stage.[13]

Congreve, meanwhile, adapted his 12- and 32-pounder (5.4 and 14.5 kg) war rockets for saving lives. They were far heavier than Trengrouse's fireworks. However, Congreve's system was meant for ship-to-shore communication only. For securing rockets to a beach, an anchor with flukes was substituted for the warhead. A double line was fastened to the stabilizing sticks, as in the Trengrouse pattern, and was rove through a pulley fixed to the ship's mast. An open, spherical lifebuoy conveyed the shipwrecked victims ashore by double-lines. In sea trials at Plymouth and Chatham in 1826, results were disappointing. The rockets failed to reach the beach, possibly because the anchor and lines made them too heavy. By that time, Congreve had gone to southern France, recuperating from an illness; he died before he could perfect the system.[14]

John Dennett of the Isle of Wight, England, also preferred the ship-to-shore mode in developing his lifesaving rocket. In a way, he continued where Congreve left off. Dennett had developed his own 3- to 32-pounder (1.3– 14.5 kg) war rockets, meant for the merchant marine as protection against pirates. "I next directed my attention towards applying their great projectile powers . . . for saving . . . lives," he later wrote.[15]

Dennett profited from the groundwork of both Trengrouse and Congreve. His 12-pounders (5.4 kg) were small yet powerful, just as Trengrouse's were weak and lighter than Congreve's excessive 60-pound (27.2 kg) anchor rocket. The 300-yard (274 m) range of the Dennett was sufficient to establish communication between ship and shore. A trial was held on the Isle of Wight on 18 January 1826. The new Royal National Institution for the Preservation of Life from Shipwreck (founded in 1824) was so pleased with the results that it adopted the apparatus and established England's first lifesaving rocket stations, on the Isle of Wight at Freshwater, Atherfield, and St. Lawrence. In two comparative tests of Dennett's rocket with the Manby lifesaving mortar, the former were superior in accuracy, reliability, and speed of operation. The British Board of Customs adopted the apparatus in 1834 for lifesaving stations under its jurisdiction. Dennett finally patented his invention, oddly calling it "Improvements in War Rockets." The misnomer notwithstanding, other countries also adopted Dennett's lifesaving projectiles.[16]

Alexander Gordon Carte, Ordnance Storekeeper and Barrack-Master of the Hull garrison depot, Yorkshire, England, worked on his own lifesaving rockets from the 1830s until his death in 1853. Interesting features were the side- and center-mounted guidestick versions, reflecting an influence by Congreve rockets. The launcher, mounted to a ship's rail, could be aimed at various elevations, like military launchers. Carte's rockets were eventually stocked at thirty-one British stations, chiefly around Durham and Yorkshire, but were not as successful commercially as Dennett's.[17]

FIGURE 12.1
Silhouette of Alexander Carte (1793–1853), British inventor of the lifesaving rocket bearing his name. (S.I. 78–2956)

Of greater importance in the history of lifesaving rockets is the name Edward M. Boxer, later Superintendent of the Royal Arsenal. Boxer's position was fortunate and led to the rocket's adoption throughout England and subsequent manufacture at the Arsenal.[18]

Boxer's main contribution was his tandem or two-step configuration to boost range and performance. The step principle had been well known since the mid-seventeenth century and dated back even earlier, as evidenced by designs in the Sibiu manuscript written in 1529–69 by rocket pioneer Conrad Haas. Boxer never claimed originality in the step technique, but he was the first to apply it to a useful invention. He produced his lifesaving rocket by 1855, but not until ten years later was it sanctioned by the Board of Trade, superseding the Dennett rocket. In 1878 Boxer's system replaced remaining Manby mortars and served until as late as 1948.[19]

Boxer's system was simple, consisting of a dozen pieces. The 2-foot (0.6 m) 12-pounder (5.4 kg) rocket (other models were available) was attached to a 9.5-foot (2.8 m) stick. Later models, like Hale rockets, were made of Atlas metal. As in Hale rocket manufacture, the propellant was hydraulically pressed at 18,000 pounds per square inch (664 kilonewtons/m²). Sheet iron topped the stick as protection against exhaust gases and the line was partly wetted prior to firing. The line was fed in and out of the hollowed top and bottom of the guidestick. A simple overhand knot secured the cord at each end and brass and India rubber washers reduced the effect of acceleration upon firing. A later modification was cork sheathing over the rocket case and nose for buoyancy.[20]

For firing, the tripod launcher with quadrant and plumb bob was raised to the elevation required to ensure that the rocket would fly over the ship. After the rocket was discharged, the shipwrecked crew grabbed the line, sometimes with "heaving canes," or hooks, drawing it in and also hauling in the "whip," or secondary double coil. Banded to the whip was a tail block that was detached and tied to the mast well above the water. Later Boxers also had a wooden tallyboard posted to the line with instructions in French, English, German, and Norwegian. Once the tail block was secured, the on-shore team dispatched a hawser and adjoining sling lifebuoy by means of the whip. The other end of the hawser was fixed to an anchor tackle on the beach. Communication thus established, one man at a time was borne off the ship to safety.[21]

The Board of Trade issued heaving canes and decreed that enameled instruction plates with Boxer-apparatus instructions be nailed or screwed to prominent places on every vessel of the merchant marine. Each officer was required to be familiar with the procedures and all lifesaving stations had to practice regularly with the apparatus. Periodic competitions were held and must have presented exciting family outings in many British coastal towns. Two- or four-wheel carts bore Boxer kits and also functioned as ambulances. Kits contained, besides the apparatus, signalling flags, portfires, lights, and assorted tools. Larger stations had horses for pulling the carts and were staffed with as many as twenty-five men, although the usual number was fewer. By the turn of the century, there were 288 rocket stations with the Boxer apparatus. Bespeaking their usefulness, in a single decade, 1870–80, some 9,407 people were rescued by the rocket lifesaving service in England alone.[22]

In England and abroad, there were several other lifesaving rocket pioneers, not all of them successful. In 1872, William Hale, Jr., patented a spin-stabilized lifesaving rocket, but he found that the projectile's rotation complicated matters and the idea was abandoned. Retired Royal Navy Paymaster James Humphrey-Singleton-Hooper of Dulwich, Surrey, also modified Hales for lifesaving. He incorporated a double-swivel for attaching the lifeline chain, but in U.S. Coast Guard demonstrations in 1880 the rocket was found to be "utterly unreliable and dangerous." British pyrotechnist William Schermuly began work on compact line-carrying rescue rockets in 1887; by 1897 his apparatus had won a gold medal at the Diamond Jubilee Exposition, though his pistol-launched apparatus was not fully developed until the twentieth century.[23]

PLATE XLI

BOXER'S LIFE-SAVING APPARATUS.

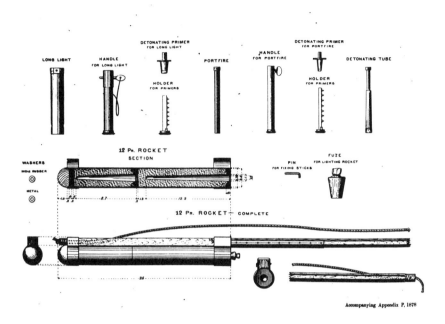

Accompanying Appendix P, 1878

FIGURE 12.3

Boxer lifesaving rocket and accompanying safety pyrotechnic signal kit, 1878. (S.I. 78–2953)

Elsewhere in Europe, Dutch artillery Captain J. van Steel, in partnership with A.C.Noodt, librarian of the Artillery and Engineering School at Delft, were apparently the second and third people after Ducarney-Blangy to build and fire lifesaving rockets. Van Steel and Noodt knew of gun-fired lifelines, but thought the rocket provided better chances. They started experiments in 1815 and obtained "extraordinary results." Encouraged, they continued working on a larger scale with Congreve rockets, but soon ran out of funds. In 1816, the two submitted their plan to the Dutch government, which appeared to be receptive. A commission collected test results and drawings but failed to direct the inventors to proceed further. A fellow Dutchman familiar with the experiments afterwards complained that the plans would probably remain in custody with the commission "until eternity." Indeed, nothing more is known of them.[24]

Better known were the lifesaving rockets of Prussian artillery Major

ROCKET LINE CARRIED OVER A WRECK.

W. W. May, F. N.

FIGURE 12.4

A lifesaving rocket in action in 1876. The rocket carried a lifeline over a ship in distress; the line was secured to the vessel's mast and by means of a block and tackle the shipwrecked were conveyed to safety by a lifebelt. (S.I. 72–3139)

Stiehler, possibly a member of the Prussian war-rocket establishment. On 17 October 1828, he demonstrated his projectiles on the beach at Memel; the Prussians were seeking replacements for lifesaving mortars, which they considered dangerous. Despite the attention received by Stiehler's rockets, they were apparently never made use of. Later, in the 1880s, the *Deutsche Gesellschaft zur Rettung Schiffbruechiger* (German Society for Shipwreck Rescue), founded in 1865, ordered the Fireworks Laboratory at Spandau to produce rescue rockets, the results of which were 2- and 3-inch (5 and 8 cm) models. These, according to historian Mitchell R. Sharpe, "were extremely well made and highly reliable." So-called Spandau rockets were consequently adopted by Germany as well as Spain, Turkey, Estonia, and other countries. (Turkey began also using Boxers along the Bosporus in 1869.) The Spandau Laboratory ceased making them in 1890, but commercial firms continued to produce similar products. By 1899, there were sixty-seven lifesaving stations along German shores that were usually supplied with 8-centimeter Spandau rockets.[25]

In France, Ducarne-Blangy's early priority was probably forgotten and not until 1849 did another lifesaving-rocket experimenter appear. Captain Nicolas-Eugene Tremblay, a retired marine artillery officer, spent years developing his *Grappin porte-amarre* (Grapnel lifesaving apparatus). Though a good demonstration was made before Emperor Napoleon III in 1855, Tremblay was unable to sell any to the Government. By 1880, the School of Maritime Pyrotechny at Toulon was manufacturing lifesaving rockets, though the French preferred lifesaving guns.[26]

Denmark's Association for the Assistance of Sailors began inquiring about rescue rockets in 1847; shortly after, the Danish Freemasons provided an apparatus that was tested at Klitmoller, facing the treacherous North Sea. The rocket worked well and was supplied to Klitmoller and other stations. By 1912, there were sixty-nine lifesaving stations; fifty had rockets.[27]

In America, as early as 1825, pyrotechnist James Cutbush in his *System of Pyrotechny* suggested "succouring, or marine rockets," but never developed them. English musician Edward Hodges, residing in the U.S., also proposed a lifesaving rocket scheme, which appeared in the *Franklin Institute Journal* in 1832; but not until 1878–80 did the American authorities begin a concrete program. Then, Ordnance Lieutenant David A. Lyle, inventor of the Lyle lifesaving gun, headed a U.S. Coast Guard committee investigating lifesaving apparatuses toward adopting the best one. Firings were carried out at the Coast Guard Station at Sandy Hook, New Jersey.[28]

After exhaustive tests of German, French, Russian, British (Boxer), and other rockets, including American designs, the Coast Guard chose Lyle's smooth-bore bronze gun that cast a line 700 yards (640 m). In 1887, however, Irish-born Patrick Cunningham of New Bedford, Massachusetts, attracted the Coast Guard's attention with his novel rocket with a hollow steel stabilizer "stick" containing the coiled faking line. Results were so laudable that the Coast Guard procured specimens from Cunningham's American Carrier Rocket Company, and several stations were supplied with them. Cunningham lifesaving rockets remained in service until the close of the century, but the Lyle gun remained the mainstay of both U.S. and Canadian lifesaving stations.[29]

In Russia, in 1851, Konstantinov suggested to the Tsar admiralty rockets for "carrying lines," but not until 1858 did he develop his ideas. He then proposed a "rocket with a double soul" to Grand Duke Michael. Similar to Boxer's pattern, Konstantinov's rocket had two steps, but contained within a single motor case to produce a low initial trajectory followed by a boost for a high parabolic flight over the ship. His rockets were tested competitively with foreign ones between 1858 and 1863. According to historian Victor N. Sokol'skii, Konstantinov's projectiles were supplied to lifesaving stations along the Baltic Sea coast but the Russians did not end their search for the best apparatus. When the Petersburg Rocket Institute closed in 1864, British Boxer lifesaving rockets came in use in Russia. However, the Nikolayev Rocket Plant opened in 1870 and Russian lifesaving rocket production resumed.[30]

Konstantinov actively pursued this humane rocket application for the remainder of his life. In 1863 he wrote *Application des Fusées au Jet des Amarres de Sauvetage* (*Application of Rockets to the Throwing of Life-Saving Ropes*), followed by *Sparsatyelniya Raketi i Sparsatyelnioy Zmyeoy* (*Life-Belt Rockets and Rescuing Kites*), published in 1869. After Konstantinov's death in 1871, the Russians reverted to a conventional, single-cavity configuration.[31]

In Sweden, Ordnance Captain Wilhelm Teodor Unge made significant advances in the development of the military rocket in the 1880s and 1890s, incorporating the de Laval exhaust nozzle; higher-energy, double-base propellant ballistite (first fired in a rocket on 12 September 1896); and effective use of spin-stabilization similar to Hale's principle. Sweden had long abandoned its *Raket Corpset*, however, and like most nations now considered artillery powder rockets obsolete. But Unge persevered and evolved a lifesaving version of his advanced war rocket. In addition to the above features, the rocket was electrically ignited. Its major drawback was its cost: $35, then exorbitant, but it was purchased by lifesaving societies in England, Austria, India, and possibly Unge's native Sweden. By 1912, Sweden had fifteen stations, only four of which had a rocket apparatus.[32]

Other countries, such as Italy and Holland, were relative latecomers in adopting lifesaving rockets, which they did by the turn of the century. Whatever their origin, it is fitting to note that during the nineteenth century lifesaving rockets appear to have saved more lives than were taken by the war rocket.[33]

The Whaling Rocket Harpoon

One of the oddest rocket applications of the nineteenth century was the harpooning of whales. Whale oil then provided illumination and served as a machine lubricant, and whaling was therefore an essential industry. The traditional Moby Dick device for killing whales was the hand-held harpoon, a dangerous and unsure means at best. Guns had been tried for throwing harpoons, but their effectiveness was uncertain.[34]

A whaling rocket was made as early as 1638 by Dutch pyrotechnist Abraham Speeck of Amsterdam, but it was long forgotten. Not until 1818 did the idea reappear. Charles Rogier, an eccentric "inventor" and professional dancer, suggested it in his *A Word for My King and Country: A Treatise on the Utility of a Rocket Armament, assisted by Balloons* (1818). Rogier drew a crude picture, which he labeled as being a "spiked rocket." The rocket was attached by a rope to a winch in a whaleboat. His description was brief: "An experiment worth trying." Yet this almost cryptic picture was probably the origin of the whaling rocket developed soon after by Congreve and Lieutenant James N. Colquhoun, Royal Artillery.[35]

In her letter of 1 February 1821 to Austrian statesman Prince Metternich, Dorothea Lieven, wife of the Russian Ambassador in London, commented that she had dined the previous day with Congreve, who told her he wished "to use his rockets for making war on the whale. . . . He wants the rocket . . . to shoot into the whale. . . . Odious man! Whales are probably delightful beings." A few months after his dinner engagement, Congreve and Colquhoun prepared modified 3- and 6-pounder (1.3 and 2.7 kg) rockets for the "odious" task. A pistolet was added so that the rocket could be hand-fired. The "warhead" contained powder to explode inside the whale once it was struck, causing instant death and producing gases to help buoy the whale so it would not sink.[36]

Accompanied by two artillery gunners as assistants, Colquhoun sailed from Hull, hub of the British whaling industry, in the ship *Fame,* to Arctic whaling waters. The vessel's captain was the well known Arctic explorer William Scoresby, Sr. On 24 June 1821, Scoresby sent back an ecstatic letter immediately published in the journals. "Sir William Congreve will," he proclaimed, "no doubt, rejoice—nay, leap mast high, on hearing . . . his rocket . . . succeeds beyond expectation." As if in anticipation of this news, Congreve and Colquhoun applied for a joint patent (No. 4563) on the harpoon on 7 June 1821. The rockets were to be made in Congreve's private factory in Bow.[37]

The enthusiasm of the partners was short-lived. Congreve-Colquhoun whaling rockets proved to be a commercial disaster. Only one other ship is known to have taken them out—the *Marguretta* of London, in 1822. Years later, in 1854, an article on Congreve rockets in *Chamber's Journal* noted that a whaling firm bought the rockets by the thousands, but they were "left idle in store rooms."

There were several reasons for the failure of the whaling rockets. Harpooners tended to distrust anything novel, especially something that threatened their well rewarded jobs. There were also many technical flaws, and the rockets were probably more expensive than ordinary iron harpoons. These problems were probably also encountered by Danish Lieutenant Wilhelm Graah, who unsuccessfully duplicated Congreve-Colquhoun whaling rocket experiments in Greenland in 1823.[38]

The idea still seemed promising to some, however and whaling rockets surfaced again in the 1840s and 1850s. One widely publicized effort was made by the American team of Captain Thomas Welcome Roys and pyrotechnist Gustavus Adolphus Lilliendahl, who also ran a whalebone manufactory. Roys, an unlettered but inventive man, had already tried to develop a whaling gun, an explosion of which cost him his right hand. He turned to the rocket and took out rocket harpoon patents beginning in 1857.[39]

FIGURE 12.5
Captain Thomas W. Roys (1816?–77), American whaling captain and co-inventor of the Roys-Lilliendahl whaling rocket harpoon. He lost his left hand in an explosion of an experimental whaling gun. (S.I. A5199; courtesy Mrs. David Byington, Aurora, Colo.)

PATENT ROCKET HARPOONS AND GUNS.

FASTEN TO AND KILL INSTANTLY WHALES OF EVERY SPECIES.

WITH PROPER LINES AND ·BOATS,·

SUCH AS WERE USED BY THE OFFICERS OF BARK REINDEER IN 1864,

ALL WHALES ARE SAVED.

N. B.—Two Months' notice required to fill an Order for the Season of 1865.

———FOR SALE BY———

G. A. LILLIENDAHL,- - - - - .- - - - NEW YORK

FIGURE 12.6

Advertisement for Roys-Lilliendahl rocket harpoon, 1866, in the New Bedford Whalemen's Shipping List. *(S.I. A3063)*

The standard Roys-Lilliendahl whaling rocket was fired from a shoulder-held launcher like the Bazooka antitank rocket of World War II. A metal hinged flap atop the barrel served as a protective visor against stray exhaust gases and sparks. Parallel rods protruded from a metal disk in back of the motor case. These were designed to counterbalance the launcher and permit exhaust gases to escape equally in all directions from the rear. The harpoon itself was a cylindrical all-metal shell with a barb. Jutting from the shell was an elongated metal loop, like a trombone. On it were sliding rings to which the rope was attached. Upon penetration of the whale, the shell exploded, causing a folded barbed toggle to spring open and secure itself to the inside of the whale. Lilliendahl manufactured the harpoons in his Unexcelled Fireworks Company in New Jersey.[40]

FIGURE 12.7
Patent model (incomplete) of Thomas Roys's whaling rocket, U.S. Patent 35,474 of 3 June 1862, now in possession of the Smithsonian Institution. (S.I. A4440–B)

After the Civil War, Roys and Lilliendahl established a whaling station at Seydhisfjordhur, on the east coast of Iceland. There, with an international crew, they tested the harpoon on several whaling expeditions, and also pioneered other innovations such as steam whaleboats and on-board processing of whale blubber on "factory ships."[41]

Yet in 1866, the daring American venture ended in financial ruin. Whales were caught, but there were many technical difficulties, and operating and research expenses reduced profits. Lilliendahl stayed on briefly. Captain Roys set sail again and by 1868 was whaling in northern Californian and Canadian waters. Bankrupt and in poor health, he laid over in San Francisco and between 1872 and 1876 was compelled to sell shares in his various patents, including the whaling rocket. Robert L. Suits thus obtained the rights and with his brother-in-law, pyrotechnist John N. Fletcher, produced the so-called California Whaling Rocket.[42]

The California Whaling Rocket, an offshoot of the Roys-Lilliendahl harpoon, was manufactured at Church Fireworks Company, San Francisco, where Fletcher worked, and for a short time it actually did a thriving business; from 1875–80 the harpoons were sold to the captains of about eighteen ships. Eventually, however, this venture also died. One reason was the gradual replacement of whale oil by petroleum. With the sinking of petroleum wells in Titusville, Pennsylvania, in 1859, and later oil strikes, the whaling industry went into steady decline until it had all but disappeared in this country by the 1920s. More importantly, perhaps, an effective whaling gun was finally invented by Norwegian Svend Foyn and came to supersede all other methods of killing and capturing whales.[43]

FIGURE 12.8

Roys-Lilliendahl rocket harpoon being tested by the inventors off the coast of Iceland during 1865–66. (S.I. A5199–A; courtesy Kendall Whaling Museum, Sharon, Mass.)

CALIFORNIA WHALING ROCKET

And Patent Bomb Lance,

MADE WITH IMPORTANT ATTACHMENTS AND IMPROVEMENTS BY

FLETCHER, SUITS & CO., SAN FRANCISCO, CAL.

Our apparatus consists of a gun metal cylinder, filled with a peculiar composition made only by ourselves, to which is attached, in front, a bomb with a barbed point; inside the bomb is an explosive charge and a chain toggle, which is released by the bursting of the shell on entering the whale; an iron shaft is attached to the rear end of the rocket, through which the whale line is spliced. There is absolutely no recoil, and it is fired from the bow of an ordinary whale boat, as illustrated above. The hinged flange is thrown up by the rocket passing out, protecting the face from injury.

The great value of the CALIFORNIA WHALING ROCKET, as made under our personal supervision, and its success and efficiency in killing and fastening to whales at THIRTY FATHOMS, is fully attested by the following whaling Captains who have witnessed its practical working, have fitted their vessels with them this present season, and who recommend them to all parties interested in the whaling business.

Capt. THOMAS W. WILLIAMS, bark Francis Palmer.	Capt. EBENEZER F. NYE, bark Mt. Wollaston.
" BERNARD COGAN, bark Rainbow,	" LEANDER C. OWEN, bark Coral,
" EZRA B. LAPHAM, bark Progress,	" WILLIAM H. KELLEY, bark Dawn,
" FREDERICK A. BARKER, schooner Leo,	" JAMES McKENNA, schooner Alaska,
" LEWIS H. WILLIAMS, brig Hidalgo·	" JAMES CAUGHILL, schooner Newton Booth.

FLETCHER, SUITS & CO., 407 Front Street, San Francisco, Cal.,
To whom all communications must be Addressed.

ALSO FOR SALE AT THIS OFFICE, 8 SOUTH SECOND STREET, NEW BEDFORD.

FIGURE 12.9

Advertisement for the California Whaling Rocket, which was briefly successful in the late 1870s off the Pacific coast and in Alaskan waters. (S.I. A4054; courtesy Kendall Whaling Museum, Sharon, Mass.)

Rocket Torpedoes

The rocket torpedo was not an invention of the eighteenth or nineteenth century. The earliest known device of this kind was described by the thirteenth-century Arab Hassan-er Rammah, although it may never have been built.[44]

In 1809, a Japanese mariner named Sato is supposed to have converted a large fishing boat into a rocket-propelled surface torpedo, but details are lacking. French naval engineer Henri-Joseph Paixhans perhaps constructed the first known rocket torpedo in the West when in 1811 he attached "a species of rocket of great dimensions" to a ship and tried it in the Basin de Villete, near Paris. It is not certain whether this was a rocket-propelled boat or torpedo to be used against enemy shipping. According to his own account, the first trial went badly because the thrust "was too far to the center of gravity. The second succeeded better." In the third trial, the "boat" went 500 feet (152 m) with "great speed." A fourth attempt was scheduled, Paixhans concludes, "but we left for Russia [i.e., Napoleon's invasion]."[45]

Another Frenchman, Captain Joseph Brussel de Brulard, who tested war rockets at Hamburg in 1813–14, likewise attached one to a boat. He achieved promising results, but the war also ended his activities. French Navy captain, rocket historian, and inventor Merigon de Montgéry was the best-known proponent of underwater rocket warfare. Among his ideas were rockets launched from submerged casemates for defending entrances to ports, and ships equipped with banks of tubes with hinged breeches to fire salvos of rocket torpedoes. De Montgéry also mentioned the work of Joshua Blair, an engineer from Baton Rouge, Louisiana, who submitted plans for a rocket torpedo to the U.S. government in 1823. It was believed that Blair's invention "could brave all the naval forces of the globe." Despite such brazen pronouncements, however, both his and de Montgéry's projects came to nought. In England, Colonel Francis Maceroni's "new sea rocket" weighing 500 pounds (226 kg) with a cast-iron head for penetrating wooden hulls also never materialized. There are scores of rocket torpedo patents, including one taken out by William Hale in 1856 based on his rotating war rocket; but these, too, were never realized.[46]

The U.S. Civil War saw its share of rocket torpedoes. One project was undertaken during 1862–63 by Captain Edward Bissell Hunt, U.S. Navy,

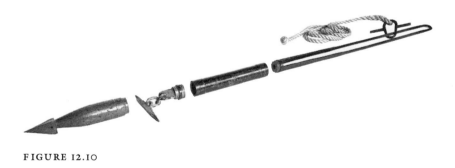

FIGURE 12.10
Specimen of a California Whaling Rocket, purchased in 1881 by the Smithsonian from one of the rocket's inventors, John N. Fletcher, for $50. Shown disassembled. (S.I. A4805)

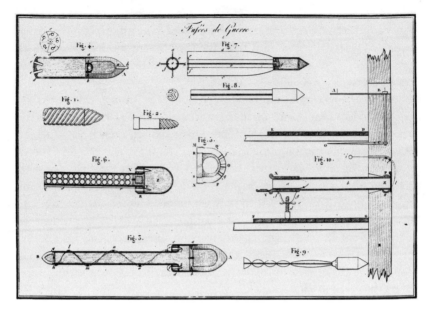

FIGURE 12.11

Schemes for rocket-propelled torpedoes, including a means for firing them from a ship's bow (Fig. 10), from Merigon de Montgéry's Recherches sur les Fusées de Guerre *(Researches on War Rockets), 1825. (S.I. A3769)*

consisting of a huge shell with cannon powder in its warhead. By encasing it in a wooden corkscrew jacket, the inventor hoped that this would impart a stabilizing spin. Launching was accomplished by a converted 11-inch (28 cm) Dahlgren gun. However, Hunt's tragic death while testing the torpedo, in which he was suffocated by gases in a submerged firing caisson, concluded the project.[47]

On 9 December 1862, President Lincoln's life was spared when a rocket-propelled torpedo was fired and exploded as he watched nearby on shore. The torpedo was the work of a gentle French-Canadian inventor and shoemaker, Pascal Plant. Plant was given permission to try his "rocket-driven submarine torpedo" against a real ship. Two cigar-shaped missiles were aimed one after the other toward a specially outfitted scow moored off a dock at the Washington Navy Yard. The first torpedo struck a mud bank, then exploded and sank. A memorandum hidden for a century in a naval ledger describes what happened to the second torpedo: "Plant's rocket sank a vessel . . . rocket fired backwards and endangered the life of President Lincoln." Plant's torpedo sank the *Diana* schooner—by mistake. Rather than displaying the expected consternation, the Navy was impressed with this proof of the powers of the torpedo. As for Lincoln, not a word was mentioned in the press that he was present at the test, much less that he was endangered.[48]

Plant was allowed to continue building a more accurate torpedo. When ready, the Navy took more stringent precautions and cleared vessels from the test area. This time the torpedo leapt out of the water, made a wild flight, plunged back into the Anacostia River, and sank, leaving bubbles. The Navy's interest in Plant's torpedo also dissolved.[49]

Instability was the most serious drawback plaguing the development of all nineteenth-century rocket torpedoes. The complex dynamics of rockets and rocket-propelled devices in the water were simply not well understood, though Hale recognized part of the problem when he noted that the rocket could not be controlled underwater due to the fact that it lost weight as the propellant was consumed. Moreover, propulsion by gunpowder was too weak for the

FIGURE 12.12

Wilhelm Unge (1845–1915), a Swedish Artillery officer who developed rotating rockets using double-base propellants and "aerial torpedo" rockets fired from airships in the 1890s and early 1900s. (S.I. A3431; courtesy Dr. Ingemaar Skoog, Immenstadt, West Germany)

task. Hence, none of the many nineteenth-century rocket torpedo projects came to full fruition. Steam-engine-powered torpedoes built by the English engineer Robert Whithead in the mid-1860s were much more reliable, however, and eventually led to the modern compressed-air-driven, gyroscopically controlled torpedoes. Modern rocket-torpedoes did not materialize until 1961 when the U.S.'s Asroc became the first such operational missile.[50]

Flying Machines

Manned flight began in the late eighteenth century. Apart from balloon ascents, a multitude of flying-machine schemes were proposed or attempted, at least two of which were adaptations of the Congreve rocket.

From Venice, Italy, in 1831, came the anonymous pamphlet *Scoperta Della Direzione del Globo Aerostatico* (*Method of Directing the Aerostatic Balloon*). Some attribute the work to the Mantua inventor Giambattista Toselli; but since Toselli was only six years old at the time, this is highly unlikely. Others simply credit the pamphlet's publisher, a Signor Molinari. The proposal itself is for a

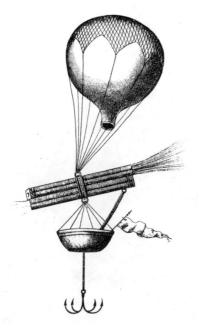

FIGURE 12.13
Balloon directed by a cluster of rockets, anonymous Italian proposal, 1831. (S.I. 72–4609)

balloon steered by a "combination" of Congreve-type rockets lashed together. Needless to say, there is no record of it ever becoming airborne.[51]

Early in the nineteenth century, pyrotechnist Claude Ruggieri is said to have lifted live rats or mice from the Champ de Mars, Paris, by a large firework rocket; the animals were recovered by parachute. In 1806, at Marseille, Ruggieri allegedly built a larger rocket, this time carrying a live sheep or ram to an estimated elevation of 200 feet (300 m). The "passenger" was similarly retrieved. But these accounts have not been verified, and neither has the stranger story of an attempt in about 1830 (or 1846 according to some sources) to lift up a young boy. However, the police intervened and the boy was prevented from going. Sometimes the youngster is identified as Wilfrid de Fonvielle, later a well known scientific balloonist. De Fonvielle himself relates quite a different version. In 1869 he "solicited rich amateurs of extraordinary adventures to come forward with the francs necessary to enable me to repeat the experiment which Ruggieri had made upon a sheep. I declared that I was ready to be shot up in a skyrocket provided its projectile powers were carefully calculated, and that it were provided with a parachute. But it was all in vain; no capitalist presented himself."[52]

Two similar accounts of attempted manned flights using giant skyrockets are known. In 1846 the showman Joel Diavolo proposed making a spectacular night ascent in a rocket for a fireworks display at London's Vauxhall Gardens. The *Illustrated London News* lampooned Diavolo with a cartoon and the comment that the rocket would be strong enough to carry him "to the moon" where he would "ultimately take up his abode there with the lunatics." The second attempt, allegedly made in Delaware in 1871, ended in an explosion and the loss of the unnamed would-be rocket traveler.[53]

In 1852, a more concrete plan for a rocket-propelled balloon was Englishman James Nye's *Thoughts on Aerial Traveling and on the Best Means of Propelling Balloons*. The Nye machine was an elongated 337-foot (103 m) airship powered by 3-pounder (1.3 kg) Congreve rockets fired successively every 7 seconds by a cartridge-fed, machine-gun-type device. One was fitted at each end of the airship for controlling forward and reverse directions. Nye calculated that the "rocket balloon" was capable of traveling 200 miles (320 km) at 15 miles per hour (24 km/hr). One noteworthy feature was Nye's preference for hot air over volatile hydrogen as the balloon's lifting gas.[54]

At about the same time, Russian rocket pioneer Konstantinov undertook actual experiments to determine the feasibility of rocket-powered flying machines. Using his rocket ballistic pendulum, he discovered that rockets of the day were "limited to one powerful impulse at the start of their action [and are] unfit for transportation of large masses during a long time, for considerable distances. Human force," he concluded, "is . . . more efficient than rockets for the propulsion of aerostats."[55]

Konstantinov was, of course, quite correct in his first conclusion but wrong in his second. The total impulse of Congreve and other gunpowder rockets of the day would have been far too feeble for any sustained propulsion. Fellow Russian Tsiolkovsky began speculating on interplanetary flight by reactive motion in the 1880s, but not until 1903 were his seminal findings published. Fittingly, it was in the same year that man first took to the air by *powered* flight, when the Wright brothers flew from Kitty Hawk. It is pertinent to add that from the mid-1890s, as liquid oxygen and other liquefied gases began to be commercially available, Tsiolkovsky started to think of liquid propellants and liquid oxidizers as far more potent and efficient than centuries-old solid fuels like gunpowder; yet ironically, these developments curiously coincided with the marked decline of the old gunpowder rocket.

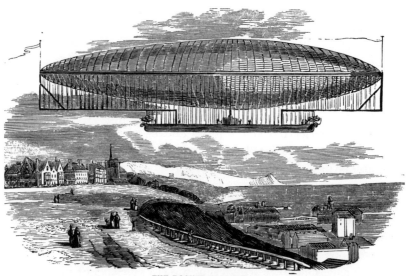

THE ROCKET BALLOON.

FIGURE 12.14

James Nye's rocket balloon, propelled by successive firings of Congreve rockets, 1852. Nye estimated that it could travel 200 miles (320 km) at 15 miles per hour (24 km/hr). (S.I. 76–7775).

Miscellaneous Applications

Congreve recognized early on the almost endless possibilities for applying the rocket principle. For example, in his second and final rocket patent (No. 9853 of 16 October 1823), he suggested that his rocket light-ball be used not only for illuminating battlefields and signalling, but also for "taking observations connected with geometrical surveys, where very distant operations are required." Congreve did not elaborate; but, in 1825, Sir Edward Sabine and astronomer Sir John Herschel conducted experiments with French officials in which rockets determined longitudinal displacements between the Greenwich and Paris observatories. In 1829, Royal Navy Captain Fitzwilliam Owen presented a similar plan. Chronometers used for measuring time were subject to error, so Owen suggested that three or more rockets be launched every evening at a given station (London or Portsmouth), and that launch schedules be posted regularly in newspapers and nautical gazettes. The times of each explosion were to be registered. Bursts seen from Greenwich were simultaneously annotated and vessels at sea were requested to record rocket sightings. The plan was for the differences between the firings and chronometer times on the ships or other points to be compared, or synchronized if necessary, to rate chronometers and for operations to be repeated weekly to determine Greenwich daily fluctuations. But such plans invariably failed in practice. Captain Sir Edward Belcher tried out a similar experiment during a survey mission of the west coast of Africa in February 1837, but many of the rockets were unable to ascend due to poor construction. Those that did rise were barely spotted at 40 miles (64 km) distance, whereas required sighting distances were twice that.[56]

The rocket's capacity for carrying a line had itself many potential applications besides lifesaving. In the 1820s, de Montgéry suggested rockets for carrying anchors over enemy ship riggings for boarding, or for scaling castles or besieged garrisons. Rockets too, he said, might establish rope and chain bridges over rivers, torrents, cliffs, and steep valleys. He added that rockets could convey flexible water pipes for pumping water to inflamed but inaccessible places. Much later, in 1882, French pyrotechnist Amedée Denisse suggested that rockets were "not also impossible" for transporting telephone wires "in the manner of lifesaving rope."[57]

Line rockets might convey salvaged equipment and other "merchandise" from a wrecked ship to shore, wrote de Montgéry in 1825. This idea was a forerunner of the mail-carrying rocket that became so popular a century later

NEW YORK FIRE DEPARTMENT TESTING DEVICES FOR THROWING LIFE LINES OVER BUILDINGS.

FIGURE 12.15

Test of projectiles for casting lines up high structures for use in fire fighting, at the foot of the Palisades, off the Hudson River, New York, in 1885. Left to right: brass barrel rocket launcher, line-throwing rifle, an air gun, and another rocket. (S.I. A5293A)

in the 1930s. In 1832, John Dennett, inventor of the Dennett lifesaving rocket, specifically mentioned rockets for fetching and dispatching mail from sinking ships in his *A Concise Description of a Powerful Species of War Rocket*. Just a year later, the mail, or message-carrying rocket, may have had its debut. During the Portuguese civil war, Bollaert, the English commander of a rocket brigade, ordered his men to wrap selected editions of newspapers around the guide-sticks of their rockets and fire them at the enemy for propaganda effects. But not until the Franco-Prussian War, while Paris was under siege, did Parisian T.D. Schneiter take out French patent No. 91160 of 31 December 1870 for such a device. Rockets could communicate the thoughts of soldiers or inhabitants of an invested town, he believed. In 1897, Otto Wilhelmi of Dusseldorf was granted a similar patent but like Bollaert, saw the rocket as a conveyor of propaganda rather than mail.[58]

The first camera-carrying rockets also date to the nineteenth century. Denisse introduced this invention in 1888 in the French journal *La Nature* of 22 September, but he probably never built it. The German Ludwig Rohrmann of Krauschwitz, Saxony, patented the concept in 1891 (British Patent No. 12669). It was left, however, to the great Swedish chemist Alfred Nobel to build the first rocket of this kind, in 1896, and from it to successfully take aerial photographs of Swedish villages when at peak altitude and suspended by parachute. More famous are the photographic reconnaissance rocket experi-

FIGURE 12.16

"Photo Rocket" of French pyrotechnist Amedée Denisse, 1888, probably the first design for a camera-carrying rocket. It had multiple, panoramic lenses. (S.I. 72-3141)

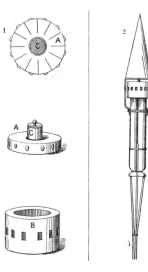

FIGURE 12.17
Photograph of the village of Karlskoga, Sweden, believed to have been taken with a camera-rocket developed by Alfred Nobel, the Swedish chemist, in about 1897. (S.I. 72–10662; courtesy Nobel Foundation, Stockholm)

ments of Alfred Maul of Dresden, carried out between 1901 and 1912, but that is beyond the scope of this book. In any case, after all those years they came to no avail because of another invention—the airplane—that was able to carry a camera to any desired spot or altitude and to take many photos, compared to Maul's single frames.[59]

Finally, although the rain-making rocket is a twentieth-century product, the idea was proposed in 1892 by Henry W. Allen, civil engineer of Goolburga, India. Allen's rocket carried a copper sphere containing the solvent ether. As the rocket ascended to colder layers of the atmosphere, it was to encounter the temperature at which ether boils violently. The fumes were to escape through spray holes around the sphere, provoking rain from cumulus or nimbus clouds. However, it is doubtful that Allen ever created rain this way.[60]

The application of rockets to chronograph rating, aerial photography, rain-making, and other purposes may or may not have been direct applications of Congreve and Hale technology, but most were probably indirect spinoffs. In this respect, among the more subtle but powerful legacies bequeathed by Congreve and Hale was proof that the simple gunpowder rocket could perform more reliably and powerfully than it had in previous centuries, and offered many potentials. It is true that the majority of these applications were neither commercially nor technically viable, but this was mainly because both the science and technology of rocketry were still crude. Nonetheless, the diversity of these ideas was an important part of the history of the nineteenth-century rocket. Further, all of these applications, whether for war or peace, were manifestations of the Industrial Revolution, which witnessed both technological triumphs and fiascoes.

Seen in a larger context, the nineteenth-century powder rocket was a multifaceted, international phenomenon that was not strictly limited to a simple battlefield shock weapon. Nor was its use confined to a brief, Napoleonic time span as has hitherto been believed. We can also see how this device, which had been neglected for centuries, was rediscovered, began to mature, flourished for another century, and went out of favor again because it did not mature fast enough within the mainstream of Industrial Revolution military technology.

Another part of the history of rocketry not told here is a repeat of what occurred from the 1200s to the 1800s; namely, a period of neglect and even disdain for the rocket, then a second rediscovery. This time, by the 1920s, the science of rocketry had begun to catch up with the technology. Thanks to the great founders of modern astronautics, Tsiolkovsky, Robert H. Goddard, and Hermann Oberth, it was recognized (and proven experimentally by Goddard) that the rocket could indeed function in a vacuum and was therefore a logical and potentially very powerful means of achieving spaceflight. These and other pioneers also concentrated at last on rocket propellants. The great breakthroughs of the development of double-base fuels and the adoption of liquid propellants finally saw the beginnings of modern rocketry (in the early 1950s came another major milestone, the introduction of castable, composite solid fuels, which almost universally replaced double-base fuels and made large-scale, solid-fuel rockets possible). Rocketry had come very far indeed from the days when all the world powers were in a race to capture the secrets of Congreve. But, to paraphrase historians Beryl Williams and Samuel Epstein, Congreve's and Hale's perseverance and faith in taming the mysterious, self-willed rocket paved the way for the men who would come after; men whose own ingenuity would supply the rocket with the power it needed to play still larger roles in our own missile and Space Age.[61]

APPENDIX

Note on Preservation
of Museum Specimens
of Hale Rockets

Several specimens of Hale rockets in the National Air and Space Museum's collections have undergone extensive restoration. An account of this process may be useful to other museums who also hold nineteenth-century powder rockets and wish to preserve them.

The first of Hale's experiments conducted by the British Army may have inaugurated a new stretch of the Royal Artillery firing range at Shoeburyness, on the southern Essex coast. According to *Jone's Woolwich Journal* of 18 August 1847: "the spot chosen was the sea shore in front of the Coast Guard station, within a few yards . . . where . . . the new practice range of the Royal Artillery will be erected. . . . The line of fire was across the Maplin Sands." Maplin Sands is a shoal extending from Shoeburyness N.E. to beyond Foulness Point.[1]

In the early 1970s, Maplin Sands was chosen as the site for a proposed airport to ease London's heavily congested air traffic. Due to pressure from environmentalists, however, the airport was never built, but in 1973–74 the

FIGURE A.1

British war rockets retrieved from the old Shoeburyness firing range, Maplin Sands, Essex, in 1975. Left to right: a 24-pounder (10.8 kg) Hale; two other 24-pounders with grooves; probably a 24-pounder Boxer; three 12-pounder (5.4 kg) Hales; and a rare 1.5-pounder (0.6 kg) Hale. (S.I. 77–4240–1)

Sands were dredged of 120 years of buried ordnance ammunition and potentially deadly explosives.[2]

Among the relics uncovered were barnacle-encrusted Congreve and Hale rockets; when the scales were removed, shiny, almost new metal was revealed underneath. Visiting Maplin Sands was Colonel John S. Weeks of the Royal Arsenal, who recognized the historical value of these specimens and the fact that they should be restored for exhibition purposes. He retrieved several rockets and was advised by ordnance engineers to submerge the specimens in barrels of oil so that oxidation, hitherto retarded by the thick barnacle covering, would not cause the rockets to start rusting rapidly when exposed to air "and disintegrate completely within three or four weeks."[3]

In 1974, the discovery of the Maplin specimens was brought to the attention of the National Air and Space Museum (NASM), Washington, D.C., by Mitchell R. Sharpe, rocket historian and curator of the Alabama Space and Rocket Center, Huntsville, Alabama. The Museum expressed an interest in obtaining some specimens. Colonel Weeks agreed to ship the rockets to the U.S. but was concerned with their condition. "My first thoughts are to cover them in thick grease, wrap them in some sort of oil-resistant paper and seal the whole thing in a plastic bag," he informed Museum officials in a letter of 13 May 1974.[4]

After conferring with Dr. Robert M. Organ, then director of the Smithsonian's Conservation Analytical Laboratory, the NASM told Weeks that "our reaction to your conservation action of submergence in oil is affirmative [to retard immediate oxidation]. If wiped off and a heavier gun grease were applied and wrapped as suggested, their condition should be completely quiescent for some months."[5]

Seven Hale rockets and one stick rocket arrived from London on 26 September 1974. They were grease-coated, wrapped in plastic, and stored in a box that remained until 1977 in a warehouse at the NASM's Preservation, Restoration and Storage Facility (PRSF), Silver Hill, Maryland. Though packed for "short-term preservation and storage" only, it was not possible to take further action at that time because of the staff's preparations for completing the new NASM in time for the Bicentennial Year of 1976.[6]

On 24 March 1977, Alfred J. Bachmeier, supervisor of PRSF Collections Management (now the Paul E. Garber Facility), stated that

FIGURE A.2

The rockets in Figure A.1 after restoration by the Smithsonian's Paul E. Garber Preservation, Restoration and Storage Facility, Silver Hill, Maryland. (s.i. 79–3563)

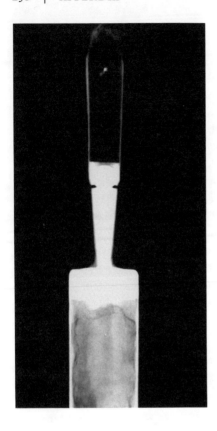

FIGURE A.3

An X-ray of the Maplin Sands central-stick (probably Boxer) rocket shown in Figure A.2. A substance was found that is probably propellant residue. Also visible are construction details, like the end closure, method of joining the stick, and nails or rivets. (S.I. 83–4028)

the method of preservation of the Hale rockets "is now causing considerable deterioration. If these rockets are . . . of an unusual grade of cast iron they should be turned over to the Conservation Analytical Lab for examination and recommendations on long-term preservation and storage. These rockets have not been examined and certified to be inert . . . they may be armed."[7]

Consequently, by early May, the still partly barnacle-covered rockets were sent to the Naval Explosive Ordnance Disposal Facility in Indian Head, Maryland. Here they were X-rayed to see if they were loaded and to determine the extent of corrosion and the location of holes. They were found to contain "a substance, possibly the original powder" but the report did not specify the location of the substance (i.e., whether in the motor case or the warhead). After X-raying, the rockets were drilled along the original seams and the substance was removed by Robert Taylor, an explosive-ordnance disposal technician.[8]

After being returned to the Garber Facility, the artifacts were subjected to the following cleaning and preservation process:

(1) First they were washed clean of powder residue using cold water under pressure.

(2) Then they were dipped in a caustic soda (lye), pH-14, a rust stripper, and rinsed in cold water.

(3) Rivets holding the nose and tail ends to the body were drilled out and removed.

(4) These were redipped in the rust stripper and rinsed with cold water.

(5) The rockets were lightly glass-beaded inside and out.

(6) Nose and tail ends were rewelded to the body.

(7) The welding area and outside of body were glass-beaded.

(8) The rockets were then dipped in iron phosphate solution at 130°F for 3 minutes.

(9) Next they were dipped in hot water at 160°F to clean and dry.

(10) "Magnus FF–111" (water white) was poured inside to coat the interior, then poured out.

(11) Finally, four coats of water white were sprayed on the exterior.[9]

After this treatment, the rockets acquired a stone-gray color, probably as a result of the phosphate. The rockets were originally black in color, but the phosphate treatment added to the rust prevention.[10]

The author then identified these rockets and accessioned them as follows:

(1) 24-pounder Hale, ungrooved, 3.75 inches (9.5 cm) in diameter; 22 inches (55.8 cm) long; 12.6 pounds (5.7 kg) in weight; Catalog No. 1979–727.

(2) 24-pounder Hale, grooved, 3.75 inches (9.5 cm) in diameter; 22 inches (55.8 cm) long; 11.75 pounds (5 kg) in weight; donated to Alabama Space and Rocket Center.

(3) 24-pounder Hale, grooved, 3.75 inches (9.5 cm) in diameter; 21 inches (53.3 cm) long; 11.87 pounds (5 kg) in weight; Catalog No. 1979–730.

(4) Probably a 24-pounder Boxer, a central-mounted stick rocket, with stick flange, 2.75 inches (6.9 cm) in diameter, 25 inches (63.5 cm) long overall; cartridge (casing) 15 inches (38 cm) long; 6.3 pounds (2.9 kg) in weight; Catalog No. 1979–728.

(5) 12-pounder Hale, grooved; 3 inches (7.6 cm) in diameter; 16 inches (40.6 cm) long; 3.3 pounds (1.5 kg) in weight; Catalog No. 1979–729.

(6) 12-pounder Hale, grooved, 3 inches (7.6 cm) in diameter; 16 inches (40.6 cm) long; 3.12 pounds (1.4 kg) in weight; donated to the Alabama Space and Rocket Center.

(7) 12-pounder Hale, grooved, 3 inches (7.6 cm) in diameter; 16 inches (40.6 cm) long; 3 pounds (1.3 kg) in weight; Catalog No. 1979–732.

(8) 3-pounder Hale, grooved, 2 inches (5 cm) in diameter; 12 inches (30.4 cm) long; 1.7 pounds (0.5 kg) in weight; Catalog No. 1979–731.

The specimens appear to date between 1865 and 1867. This is consistent with the stick rocket (artifact No. 4) being identified as a Boxer (see Chapter 4). The Boxer rocket provisionally replaced the 6-, 12-, and 24-pounder (2.7, 5.4, and 10.8 kg) Congreve rockets on 14 September 1864. Hale's 9- and 24-pounders (4 and 10.8 kg) replaced Boxer rockets in 1867.[11]

By late 1984, the Museum's Maplin Sands rockets showed new signs of deterioration. David Hallam, then a visiting conservator from the Australian War Memorial, suggested that this was caused mainly by the chlorides from the rockets' former seawater environment and that further preservation treatment was necessary. He recommended the same treatment used for cannons dug from maritime sites.[12]

Consequently, the rockets were bathed in a 2.5% caustic soda (sodium hydroxide) solution. They were then subjected to electrolysis to remove remaining chlorides and reduce the black oxides to magnetite. When the chloride level was low (a few parts per million), the rockets were placed in an inhibited chromate solution to remove the caustic hydroxide. They were then washed with an organic (amine type) inhibitor (Cortec 609) and wax-coated with a microcrystalline wax (Ilreco BE Square 185). The rockets were next put into controlled environmental storage (Hallam recommended an RH level of 55% and a temperature of 21°C, a normal museum standard).[13]

Hallam also suggested that for rockets and other ordnance recovered from a seawater environment in the future, the ideal procedure should be as follows:

(1) Strip off peeling paint, grease, and dirt.

(2) Perform electrolysis.

(3) Wash with a chromate or other inhibitor.

(4) Bathe with tannic acid to help stabilize the exterior oxides (10% acid in alcohol with pH adjusted to 2); while the object might turn black, this could be removed with the loss of minor amounts of metal.

(5) Wash with an organic inhibitor.

(6) Apply wax (or polyurethane) coating.[14]

Notes

Sources are cited by last name of author, or "anon.," if unknown. Year of publication, volume, part number (if applicable), and page number(s) follow in parentheses. Titles of sources are listed in the Bibliography by author's last name and year of publication.

Chapter 1

1. Needham (1986: 7: 108–116)
2. Needham (1986: 7: 15, 362–363)
3. Partington (1960: 42, 48–49, 200–201)
4. Winter (1979b: 468–469)
5. Needham (1986: 7: 34–35, 480, et seq.); Winter (1982: 522, 526)
6. Mitra (1963: 16); Moor (1794: 169)
7. Halim (1961: 145, 147); Irvine (1921: 29, 60–61, 325); Irvine (1962: 147–148); Briggs (1829: 3: 50, 129, 201–202, 253, 411, 459, 468); Sarkar (1960: 55); Noer (1890: 2: 331–332, 338); Winter (1979b: 468–469)

8. Craufurd (1790: 294–295)

9. Tennant (1804: 1: 244); [de la Tour] (1848: 254–256]; Irvine (1962: 149–151); Dirom (1794: 299–300)

10. Irvine (1921: 1: 148); Gold (1806: n.p.); de la Tour (1848: 48); Banerjee (1968: 151); Brock (1949: 234)

11. Kirkpatrick (1811: xciv, xcii) 12. Gold (1806: n.p.)

13. British East India Co. (1800: 256, 262–263)

14. Lenman (1968: 34–42); Sarkar (1960: 152–158); McNeill and Sedlar (1970: 68–69)

15. McNeill and Sedlar (1970: 68–69)

16. Marshall (1915: 23); Museum of Artillery (1963: i)

Chapter 2

1. Letter (1785); Congreve (ca. 1800)

2. Hogg (1963: 2: 226); Jackson and de Beer (1974: 55)

3. Thornton (1930: 8); Letter (1984)

4. Winter (1972: 334); Berkeley (1804: *passim*)

5. Anon. (1805a: 193); Letter (1785)

6. Congreve (1807: 1–2); Congreve (1827:15)

7. Sharpe (1970: 160–164); Hume (1808: 128–129); Hume (1811: 65–67); Congreve (1810: 1)

8. Congreve (1827: 15–16)

9. Congreve (1810: 1–2)

10. Congreve (1810: 1–2); Congreve (1827: 15–16)

11. Hogg (1963: 1: 590–591); Congreve (1814: 21)

12. Leigh (1951: 167)

13. Congreve (1807: 2); Congreve (1806: 21, 28)

14. Anon. (1805b: 3)

15. Anon (1805c: 2–3)

16. Laughton (1949: 155); Thompson (1944: 151)

17. Laughton (1949: 157, 175)

18. Laughton (1949: 155); Thompson (1944: 151)

19. Montú (1934: 2: 1694)

20. Congreve (1807: 3)

21. Congreve (1807: 3)

22. Congreve (1807: 4); Congreve (1827: 17); Lloyd (1952: 455–457); Letter (1810)

23. Congreve (1827: 18); Congreve (1807: 4)

24. Anon. (1806: 1)

25. Letter (1810); Congreve (1807: 15, 40); von Hoyer (1827: 6–7); Konstantinov (1861: 78); Olejar (1946: 18)

26. Congreve (1810: 15); Fyers (1808: n.p.); Winter (1978: 86–87)

27. Anon. (1807a: 3: 2, 4); Winter (1978: 85–86, 89)

28. Anon. (1807b: 2); Anon. (1807c: 2); Congreve (1808: 10); Winter (1978: 87–88)

29. Moore (1813: iii)
30. Congreve (1827: 18, 84); Chatterton (1861: 2: 127, 254, 256, 261, 263, 273, 275, 311, 323, 319, 377, 379, 382, 384–385, 389–390)
31. Letter (1810); Latham (1930: 435); Duncan (1873: 2: 225, 229); Bem (1820: 77–78)
32. Latham (1930: 425–429); Duncan (1873: 2: 37, 389–390); Whinyates (1897: 131–136); Leslie (1913: 327–332)
33. Duncan (1873: 2: 438); Latham (1930: 438–441)
34. Gurwood (1838: 2: 314); Duncan (1873: 2: 416–417)
35. Auchinleck (1855: 347–348)
36. Anon. (1829b: 412–416); Dickson (1929: 22); Marine (1913: 147–169)
37. Brant (1961: 210); U.S. Congress (1814: 163–165, 213, 251, 308); Robinson (1945: 3–4); Anon. (1814l: 247–248)
38. Anon. (1814f: 3)
39. Anon. (1814b: 144–145); Anon. (1815b: 3)
40. Anon. (1814b: 161)
41. Marine (1913: 166–167)
42. Marine (1913: 166–167)
43. Anon. (1814k: 133)
44. Anon. (1814k: 133)
45. Bassett (1927: 2: 153); Lane (1889: 24–26); Duncan (1873: 2: 398–399, 406)
46. Latour (1816: 121–122)
47. Jocelyn (1906: 495, 497–498)
48. Jocelyn (1906: 495, 498)
49. Anon. (1814a: 134); Jocelyn (1906: 495); de Grunwald (1955: 27)
50. Jocelyn (1906: 498)
51. Anon. (1824a: 640); Great Britain, War Office (1855a)
52. Jocelyn (1906: 498); Anon. (1828a: 4); Anon. (1828b: 2); Anon. (1828c: 236)

Chapter 3

1. Anon. (1836b: 35); Latham (1930: 444–445); Anon.
2. Anon. (1836b: 35); Letter (1974a)
3. Latham (1930: 446–447)
4. Latham (1930: 447); Anon. (1831:182)
5. Latham (1930: 448)
6. Trant (1827: 136, 144, 171, 175, 178, 353, 401–402)
7. Conder (1826: 53)
8. Moore Smith (1903: 292–293); Anon. (1858: 48–53)
9. Bingham (1843: 2: 36)
10. Cowan (1956: 42)
11. Anon. (1847a: 565)
12. Anon. (1847a: 574)
13. Nicaise (1859: 23); Konstantinov (1861: 25)

14. Tyrell (1855: 1: 288)
15. Nolan (1857: 2: 182)
16. Smith (1954: 120)
17. Rowbotham (1967: *passim*)
18. Hilton (1957: 160–161)
19. Jones (1859: 169–170)
20. Anon. (1826: 398); Fortescue (1924: 4: 179); Brackenbury (1874: 1: 14)
21. Fortescue (1924: 4: 21)
22. Lal (1846: 2: 464); Kaye (1857: 230, 272)
23. Hake (1891: 58, 292, 366, 504)
24. Clowes (1903: 524)
25. Anon. (1868c: 59, 215)

Chapter 4

1. Sarkar (1960: 21)
2. Congreve (1814: n.p.)
3. Congreve (1814: n.p.)
4. Hime (1904: 121)
8. Congreve (1827: 68)
9. Congreve (1807: 7–8); Congreve (1814: n.p.); Congreve (1827:70)
10. Congreve (1814: n.p.)
11. Congreve (1814: 53–55); Congreve (1827: 78); Congreve (1807: 8–11)
12. Congreve (1814: n.p.); Congreve (1807: 24)
13. Congreve (1814: n.p.); Congreve (1827: 40)
14. Congreve (1814: n.p.); Congreve (1827: 75)
15. Congreve (1827: 40)
16. Congreve (1814: n.p.)
17. Congreve (1814: n.p.); Congreve (1827: 39); Museum of Artillery (1963: 57)
18. James (1810: n.p.); Congreve (1814: n.p.)
19. James (1810: n.p.); Congreve (1814: n.p.)
20. Congreve (1814: n.p.); Congreve (1807: 7); Congreve (1810: 3); Scoffern (1852: 126, 133)
21. Congreve (1814: n.p.); Brewster (1830: 281)
22. Museum of Artillery (1963: 55); Congreve (1814: n.p.)
23. Brewster (1830: 280); Scoffern (1852: 119)
24. Congreve (1814: n.p.)
25. Congreve (1814: n.p.)
26. Congreve (1814: n.p.)
27. Anon. (1852: 3: 349–350)
28. Anon. (1852: 3: 351)
29. Congreve (1827: 60)
30. Congreve (1814: n.p.); Congreve (1827: 60–61); Scoffern (1852: 119, 122, 129–130)

31. Congreve (1827: 18, 83–84)
32. Letter (1809)
33. Clowes (1900: 5: 258, 265, 267, 272); Ellenborough (1914: 30); Chatterton (1861: 2: 254, 261, 275, 319, 384–385); Congreve (1814: n.p.)
34. Log (1814: 8: n.p.); Congreve (1814: n.p.)
35. Congreve (1827: 59)
36. Congreve (1814: n.p.); Congreve (1827: 67–68)
37. Congreve (1814: n.p.)
38. d'Arcet (1814: 134–145); Brewster (1830: 278–281); Letter (1973b)
39. Hogg (1963: 1: 590–591); Smith (1870: 7); Congreve (1815)
40. Dalkin (n.d.; n.p.)
41. Brewster (1830: 279)
42. Brewster (1830: 279); Scoffern (1852: 121); Owen (1871; 120)
43. Brewster (1830: 279); Murray (1908: 6: 611)
44. Letter (1810); Letter (1813d); Moore (1813: 21)
45. Brewster (1830: 280)
46. Brewster (1830: 280)
47. Brewster (1830: 280)
48. Brewster (1830: 280); Congreve (ca. 1810: 24)
49. Brewster (1830: 280)
50. d'Arcet (1814:138)
51. Brewster (1830: 280)
52. Brewster (1830: 281)
53. d'Arcet (1814: 136–138); Brewster (1830: 281)
54. Brewster (1830: 281)
55. d'Arcet (1814: 136–137); Brewster (1830: 281)
56. d'Arcet (1814: 141, 144); Brewster (1830: 281); Anon. (1821b: 2057)
57. Anon. (1821b: 2057); Brewster (1830: 281)
58. d'Arcet (1814: 136)
59. Brewster (1830: 281)
60. Becklake and Turvey (1987: 292–293)
61. Becklake and Turvey (1987: 292–293)
62. Great Britain, War Office (1870b: 177–178)
63. Rees (1819: 31: n.p.); Robson (1948: 147–148); Oman (1953: 470); Edwards (1924: 151, 153–154); Leslie (1924–1925: 242–244)
64. Congreve (1827: 59); Congreve (1814: n.p.); Latham (1930: 421)
65. Congreve (1827: 55–56); Congreve (1814: n.p.)
66. Latham (1930: 423–425)
67. Jocelyn (1906: 29); Latham (1930: 431–432); Duncan (1873: 2: 37–38); Whinyates (1900–1901: 27: 435–436); Secretary (1900–1901: 27: 297–300)
68. Whinyates (1900–1901: 298–300, 435–436); Anon. (1852: 349); Latham (1949: 277–283); Duncan (1872: 1: 394, 404)
69. R.G.P. (1852: 161–168, 403–409); Congreve (1814: n.p.)
70. Congreve (1814: n.p.)
71. Marmont (1862: 102)

Chapter 5

1. Congreve (1807: n.p.)
2. Winter (1965: 56–58); Brussel de Brulard (1853: 86–87)
3. Jensen (1959: 68)
4. Winter (1965: 58–59); Vaupell (1876: 2: 412)
5. Anon. (1813a: 350); Winter (1965: 59); Jensen (1959: 64); de Montgéry (1825: 640)
6. Jensen (1959: 73); Konstantinov (1861: 78–79); Tojhusmuseets (1848: 294–298)
7. Jensen (1959: 61, 66, 71–72); Winter (1965: 61–63); Teisen (1962: 143); Anon. (1853f: 7)
8. Nemetz (1957: 260); Winter (1977: 24–25); Anon. (1856: 90–91)
9. Nemetz (1957: 261–262); Winter (1977: 25)
10. Nemetz (1957: 261–262)
11. Nemetz (1957: 262–263); von Wrede (1905: 4: 194–195, 303)
12. de Montgéry (1825: 650); Nemetz (1957: 268–269); Anon. (1840a: 541–542); Dolleczek (1887: 350)
13. Konstantinov (1861: 9, 18); Anon. (1851c: 857); Anon. (1851d: 873–874); Jakobsson (1940: 91)
14. Nemetz (1957: 262–263); Anon. (1835b:458–459)
15. von Wrede (1905: 4: 533, 603–604)
16. Reisner (1860: 156–160); von Rzikowsky Dobrzisch (1860: 179–180); Konstantinov (1861: 17–18)
17. von Wrede (1905: 534); Jesser (1868: 191–195); Susane (1863: 38–45)
18. von Wrede (1905: 533); C.v.H. (1862: 413–415); Letter (1969b)
19. von Lettow-Vorbeck (1869: 1: 384–385); Dolleczek (1887: 356, 669); Anon. (1868b: 814); von Wrede (1905: 533); Konstantinov (1861: 17–18)
20. Dolleczek (1887: 353, 355–356); von Kellemes (1857: 105, 130); Anon. (1865: 14–15)
21. Anon. (1935: 417)
22. Bem (1820: 77–78); Anon. (1935: 417); Anon. (1853a: 310–311)
23. Bem (1820: *passim*)
24. Anon. (1935:417); Gembarzewski (1903: 16, 129, 127, 144–145); Los (1969: 30–31, 40, et seq.); Skoog (1977: 11); Konstantinov (1861: 61)
25. de Montgéry (1825: 184); Anon. (1812b: 659); Anon. (1818: 2)
26. Sokol'skii (1967: 22–27); Sonkin (1952: 20–25)
27. Sokol'skii (1967: 28–29, 188)
28. Sonkin (1952: 28–30)
29. Sokol'skii (1967: 3, 30–32); Sonkin (1952: 37)
30. Sokol'skii (1967: 30); Konstantinov (1861: 62); Sonkin (1952: 40–50)
31. Konstantinov (1861: 62)
32. Konstantinov (1862: 62); Sokol'skii (1967: 32–35, 61–64); Sonkin (1952: 36, 63–66)
33. Sokol'skii (1967: 35)
34. Sokol'skii (1967: 35, 40–41); Konstantinov (1863: 63); Sonkin (1952: 71–76)
35. Sokol'skii (1967: 58–59); London, Post (1848: 980); Sonkin (1952: 163–168)

36. Konstantinov (1861: 44–50, 295–296, 310–311); Sokol'skii (1967: 44–45); Sonkin (1952: 95–130)

37. Konstantinov (1861: 7, 91, 176); Sokol'skii (1967: 47, 77–78); Sonkin (1952: 142–144)

38. Trench (1874: 216–217, 219, 222); Sonkin (1952: 172); Great Britain, War (1882: 233)

39. Sokol'skii (1967:80–90); Sonkin (1952: 174–180)

40. Ley (1959: 75); Sokol'skii (1967: 80–83, 90); Sonkin (1952: 174–180); Marvin (1880: 4, 9, 15, 165, 167, et. seq.); Court (1888: 274)

41. Congreve (1827: 18, 84); Chattertoon (1861: 2: 127, 254, et. seq.); d'Arcet (1814: 135)

42. Anon. (1810a: 399–400); d'Arcet (1814: *passim*); Susane (1863: 27–29); Pralon (1883: 5); Brussel de Brulard (1853: 86–88); Letter (1973b)

43. Susane (1863: 31, 47–48); Brussel de Brulard (1853: 6, 98–99)

44. Brussel de Brulard (1853: 12–17, 20–22, 88–89, 91–93, 99–101); de Montgéry (1825: 174); Pralon (1883: 5–6)

45. Pralon (1883: 6–8); Susane (1863: 49)

46. Pralon (1883: 49–51); Susane (1863: 51)

47. Dauvé (1890: 42); Susane (1863: 51–52)

48. Pralon (1883: 8–10, 54–59); Susane (1863: 55); Konstantinov (1855: 290)

49. Dauvé (1890: 43–48, 55–56, 62, 69–74); Konstantinov (1861: 248–249); Pralon (1883: 23–26); France (1859: *passim*)

50. Dauvé (1890: 115–117); Susane (1863: 39–45); Vergnaud and Vergnaud (1865: 313–315)

51. Cordier (1906: 140–141, 255, 350); Dauvé (1890: 117–123); Pralon (1883: 61–62, 65); Susane (1863: 65)

52. Pralon (1883: 65); Susane (1863: 65)

53. Anon. (1870b: 353); Pralon (1883: 65)

54. Anon. (1872b: 156–157)

55. Anon. (1872b: 156–157); Strandh (1964: 90–91)

56. Skoog (1977: 7); de Montgéry (1825: 161, 183)

57. de Montgéry (1825: 655); Skoog (1977: 11); Jakobsson (1940: 75–78, 91–95)

58. Skoog (1977: 12); Jakobsson (1940: 78–82)

59. Skoog (1977: 12); Jakobsoon (1940: 83); Anon. (1823c: 510); de Montgéry (1825: 124)

60. de Montgéry (1825: 585); Skoog (1977: 18–19); Jakobsson (1940: 86, 88–89); Anon. (1823: 510)

61. Pictet (1848: xii–xiv); Anon. (1838b: 77–80)

62. Anon. (1876: p. unk.)

63. Konstantinov (1861: 18); Pictet (1848: *passim*)

64. Pictet (1848: xiii); von Wattenwyl (1947: 497–499); Konstantinov (1861: 18–22)

65. Konstantinov (1861: 499); Ineichen (1977: 10–14)

66. Konstantinov (1861: 18–22); Ineichen (1977: 10–14)

67. de la Llave y Garcia (1896: 47); Amiguet (1914: 480)

68. von Wattenwyl (1945: 503–504); Anon. (1867b: 134–139, 177–178); Sonkin (195: 142–144)

69. Konstantinoff (1861: 90)

70. von Wattenwyl (1945: 503–505)

Chapter 6

1. de Montgéry (1825: 654–655)
2. de Montgéry (1825: 655); Kruger (1867: 430–431); Verlohren (1910: 186); Letter (1963a); Letter (1963c)
3. Kuntzemuller (1881: 250)
4. Kaiser (195416); Konstantinov (1861: 91); Anon. (1852b: 171); Dicey (1864: 2: 169)
5. Anon. (1850h: 185); Kuntzemuller (1881: 250); Anon. 1886–7: 56); Letter (1963a)
6. Anon. (1860a: 259); Konstantinov (1861: 90–91)
7. McCabe, Jr. (1871: 115); Hauschild (1958: 28)
8. Röpnack (1961: n.p.); Brussel de Brulard (1853: 88); Letter (1962b); Anon. (1850c: 357–358); Anon. (1850f: 890); Anon. (1851a: 788–789); Anon. (1851b: 801); Anon. (1851c: 857); Anon. (1851d: 873–874); Anon. (1853b: 249–250); Anon. (1853c: 298–299)
9. Anon. (1836b: 35–36); Anon. (1836a: 113–114)
10. Osten (1849: 64–68)
11. Letter (1962a); van Geen (1840: 112, 134, 157, 198, 234, 244, 253–255, 287)
12. Anon. (1836: 114–124); the Proprietors (1829–33)
13. Madol (1930: 239–240, 265); Ananoff (1939: 310); Hale (1844b)
14. Madol (1930: 249–251, 265); Favre (1884: 291, 296–299, 310–313)
15. Anon. (1860b: 416)
16. Raikes (1846: 378–379); Letter (1810)
17. Parry (1825: 25); Marchand (1957: 3: 1156, 1174, 1176); de Montgéry (1825: 660)
18. Prothero (1966: 6: 272)
19. Röpnack (1961: n.p.); Anon. (1837b: 4: 80); Anon. (1835a: 80)
20. Röpnack (1961: n.p.); Letter (1964); Anon. (1842: 72); Schmoelzl (1857: 383–433)
21. do Nascimento (1955: 91–100)
22. Maceroni (1838: 2: 454–455)
23. de Cunha Mallos (1833: 2: 75–76, 103, 109, 177, 200, 247); Anon. (1832d: 2); Hippisley (1845: 551–559)
24. Bollaert (1870: 1: 246, 259)
25. Bollaert (1870: 1: 261–263, 267, 271, 278–279, 283, 290, 305, 309–311, 320, 331)
26. Tavares (1869: *passim*)
27. Botelho (1921: 117, 120, 187, 196, 425)
28. de Eça (1954: 2: 161–162, 181, 233, 237, 242, 422, 424, 428, 465, 622, 625)
29. Anon. (1877a: 426)
30. Winter (1965b: 183–185)
31. Letter (1962c); Winter (1965b: 185–186)
32. Winter (1965b: 186–187); Anon. (1844b: 376–377)
33. Pictet (1848: vii, xiii, 124)
34. Anon. (1850e: 87); Montù (1934: 5: 1961)
35. Konstantinov (1861: 58–59)
36. Montù (1934: 5: 1961)
37. Bormann (1864)
38. Coquilhat (1872: *passim*); Splingard (1858: *passim*)

39. Nicaise (1859: 24); Konstantinov (1861: 56)
40. Gutiérre (1963: 164); Viluma (1833: *passim*); Vigon (1947: 3: 519)
41. Gutiérre (1963: 164); Stephens (1837: 1: 219; 2: 95–96, 166, 171); Richardson (1837: 199, 228, 301); Anon. (1844a: 1: 274–275)
42. Gutiérrez (1963: 164–169)
43. Gutiérrez (1963: 164–169); Konstantinov (1861: 59–60)
44. Gutiérrez (1963: 170–173); Vigon (1947: 3: 514)
45. Nagy (1977: 45–46)
46. Nagy (1977: 46)
47. Nagy (1977: 46–47)
48. Nagy (1977: 47–48)

Chapter 7

1. Letter (1968f)
2. Letter (1813c); Anon. (1813: 2); Boston (1812–1815: *passim*)
3. Letter (1813a)
4. Anon. (1813d: 4)
5. Anon. (1814d: 2)
6. Letter (1814a); Anon. (1814f: 425)
7. Anon. (1814e: 2); Anon. (1814f: 425); Anon. (1814h: 7); Anon. (1814j: 55)
8. Anon. (1814i: 2)
9. Duncan (1814: 169); Lallemand (1820: 56); Anon. (1814h: 2)
10. Richards (1841: 1: 193)
11. Letter (1839)
12. Letter (1814b)
13. Bassett (1827: 3: 173)
14. Anon (1815a: 2)
15. Letter (1968f); Paixhans (1821: 32)
16. Birkhimer (1884; 204–205, 282); Letter (1836)
17. Letter (1939)
18. U.S. Army (1839)
19. U.S. Army (1839); Letter (1840)
20. U.S. Army (1840); Goell (1841a; 1841b)
21. U.S. Army (1840)
22. Olejar (1946: 21)
23. Preuss (1958: 63); Letter (1855a)
24. Bruce (1956: 218); Olejar (1946: 22)
25. Scoffern (1852: 56); Olejar (1946: 22–23); Knox (1946: 261)
26. Scoffern (1852: 136–139); U.S. (1880: 2: 148–156; 4: 977–979)
27. Coston (1886: 23–24); Dahlgren (1882: 125–127)
28. Olejar (1946: 24–25)
29. Myers (1917: 72); Barcena (1883: 175); U.S. (1880: 212)
30. Olejar (1946: 28–31)
31. Olejar (1946: 32–33); Donelly (1961: 75); Anon. (1858a: 1: 48–53)

32. Olejar (1946: 33); Bruce (1956: 218); Letter (1973a); Lion (1865)
33. Phisterer (1912: 2: 1558–1559, 1610–1614)
34. Merrill (1870: 148)
35. Anon. (1861c: 327); Anon. (1861d: 3)
36. Merrill (1870: 148)
37. Merrill (1870: 148)
38. Donelly (1961: 80); Anon. (1862a: 2)
39. Merrill (1870: 148, 157, 159)
40. Merrill (1870: 159–161)
41. Donelly (1961: 81)
42. Bruce (1956: 219)
43. Bruce (1956: 219); Letter (1861d)
44. Bruce (1956: 220)
45. Donelly (1961: 89–91)
46. Donelly (1961: 91–92)
47. Confederate (1861); Donelly (1961: 86)
48. Roman (1884: 1: 475–483); Donelly (1961: 77)
49. Duffey (1861); Donelly (1961: 78)
50. Roman (1884: 1: 159–160); Meade (1956: 205); Donelly (1961: 78)
51. Donelly (1961: 77–78); Davis (1950: 172–176)
52. Donelly (1961: 79)
53. Duffey (1861)
54. Donelly (1961: 81)
55. Blackford (1945: 84–85)
56. Zulavsky (1861–1865); Manarin (1966: 78)
57. Donelly (1961: 82)
58. Donelly (1961: 84)
59. Donelly (1961: 84)
60. Zulavsky (1861–1865)
61. Kellersberger (1963: 26–27)
62. Kellersberger (1963: 27)
63. Anon. (1877a: 426); Anon. (1877b: 662); Hooper (1877)
64. Graham and Humphrey (1962: 22); Anon. (1882a: 249)
65. Brazil (1853: 14–15; 1873: n.p.); Englehart (1948: 219); do Amaral (1879: 131–139); de Vasconcellos (1922: 231–232, 271); Beverina (1920: 137–139, 177, 182, 252, 259)
66. de Souza (1874: 90); Brazil (1867: n.p.); Brazil (1869: n.p.); Brazil (1873: n.p.); Brazil (1869: n.p.); Brazil (1873: n.p.); Best (1934: 3: 61, et. seq.); Fragaso (1959: 3 & 4: *passim*); Letter (1968)
67. Brazil (1874: n.p.); do Amaral (1879: n.p.)
68. Dundonald (1859: 1: 25–26)
69. Dundonald (1859: 1: 25–27, 47)
70. Peru (1851: 5); Peru (1858: 12); Peru (1860: 10)
71. Lion (1865)
72. Lion (1865)
73. Kirbus (1968: 88)
74. Beverina (1923:312); Diaz (1843: 94, 130, 143, 245, 253, 301); Englehardt (1948:

223); Argentina (1868: n.p.)

75. de la Pezuela (1833: 21)

76. Anon. (1853f: 7); Anon. (1896:5)

77. Myers (1917: 65); U.S. Army (1880: 2: 209)

78. Kolinski (1965: 45, 119, 179); Acosta (1948: 235)

79. Letter (1865a); Burton (1870: 21, 91, 322)

80. Acosta (1948: 30–32, 87–89, 100–101, 214); Barroso (1929: 231); London, Post Office (1860: 838)

Chapter 8

1. Carnacticus (1820: 171, 182, 256, 258); Welsh (1830: 1: 9); Jocelyn (1915: 117, 301)

2. Buckle (1853: 330–331); Kaestlin (1957: 26–27)

3. Congreve (1827: 19); London, Post Office (1848: 1128); Kaestlin (1957b: 291)

4. Kaestlin (1957b: 297)

5. Congreve (1827: 45–47)

6. Anon. (1824c: 42); Anderson (1862: 270–271, 276–282); Anon. (1825: 285–286)

7. Congreve (1824: *passim*); Congreve (1827: 19); London, Post Office (1859: 1405)

8. Kaestlin (1947b: 299); Kaestlin (1957a: 27); Anon. (1829a: 252–253)

9. Anon. (1841a: 43)

10. Bingham (1843: 1: 26; 2:206–207, 222)

11. Yuan (1888: 54); Teng (1961: n.p.)

12. Anon. (1857: 153); Anon. (1854a. 556

13. Anon. (1870a: 194–195); Bax (1870: 280); Great Britain, Army (1867: 5: 7)

14. Matignon (1900: 49)

15. de Montgéry (1825: 660); Hughes (1830: 2: 216, 276, 280, 282)

16. Weygand (1936: 1: 171); Konstantinov (1855: 267)

17. Anon. (1838a: 32–33); Meyer (1837: 304–305, 311)

18. Anon. (1832b: 221, 223)

19. Anon. (1838a: 32–33); Anon. (1883: 2)

20. Anon. (1883: 18)

21. Emin-Pascha (1840: 23); Lake (1857: 193)

22. Great Britain (1827); Anon. (1841c: 104–105); Colombari (1853: 678); Anon. (1856b: 183); v.E. (1878: 175); London, Post Office (1848: 1128)

Chapter 9

1. Letter (1968c); Winter (1973a: 31–33)

2. Hale, patent (1827); Hale (1868: 10)

3. Hale (1832: 48); Hale (1865: 27); Benham (1892: 28); Anon. (1832c: 2)

4. Hale (1865: 19); Hale, patent (1834); Hale, patent (1838); Hale and Purt, patent (1842); Letter (1969a)

5. Hale and Dell, patent (1841); Hogg (1963: 2: 1151, 1165, 1282); Hale (1865: 26)

6. Hale (1865: 1, 4)

7. Hale, patent (1844a); Hale, patent (1844b); Hale (1865: 4–5); de Ponticny (1845: 434); Letter (1968c)

8. Bruce (1956: 218); Letter (1846b); de Ponticny (1845: 435; 1846; 434–435); Letter (1846a); Anon. (1846b)

9. Nagy (1977: 45); Great Britain, War Office (1854–1855); Letter (1849)

10. Scoffern (1852: 135); Henderson (1966: 118); Hale (1857); Langhans (1938: 28); Hale, patent (1857); Sonkin (1952: 162–167); Sokol'skii (1967: 59); London, Post Office (1848: 980)

11. Hale (1865: 5); Anon. (1850d: 5: 3); Letter (1865a); Olejar (1946: 33); Anon. (1853f: 7)

12. Anon. (1853f: 7); Anon. (1853i: 407)

13. Nagy (1974: 4, 8); Anon. (1853f: 7); Anon. (1853d: 55); Anon. (1853g: 275)

14. Anon. (1853f: 7); Anon. (1853d: 55–56); Great Britain, War Office (1854–1855); Nagy (1974: 4–5)

15. Anon. (1853f: 7)

16. Anon. (1853: 292); Marx (1853: 5); Anon. (1853g: 275); Duncombe (1868: 2: 132–133); Bell (1936: 2: 80); Great Britain, Parliament (1853: 452–453)

17. Anon. (1853f: 7)

18. Hale, Jr. (1853: 261)

19. Anon. (1853d: 55–56); Great Britain, War Office (1854–1855); Nagy (1974: 8)

20. Duncombe (1868: 2: 132–133); Great Britain, War Office (1853); Hale (1865: 7)

21. Hale (1865: 5–7, 16–17, 24); Hogg (1963: 2: 751); Great Britain, War Office (1854–1855)

22. Olejar (1946: 33); Letter (1969); Great Britain, War Office (1854–1855); Langhans (1938: 28)

23. Pralon (1883: 13–14, 46–47); Letter (1861d); Konstantinov (1869: 115, 119); Anon. (1867a: 403)

24. Konstantinov (1869: 115, 119)

25. Pralon (1883: 13–14, 46–47); Konstantinov (1869: 115, 119); Letter (1861e)

26. Bruce (1956: 219); Letter (1861a); Letter (1861c)

27. Sharpe (n.d.: 38–42); London, International Exhibition (1863: XI: 15); London, International Exhibition (1862: 11: 41; 12: 43); Hale, Jr. (1875)

28. Anon (1867c: 504); Hogg (1963: 2: 1377); Great Britain, War Office (1881: 302)

29. Hale (1867: *passim*); Anon. (1868a: 284–285); Commission Militaire (1869: 186–187); Dolleczek (1887: 352–356)

30. Hale (1870); Letter (1968e); International Astronomical Union (1970: 35); Winter (1973a: 33)

Chapter 10

1. Hale, patent (1844)

2. Hale, patent (1858); Dolleczek (1887: 355)

3. Hale, patent (1858); Hale, patent (1862)

4. Hale, patent (1862); Great Britain, War Office (1887: 321)

5. Great Britain, War Office (1870b: 181); Great Britain, War Office (1881: 302, 304)

6. Great Britain, War Office (1881: 302)

7. Great Britain, Ordnance Dept. (1865b: 291–292); Great Britain, War Office (188b: 179); Great Britain, War Office (1887: 321–323); Great Britain, War Office (1897: 410)

8. Great Britain, War Office (1881: 302, 305); Great Britain, War Office (1870b: 179); Letter (1855e)

9. Great Britain, War Office (1870b: 181–182); Great Britain, War Office (1881: 303–305); Great Britain, War Office (1892: 406)

10. Cole (1878: 8); Great Britain, War Office (1881: 302); Great Britain, War Office (1887: 322)

11. Letter (1855e); Cole (1877: 2)

12. Moore (1813: 21); Anon. (1834: 457–461); Letter (1810); Letter (1823d)

13. Letter (1852a); Letter (1852b); Letter (1852e)

14. Letter (1852b)

15. Letter (1852e); Letter (1852c); Letter (1852d)

16. Letter (1852e)

17. Letter (1852e)

18. Letter (1852e); Anon. (1855: 411); Hogg (1963: 1: 751)

19. Anon. (1855: 411); Great Britain, War Office (1887: 322)

20. Great Britain, War Office (1870b: 179–180); Letter (1865b); Letter (1863a)

21. Anon. (1879a: 21); Great Britain, War Office (1881: 302)

22. Great Britain, War Office (1887: 321)

23. Great Britain, War Office (1870b: 181); Great Britain, War Office (1881: 303)

24. Great Britain, War Office (1881: 303, 306); Great Britain, War Office (1887: 322–323)

25. Great Britain, War Office (1881: 303)

26. Great Britain, War Office (1887: 321, 324); Great Britain, War Office (1870b: 181)

27. Great Britain, War Office (1886: 393)

28. Letter (1851)

29. Letter (1855b); Letter (1855c); Letter (1855d)

30. Owen (1871: 144); Great Britain, War Office (1870b: 182–184, 186); Great Britain, Ordnance Dept. (1865a: 102)

31. Scoffern (1852: 134); Great Britain, Ordnance Dept. (1865a: 102)

32. Hale, patent (1844a); Hale, patent (1860); Great Britain, War Office (1870b: 182); Great Britain, Ordnance Dept. (1877: 6–7); Hale, Jr., patent (1873)

33. Great Britain, War Office (1870b: 183)

34. Great Britain, Ordnance Dept. (1878a: 184)

35. Great Britain, Ordnance Dept. (1878a: 174)

36. Great Britain, Ordnance Dept. (1878b: 78)

37. Owen (1871: 144)

38. Great Britain, War Office (1870b: 186)

39. Owen (1871: 144); Wolseley (1882: 40–41)

40. Cole (1878: 9, 16, 18); Great Britain, War Office (1881: 308, 400); Wolseley (1882: 40–41)

41. Mauncy (1962: 14)

42. Rogers (1971: 101–102, 115)

43. Rogers (1971: 117–118, 120, 124)

44. Wolseley (1882: 400)

Chapter 11

1. Gordon (1962:202); Browne (1867:452–453, 457–458); Chapman (1880: 182, 197–199); Simpson (1891:201)
2. Henty (1874: 411–412)
3. Great Britain, War Office (1870a:2:37, 57–58, 473); Napier (1927:240–243)
4. Napier (1927: 21)
5. Brackenbury (1874: 1: 63, 94–95, 126, 254–255); Maurice (1874: 113, 328)
6. Brackenbury (1874: 1: 206); Morris (1965: 32–323, 327, 355, 359)
7. Ashe and Edgell (180: 48, 50, 157); Morris (1965: 368); Grant (n.d.: 4: 230, 303); Headlam (1940: 3: 294)
8. Morris (1965: 327); Grant (n.d.: 4: 303)
9. Morris (1965: 462); Headlam (1940: 3: 294)
10. Shaw (1929–1930: 335, 337); Carter (1903: 260–261)
11. Headlam (1940: 2: 21)
12. Slade (1881: 257, 262); Grant (n.d.: 4: 16, 29)
13. Mansel (1881: 267); Gordon (1962: 239)
14. Hickley (1895: 191–193, 196); Anon. (1882: 24); Royle (1900: 257, 543, 549); Grant (n.d.: 4: 392, 411, 417, 454, 611)
15. Headlam (1940: 3: 115); H.B. (1949: 89)
16. Headlam (1940: 3: 117)
17. Chalmers (1934: 33); Anon. (1949: 88)
18. Churchill (1900: 235)
19. Gordon (1962: 265); Great Britain, War Office (1915a: 21); Great Britain, War Office (1915b: 220)
20. J.H.L. (1921: 77); Great Britain, War Office (1892: 408); Headlam (1940: 1: 184)
21. Anon. (1921: 77); Hogg (1962: 2: 1379)

Chapter 12

1. Mariotte (1686: 187); Mandryka (1962: 447–460); Buffon (1742: 105–110); Desaguliers (1744: 62–65); [de la Hire] (1720: 11–13)
2. Congreve (1807: [1–81]); Moore (1813: 9, 24, 36, 39, 110–117)
3. Moore (1813: 32–33)
4. von Hauser (1819: 218–231); Meyer (1819: 1077–1079); von Sonnenfield (1850: *passim*)
5. Ruffini (1833: 56–78)
6. Munier (1830: 114–129); Kahl (1859: 279–284); Coquilhat (1873: 1–33)
7. Pralon (1883: 21, 24); Konstantinov (1861: 21); Sokol'skii (1967: 61–64)
8. Ruggieri (1802: 303–304); Anon. (1839a: 1133)
9. Ducarney-Blangy (1801: *passim*); Sharpe (n.d.: 2–3)
10. Sharpe (n.d.: 3)
11. Sharpe (n.d.: 4)
12. Sharpe (n.d.: 4)

13. Anon. (1809a: 398); Anon. (1810b: 188–292)

14. Sharpe (n.d.: 7); Anon. (1823a: 676–677)

15. Dennett (1832: 3–4)

16. Dennett (1832: 11–19); Dennett, patent (1838); Sharpe (n.d.: 13)

17. Sharpe (n.d.: 19–20)

18. Sharpe (n.d.: 20–22, 26); Winter and Sharpe (1974: 427–429)

19. Sharpe (n.d.: 21–22, 25–26); Carafoli and Nita (1972: 1: 3–5)

20. Sharpe (n.d.: 22–26)

21. Sharpe (n.d.: 26); Anon. (1887: 9239); Lewis (1874: 232–236); Anon. (1897: 2–3); Great Britain, Board of Trade (1881: *passim*); Gray Jones (1876: 164–168)

22. Sharpe (n.d.: 26)

23. Sharpe (n.d.: 29–32, 38–42); Anon. (1877c: 716); Hooper, patent (1876); Hale Jr., patent (1872)

24. Anon. (1822b: 66–69, 162)

25. Sharpe (n.d.: 42–45); Anon. (1872a: 276)

26. Sharpe (n.d.: 62–65); Anon. (1859: 194–199); France (1877: 12–15); de Bonnefoux (1854: 245–250); Figuier (1857: 307–312)

27. Methley (1912: 228)

28. Cutbush (1825: 544); Hodges (1832: 193–199); Barnett (n.d.: 45–55); Mater (1944: 14)

29. Sharpe (n.d.: 34–36); Sokol'skii (1967: 91–94)

30. Sharpe (n.d.: 55–57); Sokol'skii (1967: 91–94)

31. Sokol'skii (1967: 91–94)

32. Skoog (1974: 266)

33. Anon. (1872a: 276); Sharpe (n.d.: 58–65); Meijer (1880: 291–293); Meijer (1881: 49–53); de Br. (1880: 148–151)

34. Schmitt, de Jong and Winter (1980: 89)

35. Winter and Sharpe (1971: 361); Rogier (1818: 5)

36. Johnson (1959: 1: 76–77)

37. Congreve and Colquhoun, patent (1821); Anon. (1821: 102)

38. de Montgéry (1825: 660); Anon. (1854: 558); Anon. (1822a: 411–412)

39. Schmitt, de Jong, and Winter (1980: 22–27, 92, 71, 200–201); Johnson (1959: 1: 101–102)

40. Anon. (1879b: 1); Anon. (1877c: 565)

41. Tvede (1868: 50–69)

42. Johnson (1959: 1: 80); Mater (1944: 14)

43. Tvede (1968: 67–69); Winter and Sharpe (1971: 351–352, 355, 359, 355); Anon. (1877c: 565); Schmitt, de Jong, and Winter (1980: 202–203)

44. Partington (1960: 203)

45. Endo (1960: 4); Paixhans (1821: 43–45)

46. Brussel de Brulard (1853: 81); de Montgéry (1825: 708–711, 735); Letter (1963b); Macaroni (1838: 454); Hale, patent (1856)

47. Barber (1874: 27–28)

48. Winter (1974a: 80–82); Bruce (1956: 177–178); Anon. (1862b: 3)

49. Winter (1974a: 81–82)

50. Ley (1958: 79); Hale (1863: 18–20)

51. Boffito (1928: 209–211); Winter (1969: 13)

52. Duhem (1943: 300); Glaisher, de Fonvielle, et al. (1871: 234–235)

53. Anon. (1846b: 370); Anon. (1871: 251)

54. Nye (1852: 14–20); N.B. (1853: 167–168)

55. Konstantinov (1857: 99–101)

56. Congreve, patent (1823); Anon. (1829: 616–619); Herschel (1828: 77–126); Kane (1900: 247)

57. de Montgéry (1825: 700–702); Ley (1964: 50); Denisse (1882: 83)

58. de Montgéry (1825: 713); Dennett (1832: 7–8); Bollaert (1870: 1: 290); Wilhelmi, patent (1891); Schneiter, patent (1870); Kronstein (1878: 46–47)

59. Anon. (1888: 263); Rohrmann, patent (1891; Sohlman (1950: 260–261); Nobel, patent (1896); Winter (1973b: *passim*)

60. Anon. (1892: 13631–13632)

61. Williams and Epstein (1958: 30)

Appendix

1. Anon. (1847b: 137); Walton (1973: 26)

2. Walton (1973: 26)

3. Letter (1974a)

4. Letter (1974a)

5. Letter (1974b)

6. Memorandum (1977)

7. Memorandum (1977)

8. National Air and Space Museum (1980)

9. National Air and Space Museum (1980)

10. Great Britain, War Office (1870b: 182; 1881: 303; 1887: 322)

11. Hogg (1963: 1377–1378)

12. Interview (1984)

13. Interview (1984)

14. Interview (1984)

Bibliography

Information not included on the title page of a source appears within brackets in this bibliography. In some cases where there is no article title, the subject of the article is enclosed within brackets. For the sake of brevity, some longer titles have been shortened.

Acosta, Juan F.
   1948   *Carlos Antonio Lopéz Obrero Maximo* (Asunción).

Amaral, António José do
   1879   *Nomenclature Explicada de Artilharia e Guia do Fogueteiro de Guerra* (Rio de Janeiro).

Amiguet, Maj. Frédéric
   1914   *Les Milices Vaudoises.* (Lausanne).

Ananoff, Alexandre
   1939   L'Histoire des Fusées. *La Nature* (Paris). 15 May 1939: 310.

Anderson, Col. William
   1862   *Sketch of the Mode of Manufacturing Gunpowder at Ishapore Mills* (London).

Anon.

1805a   Floating Mortar Battery. *The Naval Chronicle* (London). 13: 193.
1805b   Expresses from off Boulogne, and from Dover. *The Times* (London). 23 Nov.: 2: 3.
1805c   Operations off Boulogne. *The Times* (London). 25 Nov.: 3: 2–3.
1806   *Le Moniteur Universel* (Paris). 15 Oct.: 1.
1807a   Ship News [and other untitled item about rockets at Copenhagen]. *The Times* (London). 6 Aug.: 3: 2, 4.
1807b   Mr. Congreve's Rockets [at Copenhagen]. *The Times* (London). 26 Sept.: 2: 1–2.
1807c   [Congreve rockets at Copenhagen] *The Times* (London). 5 Oct.: 2: 3.
1809a   *The Naval Chronicle* (London). 21: Jan.–Jun.: 398.
1809b   Confutation of the Pretended Discovery of the Congreve Rockets by the French. *The Times* (London). 27 Oct.: 3: 4.
1810a   English Incendiary Fusees Examined. *The Emporium* (Philadelphia). 1: 399–400.
1810b   Correspondence. *The Naval Chronicle* (London). 21: Jan.–Jun.: 188–190; 291–292.
1812a   *The Examiner* (London). 11 Oct.: 648.
1812b   *The Examiner* (London). 18 Oct.: 659.
1813a   *Annual Register* (London). 55: 21.
1813b   Spring Rocket [of John Beath]. *Naval Chronicle* (London). 30: 2.
1813c   Congreve Rocket. *National Intelligencer* (Washington, D.C.). 5 June: 1.
1813d   Congreve Rocket. *The Enquirer* (Richmond). 15 June: 4: 1.
1814a   *Annual Register* (London). 56: 134.
1814b   Surrender of Alexandria, et al. *Niles Weekly Register* Supplement (Baltimore). 7: 144–161.
1814c   *The Enquirer* (Richmond). 15 June: 4.
1814d   Congreve Rocket. *Boston Gazette* (Boston). 28 Jul.: 2.
1814e   *Baltimore Telegraph* (Baltimore). 27 Aug.: 2.
1814f   Congreve Rocket. *Niles Weekly Register* (Baltimore). 6: 20 Aug.: 425.
1814g   *New York Evening Post* (New York.) 29 Aug.: 3.
1814h   Rocket Battery. *Boston Gazette* (Boston). 22 Sept.: 2: 5.
1814i   Miscellaneous Items of News, &c. [rockets of M. de Fauvel]. *Boston Gazette* (Boston). 26 Sept.: 2: 5.
1814j   Rocket Battery. *Niles Weekly Register* (Baltimore). 7: 6 Oct.: 55.
1814k   Defence of Stonington. *Niles Weekly Register* (Baltimore) 7: 5 Nov.: 130–133.
1814l   *Niles Weekly Register* (Baltimore). 7: 17 Dec.: 247–248.
1815a   Expedition to Algiers. *The Albany Argus* (Albany, N.Y.). 25 Apr.: 3: 1–2.
1815b   [*Erebus* rocket ship, return of]. *The Times* (London). 1 May: 3: 3.
1821a   *Annual Register* (London). 63: 102.
1821b   Sir William Congreve's Zündraketen. *Militär-Wochenblatt* (Berlin). 4: 1 Dec.: 2057–2058.
1822a   Lettre du Capitaine Kay, Relative a l'Emploi des Fusées à la Congreve

pour la Pêche de la Baleine. *Annales Maritimes et Coloniales* (Paris). 2: 2: 411–412.

1822b   [Correspondence]. *Algemeene Konst- en Letter-Bode* (Haarlem, Holland). 1: 66–69, 162.

1823a   Anchor-Rockets. *The Imperial Magazine* (London). 5: Jul.: 676–677.

1823b   Rockets. *New Monthly Magazine* (London). 1 Dec.: 510.

1824a   *Gentleman's Magazine* (London). 94: 2: 640.

1824b   Explosion at Sir William Congreve's Rocket Manufactory. *Supplement to The Morning Chronicle [The Times]* (London). 12 June: 2: 4.

1824c   *India Gazette* (Calcutta). 3 June: 42.

1825   Capt. Parlby's Rockets. *Asiatic Journal* (London). 19: Mar.: 285–286.

1826   Miscellen. *Allgemeine Militär-Zeitung* (Leipzig). 50: 20 Dec.: 398.

1827   Rocket Life Preservers. *The Naval and Military Magazine* (London). 2: Sept.: 313–314.

1828a   [obit., Sir William Congreve] *Journal Politique et Literaire de Toulouse.* (Toulouse). 21 May: 4.

1828b   Sir. Wm. Congreve, Bart. F.R.S. [obit.]. *The Gentleman's Magazine* (London). 98: Aug.: 2.

1828c   *The Annual Register* (London). 236.

1829a   General Orders. Indian Army. Calcutta. Rockets and Rocket-Troop. *United Service Journal* (London). 1: Feb.: 252–253.

1829b   Memoir of Major General Robert Ross. *United Service Journal* (London). 1: Apr.: 412–416.

1829c   Capt. W.F.W. Owen's plan for Rating Chronometers. *United Service Journal* (London). 1: May: 616–619.

1831   [From the journal of an officer of Lord Exmouth's fleet] Algiers in 1816. *United Service Journal* (London). 29: Feb.: 177–189.

1832a   *The Mirror* (London). 19: 14 Apr.: 249.

1832b   The Siege of Acre and Military Resources of Egypt. *United Service Journal* (London). 9: Jun.: 220–224.

1832c   *Essex Standard and Colchester County Advertiser* (Colchester, England). 15 Sept.: 2.

1832d   (From the *Chronica Constitutional.*) Oporto. Sept. 18. *The Times* (London). 27 Sept.: 2: 3.

1833   Experiments at Yarmouth with Apparatus for Saving Life. *The Naval Magazine* (London). 2: 861–862.

1834   Substitution de la Presse Hydraulique au Mouton dans le Chargement des Fusées. *Journal des Armes Spéciales* (Paris). 1: 1: 457–461.

1835a   *Annual Register* (London). 80.

1835b   Note sur les Fusées a la Congreve. *Spectateur Militaire* (Paris). 18: Jan.: 458–459.

1835c   Congreve Rockets. *The Military and Naval Magazine of the United States* (Washington, D.C.). 5: Apr.: 144.

1835d   Expériences faites a la Fère, sur les Fusées de Guerre anglais et françaises en Janvier 1834. *Journal des Sciences Militaires* (Paris). 2: 9: Feb.: 135–150.

1836a   Overzigt van de Hier te Lande Genomene Proeven met Oorlogs-Vuurpijlen. *De Militaire Spectator* (Breda, Holland). 5: 113–114.

1836b   Some Recollections of the Battle of Algiers [by "An Officer Serving Aboard the Queen Charlotte"]. *United Service Journal* (London). Sept.: 35–41.

1837a   Rocket Communication with Distressed Vessels. *Nautical Magazine* (London). 1: 400–402.

1837b   Versuche mit Kriegsraketen in Griechland. *Helvetische Militär-Zeitshrift* (Bern). 4: 5: 80.

1837c   Rocket Communication with Vessels in Distress. *Army and Navy Journal* (Washington, D.C.) 5: 21 Sept.: 181.

1838a   Manuel Historique de la Technologie des Armes a Feu. *Journal des Sciences Militaires* (Paris). 22: April: 1–64.

1838b   Üeber Kriegsraketen als Ersass für die ehemaligen Bataillons-Kanonen. *Helvetische Militär-Zeitschrift* (Bern). 5: 5: 77–80.

1839a   Nouvel essai de fusées de sauvetage, à Boulogne. *Annales Maritimes et Coloniales* (Paris). 24: 2: 1133.

1839b   Egypt and Mehemet Ali. *United Service Journal* (London). 31: Nov.: 289–299.

1840a   *Annual Register* (London). 82: 541–542.

1840b   Military Establishments and Discipline of the Chinese. *United Service Journal* (London). 32: Jan.: 19.

1841a   *Annual Register* (London). 83: 43.

1841b   Die Rachette [sic], als Waffe für de Schweiz. *Helvetische Militar-Zeitschrift* (Berne). 8: 160–184.

1841c   Persia: The Artillery. *United Service Journal* (London). 36: May: 104–105.

1842   Notices of the Naval and Military Establishments of Greece. *United Service Journal* (London). 39: May: 72–78.

1844a   Cohetes a la Congrewe [sic]. *Memorial de Artillería* (Madrid). 1: 30 Nov. : 273–278.

1844b   De L'Organisation de l'Artillerie . . . *Journal des Science Militaires* (Paris). 3: 20: Dec.: 361–398.

1846a   Hale's War Rocket. *Mechanic's Magazine* (London). 144: 4 Apr.: 256.

1846b   *Illustrated London News* (London). 8: 6 June: 370.

1847a   The Rocket Battery at St. Lorenzo, on the Parana. *United Service Journal* (London). 53: April: 562–575.

1847b   Mr. Hale's War Rockets. *Jone's Woolwich Journal* (Woolwich). 5: Sept.: 137.

1849a   *The London Gazette* (London). 2: 3287.

1849b   Köngriech Sachsen. *Allgemeine Militär-Zeitung* (Leipzig and Darmstadt). 115: 25 Sept.: 913–914.

1850a   *The London Gazette* (London). 1: 750.

1850b   Bayern. *Allgemeine Militär-Zeitung* (Leipzig and Darmstadt). 43: 9 Apr.: 342.

1850c   Bayern. *Allgemeine Militär-Zeitung* (Leipzig and Darmstadt). 45: 13 Apr. 357–358.

1850d   Experiments with Rockets. *The Times* (London). 27 May: 5: 3.

1850e   Experiments with Rockets at Shoeburyness. *Jone's Woolwich Journal* (Woolwich). 6: Jun.: 87.

1850f   Bayern. *Allgemeine Militär-Zeitung* (Leipzig and Darmstadt). 112: 17 Sept.: 890.

1850g   Kongreich Sachsen. *Allgemeine Militär-Zeitung* (Leipzig and Darmstadt). 123: 12 Oct.: 978–979.

1850h   Mr. Hale's Rockets. *Jone's Woolwich Journal* (Woolwich). 6: Dec.: 185.

1851a   Bayern. *Allgemeine Militär-Zeitung* (Leipzig and Darmstadt). 98: 16 Aug.: 788–789.

1851b   Württemburg. *Allgemeine Militär-Zeitung* (Leipzig and Darmstadt). 99: 19 Aug.: 801.

1851c   Württemburg. *Allgemeine Militär-Zeitung* (Leipzig) 105: 2 Sept.: 857.

1851d   Württemburg. *Allgemeine Militär-Zeitung* (Leipzig) 107: 6 Sept.: 873–874.

1852   *Aide-Mémoire to the Military Sciences* (London). 3: 348–353.

1853a   Joseph, Bem. *Nouvelle Biographie Universelle* (Paris). 5: 310–311.

1853b   Bayern. *Allgemeine Militär-Zeitung* (Leipzig). 30: 10 Mar.: 249–250.

1853c   Bayern. *Allgemeine Militär-Zeitung* (Leipzig). 36: 24 Mar.: 298–299.

1853d   *Annual Register* (London). [Apr.]: 55–56.

1853e   Bayern. *Allgemeine Militär-Zeitung* (Leipzig). 49: 23 Apr.: 402.

1853f   The War Rocket Factory and the Government. *The Times* (London). 29 Apr.: 7.

1853g   The Witness Against M. Kossuth. *The Examiner* (London). 30 Apr.: 275.

1853h   *The Examiner* (London). 1 May: 292.

1853i   Grossbritannien. *Abendblatt der Öesterreichische Kaiserlichen Weiner Zeitung* (Vienna). 6 May: 407.

1853j   Parliamentary Intelligence. House of Commons . . . Prosecution of Mr. Hale. *The Times* (London). 6 May: 3: 3–5; 4: 1.

1853k   Bayern. *Allgemein Militär-Zeitung* (Leipzig). 56: 10 May: 457.

1853l   Bayern. *Allgemein Militär-Zeitung* (Leipzig). 74:21 June: 601.

1853m   Bayern. *Allgemeine Militär-Zeitung* (Leipzig). 131: 1 Nov.: 1065.

1854a   What Is a Congreve Rocket? *Littell's Living Age* (London). 41: 17 Jun.: 556–558.

1854b   Hale's Rockets and Musket Rockets. *Mechanic's Magazine* (London). 18 Nov.: 21.

1855   War Rockets and Their Manufacture. *The London Illustrated News* (London). 26: 22 Apr.: 411.

1856a   Augustin, Vincenz Freiherr. *Biographic Lexicon des Kaiserthums Österreich* (Vienna). 1: 90–91.

1856b   Kurze Notizen über die Persische Armee. *Archiv für Offizieren der Königlich Preussischen Artillerie und Ingenieur-Corps*. (Berlin). 39: 180–184.

1857   *Harper's Weekly* (New York). 1: 7 Mar.: 153.

1858   Report of Experimental Rocket Practice in Canada *Minutes of Proceedings of the Royal Artillery Institution* (Woolwich). 1: 48–53.

1859   Appareils de Sauvetage. *Bulletin de la Société d'Encouragement* (Paris). 58: 2: 6: 194–199.

1860a   Öesterreichen Monarchie. *Allgemeine Militär-Zeitung* (Darmstadt). 22: 2 June: 259.

1860b   Niederlande. *Allgemeine Militär-Zeitung* (Darmstadt). 34: 1 Sept.: 416.

1861a   Formidable Weapon. *Scientific American* (New York). 5: 23 Nov.: 327.

1861b   *The Daily National Intelligencer* (Washington, D.C.). 11 Dec.: 3.

1862a   Our Military Budget . . . Self-Propelling Projectile. *The Evening Star* (Washington, D.C.). 23 Apr.: 2: 1.

1862b   Schooner Sunk. *The Evening Star* (Washington, D.C.). 11 Dec.: 3: 1.

1865   Öesterreichische Rotationsraketen. *Zeitschrift für die Schweizerische Artillerie* (Frauenfeld, Switzerland). Dec.: 14–15.

1866   Rocket Gun. *The Mechanic's Magazine* (London). 84: Feb.: 70.

1867a   *Memorial de l'Artillerie* (Paris). 8: 403.

1867b   Die Bundesbesbeschlusse über Umänderung von Artillerie Material und Umwandlung der Raketen-Batterien. *Zeitschrift für die Schweizerische Artillerie* (Berne). Aug.: 134–139.

1867c   [William Hale's rockets purchased by British Government]. *The Engineer* (London). 24: Dec.: 504.

1868a   Critical Notices. Treatise on . . . Vessels . . . Propelled by Steam Power. By William Hale, C.E. *Colburn's United Service Journal* (London). 117: June: 284–285.

1868b   *Üeber Land und Meer. Allgemeine Illustrierte Zeitung* (Stuttgart). 16: Sept.: 814.

1868c   Our Latest 'Little War;' or, Campaigning in Honduras. *Colburne's United Service Magazine* (London). 118: Sept. 52–59, Oct.: 212–218.

1869   *Artilleriski Zhurnal* (St. Petersburg). Aug.: 105–126.

1870a   Description of Shanghai Imperial Arsenal, in 1869. *Siam Repository* (Bangkok). 2: Apr.: 193–195.

1870b   Fusee Satan. *Scientific American* (New York). 23: 3 Dec.: 353.

1871   Transatlantic Clippings. *The Graphic* (London). 4: 9 Sept.: 251.

1872a   Rocket Apparatus and Life Boats in the Bosphorus. *The Nautical Magazine* (London). 41: Mar.: 276.

1872b   Fusées de Guerre. *Revue d'Artillerie* (Paris). 1: Nov.: 156–157.

1873   Rocket and Mortar Apparatus for Saving Life. *The Cornhill Magazine* (London). 20: July: 72–73.

1876   Adolphe Pictet [obit]. *Journal de Genève* 16 Jan.: p.unk.

1877a   New Projectiles—The War Rocket—Hale's Patent. *Army and Navy Journal* (New York). 14: 10 Feb.: 426.

1877b   *Army and Navy Journal* (New York). 14: 10 May: 662.

1877c   The New Method of Whaling. *The Wasp* (San Francisco). 28 July: 565.

1877d   Mr. Singleton Hooper. *The Broad Arrow* (London). 19: 1 Dec.: 716.

1878   *Jahresberichte über die Veränderung, und Fortschritte im Militärwesen* (Berlin). 5: 175.

1879a   War Rockets. *Scientific American Supplement* (New York). 7: 8 Feb.: 2580.

1879b   The Roys and Lilliendahl Whaling Rocket. *Mining and Scientific Press* (San Francisco). 5 Apr.: 1.

1882   The War in Egypt. *Illustrated London News* (London). 81: 22 July: 130.

1883   *Army and Navy Journal* (New York). 21: 4 Aug.: 18.

1886–87   *Die Geschichte des Feuerwerkwesens* (Berlin), 1.

1887   The British Life Saving Rocket Service. *Scientific American Supplement* (New York). 23: 5 Feb.: 9239.

1888   La Photo Fusée. *La Nature* (Paris). 116: 22 Sept.: 263.

1892   A Proposed Rain-Making Rocket. *Scientific American Supplement* (New York). 33: 7 May: 13631–13632.

1896   Collazo Safely Landed. Arms and Ammunition Furnished to the Cuban Insurgents. *New York Times* (New York). 19 Mar.: 5: 3.

1897   Life-Saving on Our Coasts. *The Navy and Army Illustrated* (London). 4: 28 May: 2–3.

1921   Questions. Rockets. *Journal of the Army Historical Research* (London). 1: Dec.: 77.

1935   Bem, Jozef Zacharjasz. *Polski Slownik Biograficzny* (Cracow). 1: 417.

1949   War Rockets in the Nineteenth Century. *Journal of the Society for Army Historical Research* (London). 27: Summer: 88.

d'Arcet [Joseph]
1814   Notice sur les fusées incendiaries de Congrêve. *Bulletin de la Sociétié d'Encouragement* (Paris). 3: 134–145.

Argentina, Republic of, Ministerio de Guerra
1868   *Memoria presentada por el Ministerio de Estado* (Buenos Aires).

Ashe, Maj. Waller, and Capt. E.V. Wyatt Edgell
1872   *The Story of the Zulu Campaign* (London).

Auchinleck, G.
1855   *A History of the War Between Great Britain and the United States of America* (Toronto).

Banerjee, Anil Chandra
1968   *Peshwa Madhav Rao I* (Calcutta).

Barber, Lt. Francis Morgan
1874   *Drifting and Automatic Moveable Torpedoes, Submarine Guns, and Rockets* (Newport, R.I.)

Barcena, José Maria Roa
1883   *Recuerdos de la Invasión Norte-America 1846–1848* (Mexico City).

Barnett, J.P.
1972   The Lifesaving Guns of David Lyle. *Nautical Research Journal* (Washington, D.C.). Spring: 21–26.

Barroso, Gustavo
    1929   *A Guerra do Rosas* (São Paulo).

Bassett, John Spencer, ed.
    1927   *Correspondence of Andrew Jackson* (Washington, D.C.), 2.

Becklake, E.J., and P.J. Turvey
    1987   Congreve at the Rotunda. *Journal of the British Interplanetary Society* (London). 40: July: 291–298.

Bell, Herbert C.F.
    1936   *Lord Palmerston* (London), 2.

Bem, Josef
    1820   *Erfahrungen über die Congrev'schen Brand-Raketen, bis zum Jahre 1819 in der Königl. Polnischen Artillerie* (Weimar).

Benham, Charles E.
    [1892]   *Colchester Worthies: A Biographical Index of Colchester* (London).

Berkeley, Hon. Sir George Cranfield
    1804   *The Trial of James Whiting, John Parsons and William Congreve* (Buckingham, England).

Bernard, W.D.
    1844   *Narrative of the Voyages and Services of the Nemesis* (London), 1–2.

Best, Félix
    1934   *Compendio de las Campañas Militares Argentinas* (Buenos Aires).

Beverina, Capt. Juan
    1911   *Caseros (3 de Febrero de 1852)* (Varese, Italy).
    1923   *Las Campañas de los Ejércitos Libertadores 1838–1852* (Buenos Aires).

Bingham, Cmdr. J. Elliot
    1843   *Narrative of the Expedition to China* (London), 2.

Birkheimer, William E.
    1884   *Historical Sketch of the . . . Artillery.* United States Army *(Washington, D.C.).*

Blackford, Lt. Col. William C
    1945   *J.E.B. Stuart* (New York).

[Boffito, Giuseppe] (B.G.)
    1928   Al Margini dell Storia l'Aeronautica nelle cittu Italiane. *Rivista Aeronautics* (Rome). 4: July: 209–211.

Bollaert, William
    1870   *The Wars of Succession of Portugal and Spain, from 1826* (London), 1.

de Bonnefoux, Capt.
  1854   Grappin Porte-Amarre de M. Tremblay. *Nouvelles Annales de la Marine et des Colonies* (Paris). 11: March: 245–250.

Bormann, Maj. Gen. [Charles William]
  1864   Memoir on Hail Shells and War Rockets, with accompanying letters. [Brussels]. Unpub. Records of the Quartermaster General, Record Group 92, National Archives.

Boston, City of
  1812–15   *Boston City Directories* (Boston).

Botelho, José Justino Teixera
  1921   *História Militar e Politica dos Portugêses em Moçambique* (Coimbra).

de Br.
  1880   De vuurpijltoestel van Kapt. Meijer. *De Zee* (Amsterdam). 2: 4: 148–151.

Brackenbury, Henry
  1874   *The Ashanti War.* (Edinburgh), 1–2.

Brant, Irving
  1961   *James Madison* (New York), 6.

Brazil, Minister of War
  1853   *Relatorio da Reparticao dos Negócios da Guerra* (Rio de Janeiro).
  1867   *Relatorio da Reparticao dos Negócios da Guerra* (Rio de Janeiro).
  1869   *Relatorio da Reparticao dos Negócios da Guerra* (Rio de Janeiro).
  1872   *Relatorio Apresentado á Assembléa Geral Legislativa* (Rio de Janeiro).
  1873   *Relatorio Apresentado á Assembléa Geral Legislativa* (Rio de Janeiro).

Brewster, David
  1830   Pyrotechny—Construction of Iron Rockets. *The Edinburgh Encyclopaedia* (Edinburgh), 17: 279–281.

Briggs, John
  1829   *History of the Rise of Mahomedan Power in India* (London), 3.

British East India Co.
  1800   *Copies and Extracts of Advices to and from India* (London).

Brock, Alan St. H.
  1949   *A History of Fireworks* (London).

Browne, Capt. C.O.
  1867   Mountain Train Formed for Service in Abyssinia. *Minutes of Proceedings of the Royal Artillery Institution* (Woolwich), 5: 452–458.

Bruce, Robert V.
  1956   *Lincoln and the Tools of War* (Indianapolis).

Brussel de Brulard, [Auguste]

1853   *Memoirs sur lés Fusées de Guerre Fabrique á Hambourg en 1813* (Paris).

Buckle, Capt. E.

1852   *Memoir of the Services of the Bengal Artillery* (London).

[Buffon, Georgés Louis Le Clerc, Compte de]

1742   Sur les Fusées Volantes. *Histoire de l'Académie Royale des Sciences* (Paris), 105–110.

Burton, Capt. Richard F.

1870   *Letters from the Battlefields of Paraguay* (London).

C.v.H.

1862   Die Raketen und das 3 pfundige Gebirgsgeschütz. *Österreichische Militär Zeitschrift* (Vienna). 4: 413–415.

Carnaticus, pseud.

1820   *Summary of the Mahrata and Pindarree War during 1817, 1818, and 1819* (London).

Carter, Thomas Fortescue

1903   *A Narrative of the Boer War* (London).

Chalmers, Rear Adm. W.S.

1934   *The Life and Letters of David, Earl Beatty* (London).

Chapman, Lt. E.F.

1880a   The Abyssinian Expedition. *Minutes of the Proceedings of the Royal Artillery Institution* (Woolwich). 6: 167–190.

1880b   Notes on the Equipment . . . Employed in Abyssinia. *Minutes of the Proceedings of the Royal Artillery Institution* (Woolwich). 6: 194–202.

Chatterton, Lady Georgiana

1861   *Memorials . . . of Admiral Lord Gambia* (London), 2.

Churchill, Winston S.

1899   *The River War* (London).

Clowes, Sir William Laird, et al.

1900–1903 *The Royal Navy—A History from the Earliest Times* (London), 5–7.

Cockburn, James

1858   Alteration in the Construction of Rockets. *Minutes of Proceedings of the Royal Artillery Institution* (Woolwich). 1: 42–46.

Cole, Joshua

1878   On an Improved War Rocket. *Journal of the Royal United Service Institution* (London). 21: 1–20.

Colombari, Col. F.

1853   Observations sur l'Armée Persane—artillerie de Campagne a Dromadaire. *Spectateur Militaire* (Paris). 2: 5: Sept.: 678.

Commission Militaire de la Exposition Universelle de 1867
1869   *Rapport de la Haute Commission Militaire—Exposition Universelle de 1867 à Paris* (Paris).

Conder, Josiah
1826   *The Modern Traveler* (London).

Confederate States of America, Army, Ordnance Dept.
1861   In War Dept., Collection of Confederate Records, Misc. Items, Orders and Circulars, Ordnance Dept. Unpub. Record Group 109, Entry 39. National Archives.

Congreve, William
ca. 1800   A Second Century of Inventions. Unpub. MS. 38844 in British Museum Library.
1806   *Memoir on the Possibility, the Means, and the Importance of the Destruction of the Boulogne Flotilla* (London).
1807   *A Concise Account of the Origin and Progress of the Rocket* (London).
1808   *Postscript to the Concise Account of the Origin and Progress of the Rocket System.* (London).
1809   *General View of a Complete Course of Experiments* (London).
1810   *The Different Modes of Use and Exercise of Rockets* (London).
ca. 1810   *General View of a Complete Course of Experiments . . . of the Rocket System.* (London).
1814   *Details of the Rocket System* (London).
1815   British patent No. 3937 for "Machine for the Manufacture of Gunpowder," 2 Jan.
1823   British patent No. 4853 for "Fireworks," 16 Oct.
1824   *An Appeal to the British East India Company* (London).
1825   *Sir William Congreve's Method of Saving the Crews* (London).
1827   *A Treatise on the General Principles . . . of the Rocket System* (London).

Congreve, Sir William, and James Nisbett Colquhoun
1821   British patent No. 4563 for "Application of Rockets to Destruction and Capture of Whales, &c.," 7 Dec.

Coquilhat [Casimir-Erasmé]
1873   Trajectories des Fusées Volantes dans le Vide. *Mémoires de la Société Royal des Sciences de Liége* (Brussels). 5: Nov.: 1–33.

Cordier, Henri
1906   L'Expédition de Chine de 1860 (Paris).

Coston, Martha J.
1882   *A Signal Success* (Philadelphia).

Court, Capt. C.A.
1888   The Russian Artillery in 1888. *Journal of the Royal United Service Institution* (London). 32: 274.

Cowan, James
  1956   *The New Zealand Wars—A History of the Maori Campaigns* (Wellington, New Zealand).

Cox, Hiram
  1821   *Journal of a Residence in the Burmhan Empire* (London).

Craig, Col. H.K.
  1851   Certificate of Col. H.K. Craig and Attestation of Hon. C.M. Conrad, Secretary of War. Unpub. 22 Oct. in U.S. Ordnance Papers, Record Group 156, National Archives.

Crauford, Quintin
  1790   *Sketches Chiefly Relating to the . . . Hindoos* (London).

Cunha Mallos, Raimundo José da
  1833   *Memorias da Campanha* (Rio de Janeiro), 2.

Cutbush, James
  1825   *A System of Pyrotechny* (Philadelphia).

Dahlgren, Madeleine Vinton
  1882   *Memoir of John A. Dahlgren* (Boston).

Dakin, Douglas

  1955   *British and American Philhellenes During the War . . . 1821–1833* (Thessalonika, Greece).

Dalkin, A.J.
  n.d.   Notes on 24-pounder Hale rocket in the Rotunda, Royal Artillery Museum, Woolwich, unpub. In "Hale Rockets" file, National Air and Space Museum.

Dauvé, Henri P.E.
  1890   *Historique de 12ᵉ Régiment d'Artillerie 1834–1890.* (Paris).

[Davis, Varina Howell]
  1890   *Jefferson Davis: A Memoir by His Wife* (New York), 2.

[de la Tour, Maistre] M.M.D.L.T.
  1848   *The History of Hyder Shah alias Hyder Ali Khan Bahadur* (London).

Denisse, Amedée
  1882   *Traité Practique Complet des Feux d'Artifice* (Paris).

Dennett, John
  1832   *A Concise Description of a Powerful Species of War Rockets* (London).
  1838   British patent No. 17759 for "Mortar and War Rockets," 2 Aug.

Desaguliers, J.T.
  1744   *A Course of Experimental Philosophy* (London).

Diaz, Gen. César
    1843   *Memorias 1842–1852* (Buenos Aires).

Dicey, Edward
    1864   *The Schleswig-Holstein War* (London), 2.

Dickson, Col. Sir Alexander
    1929   Artillery Services in North America in 1814 and 1815. *Journal of the Society of Army Historical Research* (London) 8: April, July, and Oct.: 220–222.

Dirom, Major
    1794   *A Narrative of the Campaign in India* (London).

Dolleczek, Anton
    1887   *Geschichte der Österreichische Artillerie* (Vienna).

Donelly, Ralph W.
    1961   Rocket Batteries in the Civil War. *Military Affairs* (Washington, D.C.) 25: Summer: 69–93.

Dontas, Domna N.
    1966   *The Last Phase of the War of Independence in Western Greece* (Thessalonika, Greece).

Ducarne-Blangy, M.
    1801   *A la Nation Francaise . . . Moyens propres a sauver les equipages d'une partie des Vaisseaux gui viennent échouer et perir a la côte* (Paris).

Duffey, George
    1861   In Compiled Service Records of Confederate General and Staff Officers & Non-Regimental Enlisted Men, Unpub. Microcopy 331, Roll No. 80, National Archives.

Duhem, Jules
    1943   *Histoire des Idées Aeronautiques avant Montgolfier* (Paris).

Duncan, Maj. Francis
    1872–73   *History of the Royal Regiment of Artillery* (London), 1–2.

Duncan, William R.
    1814   General Orders. *Niles Weekly Register* (Baltimore). 7: 15 Oct.: 68–69.

Duncombe, Thomas H.
    1868   *The Life and Correspondence of Thomas Slingsby Duncombe* (London), 2.

Dundonald, Thomas, 10th Earl of
    1859   *Narration of Services in . . . Chile, Peru, and Brazil* (London), 1.

Eca, Filipe Gastão de Almedia de
    1954   *História das Guerras no Zambeze* (Lisbon), 2.

Edwards, Lt. H.N., ed.
    1924   The Diary of Lieutenant C. Gilmor, R.N.—Portugal—1810. *Journal of the Army Historical Research* (London). 3: July: 148–156.

Egerton, Wilbraham
    1880   *An Illustrated Handbook of Indian Arms* (London).

Ellenborough, Lord
    1914   *The Guilt of Lord Cochrane* (London).

Elliott, H.M.
    1875   *The History of India as Told by Its Own Historians* (London), 4.

Emin-Pascha [Mahomet]
    1840   *Memoir sur un Nouveau Système de Confection des Fusées de Guerre* (Paris).

Endo, Koji, et al.
    1960   *Roketto kogaku* (Tokyo).

Englehardt, Armin
    1948   The Battle of Caseros—The Dawn of Modern Argentina. *Military Affairs* (Washington, D.C.). 12: Winter: 219.

Favre, Jules
    1884   *Louis XVII Plaidoire* (Paris).

Forbes, Archibald, G.A. Henty, et al.
    1897   *Battles of the Nineteenth Century* (London), 1–2.

Fortescue, John W.
    1924   *A History of the British Army* (London), 4.

Fragaso, Augusto Tasso
    História da Guerra entre a Tríplice Alanca e o Paraguai (Rio de Janeiro), 1–5.

France, Ministére de la Guerre
    1859   *Guerre d'Orient—Siège de Sebastopol—Historique du Service de l'Artillerie (1854–1856)* (Paris), 1–2.

Fyers, Capt. Peter
    1808   *Memoranda to Accompany Capt. Fyers' Plan of Copenhagen* (Colchester, England). Copy in the Royal Artillery Institution Library, Woolwich.

van Geen, J.J.
    1840   *Celebes* (Breda, Holland).

Glaisher, James, Wilfrid de Fonvielle, et al.
    1871   *Travels in the Air* (London).

Glover, Richard
    1963   *Peninsular Preparation* (Cambridge, England).

Gode, P.K.
    1939   Use of Guns and Gunpowder in India from A.D. 1400 Onwards. In *A Volume of Indian and Iranian Studies* (Bombay).

Goell, A.C.

1841a   U.S. Patent No. 1,986, "Improvement in the press employed for filling War Rockets."

1841b   U.S. Patent No. 2,009, "Improvement in machines for Boring War-Rockets."

Gold, Capt. Charles

1806   *Oriental Drawings* (London).

Gordon, Maj. Lawrence L.

1962   *British Battles and Medals* (Aldershot, England).

Graham, Gerald S., and R.A. Humphreys, eds.

1962   *The Navy and South America* (London). Navy Records Society Publications 94.

Grant, James

n.d.   *British Battles on Land and Sea* (London).

Gray Jones, Capt. C.

1876   The Rocket Apparatus and Its Work. *The Leisure Hour* (London). 25: 11 Mar.: 164–168.

Great Britain, Army

1859   List. Shewing the Number of Serviceable Congreve Rockets at the Various Stations. Unpub. Royal Artillery Institution Library, Woolwich.

Great Britain, Board of Trade, Marine Dept.

1881   *Tables Issued by the Board of Trade Relating to Life Salvage* (London).

Great Britain, Ordnance Dept.

1865a   *Extracts from the Proceedings of the Department of the Director of Artillery* (London). 3: 2: 102.

1865b   *Extracts from the Proceedings of the Department of the Director of Artillery* (London). 3: 4: 291–292.

1867   *Proceedings of the Ordnance Select Committee* (London), 5: 1.

1873   *Extracts from the Proceedings of the Department of the Director of Artillery* (London). 11: 7.

1877   *Extracts from the Proceedings of the Department of the Director of Artillery* (London). 15: 2: 57–58.

1878a   *Extracts from the Proceedings of the Department of the Director of Artillery* (London). 15: 3: 174.

1878b   *Extracts from the Proceedings of the Department of the Director of Artillery* London). 15: 6–7.

1878c   *Extracts from the Proceedings of the Department of the Director of Artillery* (London). 16: 2: 78.

Great Britain, Parliament

1853   *Hansard's Parliamentary Debates* (London). 126: 3: 452–453.

Great Britain, War Office
  1827   W.O. 44/505. Unpub. in Public Record Office, London.
  1848   W.O. 44/627/353. Unpub. in Public Record Office, London.
  1853   P.O. 44/627/354. Unpub. in Public Record Office, London.
  1855a   W.O. 44/644, Inventions—"Thunderbolt" [rocket] by Sir Wm Congreve, Ordnance Correspondence, Royal Laboratory. Unpub. in Public Record Office, London.
  1855b   W.O. 47/2752 and W.O. 47/2753. Unpub. in Public Record Office, London.
  1860   *Treatise on Ammunition* (London).
  1870a   *Record of the Expedition to Abyssinia* (London). 2.
  1870b   *Treatise on Ammunition* (London).
  1881   *Treatise on Ammunition* (London).
  1882   *The Armed Strength of Russia* (London).
  1886   *Priced Vocabulary of Stores Used in Her Majesty's Service* (London).
  1887   *Treatise on Ammunition* (London).
  1897   *Treatise on Ammunition* (London).
  1905   *Treatise on Ammunition* (London).
  1915a   *Priced Vocabulary of Stores Used in His Majesty's Service* (London).
  1915b   *Treatise on Ammunition* (London).

de Grunwald, Constantin
  1955   *Tsar Nicholas I.* (New York).

Gurwood, Lt. Col. John
  1838   *Dispatches of . . . The Duke of Wellington* (London). 6, 12.

Gutiérrez, Juan Barrios
  1963   Cohetes de Guerre en el Siglo XIX. *Revista de Historia Militar* (Madrid). 7:139–173.

H.B.
  1949   War Rockets in the Nineteenth Century. *Army Historical Research* (London). 27: Summer: 88.

Hake, A. Egmont
  1891   *Events in the Taeping Rebellion* (London).

Hale, William
  1827   British patent No. 5594 for "Improvements in Propelling Vessels," 22 Dec.
  1832   Account of a New Mode of Propelling Vessels in *Abstracts of the Papers Printed in the Philosophical Transactions of the Royal Society Proceedings* (London). 5: 3: 1830–1832: 48.
  1834   British patent No. 6649 for "Windmills," 26 July.
  1838   British patent No. 7586 for "Rotary Engine," 8 Mar.
  1844a   British patent No. 10,008 for "Improvements in Rockets," 11 Jan.
  1844b   Dutch patent No. 192 for "Improvements in Rockets," 4 Sept.
  1856   British patent No. 410 for "Marine Propulsion," 18 Feb.

1857	British patents No. 709 and 1510 for "Rolling Iron and Steel," 11 Mar. and 27 May, respectively.

1857   British patents No. 709 and 1510 for "Rolling Iron and Steel," 11 Mar. and 27 May, respectively.

1858   British patent No. 2497 for "Improvements in Rockets," 8 Nov.

1860   British patent No. 1578 for "Impelling Shells or Shot," 29 Jan.

1862   British patent No. 1220 for "Rockets," 24 Oct.

1863   *The Comparative Merits of a Rifle Gun and Rotary Rocket* (London).

1865   *Hale's War Rockets. Statements for the Referee* (London).

1867   British patent No. 479 for "Improvements in Propelling Vessels," 21 Feb.

1868   *Treatise on the Mechanical Means by Which Vessels are Propelled by Steam Power* (London).

1870   Death Certificate. No. 545605, Unpub. in General Register Office, Somerset House (London)

Hale, William, and George Purt

1842   British patent No. 9545 for "Aerated Liquors," 8 Dec.

Hale, William, and Edward Dell

1841   British patent No. 9047 for "Improvements in Cases and Magazines for Gunpowder," 13 Aug.

Hale, William, Jr.

1853   The Charge Against M. Kossuth. *The Lady's Newspaper* (London). 13: 23 Apr.: 261.

1873   British patent No. 2607 for "War Rocket Apparatus," 1 Aug.

1874   Rockets for Ashantee. *The Times* (London). 9 Jan.: 12: 1.

Hale's Rocket Co., Ltd., Board of Trade papers, B.T. 31/237c,

1875   Public Records Office, London

Halim, Abdul

1961   *History of the Lodi Sultan of Delhi and Agra* (Dacca, Pakistan).

Hauschild, Reinhard, and Hellmut H. Fuhring

1958   *Raketen* (Bonn).

von Hauser, Freiherrn

1819   Bemerkungen über die von dem Freiherrn von Hauser . . . ausgestellen Theorie der Raketen. *Öestreichische Militärische Zeitschrift* (Vienna). 1: 218–230.

Headlam, Maj. Gen. Sir John

1931–40   *The History of the Royal Artillery* (Woolwich), 3.

1944   The Use of Rockets in the Artillery. *The Journal of the Royal Artillery* (Woolwich). 71: 2: Apr.: 81–85.

Henderson, W.O.

1966   *J.C. Fischer and his Diary of Industrial England 1814–1851* (London).

Henty, G.A.

1874   *The March to Coomasie* (London).

Herschel, J.F.W.
    1828   Account of a Series of Observations . . . for the Purpose of Determining
                the Difference of Meridians of the Royal Observatories of Greenwich
                and Paris. *Philosophical Transactions of the Royal Society* (London). 1: 77–
                126.

Hickley, Lt. J.D.
    1895   An Account of the Operations on the Benin River in August and Septem-
                ber, 1894. *Journal of the Royal United Service Institution* (London). 39:
                Feb.: 191–198.

Hilton, Maj. Richard
    1957   *The Indian Mutiny* (London).

Hime, Henry W.L.
    1904.   *Gunpowder and Ammunition, their Origin and Progress* (London).

de la Hire, Phillipe
    1720   Sur les Effets du Ressort de L'Air dans la Poudre á Canon, & dans le
                Tonnerre. *Histoire de l'Acadèmie Royale des Sciences.* (Paris)

Hodges, Edward
    1832   Observations on the Preservation of Lives from Shipwreck, with a Sug-
                gestion for the Employment of Sky Rockets. *Journal of the Franklin
                Institute* (Philadelphia). 9: 193–199.

Hogg, Brig. O.F.G.
    1963   *The Royal Arsenal* (London), 1–2.

Hooper, James Humphrey Singleton
    1876   British patent No. 3871 for "Rockets for Saving Life, &c.," 6 Oct.

von Hoyer, Maj. Gen. D.J.G.
    1827   *System der Brandraketen nach Congreve und Andern* (Leipzig).

Hughes, B.P., Major-General
    1969   *British Smooth-bore Artillery: The Muzzle-loading Artillery of the 18th and
                19th Centuries* (Harrisburg, Pennsylvania).

Hughes, T.S.
    1830   *Travels in Greece and Albania* (London), 2.

Hume, Joseph.
    1808   [Hume's claim for the priority of Congreve rockets] *Gentlemen's Maga-
                zine* (London). 78 (Feb): 128–129.
    1811   Remarks on Military Rockets. *Nicholson's Journal of Natural Philosophy,
                Chemistry, and the Arts* (London). 28: 63–67.

Ineichen, Hugo
    1977   Die Schweizerischen Raketenbatterien im 19. Jahrhundert. *Bulletin
                Schweizerische Gessellschaft der Offiziere des Munitiondientes* (Matten-
                Interlaken). 2: 7–20.

International Astronomical Union

1970   *Lunar Nomenclature—Report of the Working Group of IAU Commission 17, The Moon—Proposed Names for Craters on the Moon's Far Side* (Brighton, England).

Interview

1984   With David Hallam, by author, Washington, D.C., 21 Dec. Notes in "Hale Rockets" file, National Air and Space Museum.

Irvine, William

1921   *Later Mughals,* edited by Jadunath Sarkar. (Calcutta).
1962   *The Army of the Indian Moghuls: Its Organization and Administration* (New Delhi).

J.H.L.

1921   Rockets. *Journal of Army Historical Research* (London). 1:Dec.:77.

Jackson, Melvin H., and Carol de Beer

1974   *Eighteenth Century Gunfounding* (Surrey, England).

Jahns, Max

1890   *Geschichte der Kriegswissenschaften Vornehmlich in Deutschland* (Munich), 2.

Jakobsson, Theodor

1940   Kongl. Raket Corpsen. *Förenings Armémusei Vänner* (Stockholm). 3: 72–95.

James, Charles

1810   *A New and Enlarged Military Dictionary* (London), 2.
1816   *An Universal Military Dictionary in English and French* (London), 2.

Jensen, Lt. Col. B. Allerslev

1959   Fra Leipzig til London. *Dansk Artilleri Tidsskrift* (Copenhagen). 3: June: 67–79.

Jesser, Moritz

1868   August Friedrich Ritter von Schmidt . . . Nekrolog. *Österreichische Militärische Zeitschrift* (Vienna). 9: 7: 191–195.

Jocelyn, Col. J.R.J.

1906   The Connection of the Ordnance Department . . . with Fire-works, Including Some Account of . . . Sir William Congreve (2nd Baronet). *Journal of the Royal Artillery* (Woolwich). 32: 11: Feb.: 481–503.
1915   *The History of the Royal and Indian Artillery in the Mutiny of 1857* (London).

Johnsen, Arne Odd

1959   *Den Moderne Hvalfangst Historie* (Oslo), 1.

Jones, Capt. Oliver J.

1859   *Recollections of a Winter Campaign in India in 1857–58* (London).

Kaestlin, Maj. J.P.

    1957a   Lieutenant General William Whish. *The Journal of the Royal Artillery* (Woolwich). 89: Jan.: 25–29.

    1957b   Who Killed Cock Robin? Notes on Our Indian Rocket Troops. *The Journal of the Royal Artillery* (Woolwich). 84: 4: Oct.: 291–299.

Kahl, Emil

    1859   Ueber die Berechnung der Steighöhe der Raketen. *Zeitschrift für Mathematik und Physik* (Leipzig). 4: 279–284.

[Kane, John]

    1900   *List of Officers of the Royal Regiment of Artillery* (Woolwich).

Kaiser, Hans K.

    1954   *Les Fusées* (Paris).

Kaye, John William

    1857   *History of the War in Afghanistan* (London).

Kellemes, Andor Melczer von

    1857   *Grundzuge über den Gebrauch der Artillerie im Felde und der Kriegswaffen Uberhaupt* (Vienna).

Kellersberger, Lt. Col. Getulius

    1963   The First (and Last) Rocket Battery of the Confederate Army. *Civil War Times* (Valley Forge, Pa.). June: 24–25.

Kirbus, Federico B.

    1968   El Desarollo de los Cohetes. *Boletin del Centro Naval* (Buenos Aires). Jan.–Mar.: 88.

Kirkpatrick, William

    1811   *Select Letters* (London).

Knollys, Henry

    1875   *Incidents in the China War of 1860* (London).

Knox, Dudley W.

    1946   Early Use of Rocket Weapons. *U.S. Naval Institute Proceedings* (Annapolis, Md.). 20: Feb.: 257–261.

Kolinski, Charles J.

    1965   *Independence or Death! The Story of the Paraguayan War* (Gainesville, Fla.).

Konstantinov, Konstantin I.

    1854   *Vozdushoplavania* (St. Petersburg).

    1855   O vvenia i oopotrebdeniya boevichya raketya. *Morskoi Sbornik* (St. Petersburg). 18: 10: 261–299.

    1861   *Lectures sur les Fusées de Guerre* (Paris).

    1863   *Application des Fusées au Jet des Amarres de Sauvetage* (St. Petersburg).

    1865   Nekotorye svedeniya o nyneshnem sostoyanii raketnogo. *Artilleriiskii Zhurnal* (St. Petersburg). 9: 226–228.

1869   Boyevyya rakety v Abissinsky expeditsii—Vrashchtel'noye drizheniye
            dlya napravleniya raket. *Artilleriski Zhurnnal* (St. Petersburg). 8: 105–126.

Kronstein, Max
1978   *The Airpost Journal* (Albion, Pa.). 50: Nov.: 46–47.

Kruger, A.
1867   *Chronik der Stadt und Festung Spandau* (Berlin).

Kuntzemuller, Otto
1881   *Urkundliche Geschichte der Stadt und Festung Spandau* (Spandau).

Lake, Col. Atwell
1857   *Narrative of the Defense of Kars* (London).

Lal, Mohan
1846   *Life of the Amir Dost Mohammed Khan of Kabul* (London).

Lallemand, H.
1820   *A Treatise on Artillery* (New York).

Lane, Maj. F.W.
1889   *Memoir of Maj. Henry Bowyer Lane of the Royal Artillery* (Usk, England).

Langhans, Dr. A.
1938   Geschichtestafeln der Werhrchemie. *Zeitschrift für das gesamte Schiess und
            Sprengstoffwesen* (Munich). 33: Dec.: 24–28.

Latham, Capt. H.B.
1930   The Rocket Service and the Award of the Swedish Decorations. *The
            Journal of the Royal Artillery* (Woolwich). 56: Jan.: 419–452.
1949   The Disbandment of the Rocket Troop in 1816. The Last Word. *Journal of
            the Royal Artillery* (Woolwich). 76: Oct.: 277–280.

Latour, A. [rsene] Lacarriere
1816   *Historical Memoir of the War in West Florida and Louisiana in 1814–15*
            (Philadelphia).

Laughton, Sir John Knox, ed.
1949   *Letters and Papers of Charles, Lord Barham, Admiral of the Red Squadron,
            1758–1813, Vol. 3.* (London), Navy Records Society Publications, 39.

Leigh, Ione
1951   *Castlereagh* (London).

Lenman, Bruce
1968   The Weapons of War in 18th Century India. *Journal of the Army Historical
            Research* (London). 56: Spring: 33–43.

Leslie, Maj. J.H.
1913   Swedish Medals Granted to the Rocket Brigade, R.H.A., for the Battle of
            Leipzig, October 16–18, 1813. *The Journal of the Royal Artillery* (Wool-
            wich). 40: Oct.: 327–332.

1924–25   The Services of the Royal Regiment of Artillery in the Peninsular War, 1808 to 1814. *Journal of the Royal Artillery* (Woolwich). 51: Oct.: 242–244.

Letters

1785   Congreve, William (the younger) to his father. Unpub. in Royal Artillery Institution Library, Woolwich, England.

1809   Capt. Guillaume Marcelin Proteau, 21 June. Unpub. Ministere d'État Charge de la Defense Nationale (Marine), État-Major, Service Historique, Paris.

1810   William Congreve to Board of Ordnance, 27 Nov. Unpub., W.O. 44/642, Public Record Office, London.

1813a   George Bomford to Ordnance Dept., 29 Mar. Unpub. Record Group 156, Special Files Ex-8–1, U.S. Ordnance Dept. National Archives.

1813b   J. Ellison, testamonial, 3 Apr. Unpub. Record Group 156, Entry 199. National Archives.

1813c   William Congreve to Board of Ordnance, 11 Nov., in W.O. 44/642, Public Record Office, London.

1814a   Joshua Barney to Sec. of the Navy, 9 June. Unpub. Record Group 45. National Archives.

1814b   Capt. Alden Partridge to Ordnance Office, 9 Sept. Unpub. Record Group 156, Special Files Ex-4 & 5-#3, U.S. Ordnance Office. National Archives.

1836   Capt. Benjamin Huger to Col. George Bomford, 5 Sept. Unpub. Record Group 156, Book 27, No. 10. National Archives.

1839   Lt. Col. George Talcott to Sec. of War, 8 Apr. Unpub. Record Group 156, Letters Sent, 7: 72. National Archives.

1840   Alvin C. Goell to Capt. John Symington, 9 Nov. Record Group 156. National Archives.

1846a   Thomas Aspinwall to Lt. Col. J. Talcott, 3 Sept. Record Group 156. National Archives.

1846b   R.G. Fairbanks and J.B. Hyde to Thomas Aspinwall, 26 Sept. Unpub. Record Group 156. National Archives.

1849   K. Stolzman to Ferenc Pulszky, 16 May. Ferenc Pulszky Archives, Budapest.

1851   Robert Hale to U.S. Ordnance Dept., 16 May. Unpub. Record Group 156. National Archives.

1852a   John Tylden to James Nasmyth, 7 Sept. Unpub. W.O. 44/644, Public Record Office, London.

1852b   James Nasmyth to John Tylden, 13 Oct. Unpub. W.O. 44/644, Public Record Office, London.

1852c   John Tylden to James Nasmyth, 30 Oct. Unpub. W.O. 44/644, Public Record Office, London.

1852d   James Nasmyth to John Tylden, 1 Nov. Unpub. W.O. 44/644, Public Record Office, London.

1852e   John Tylden to Board of Ordnance, 17 Nov. Unpub. W.O. 44/644, Public Record Office, London.

1855a   Capt. William Maynadier to G.T. Balch, 16 July. Unpub. Letters to Ordnance Office, v. 15, p. 305, Record Group 156, National Archives, Washington, D.C.

1855b   Robert Hale to Jefferson Davis, 13 Nov. Unpub. Record Group 156. National Archives.

1855c   Maj. William H. Bell to Jefferson Davis, 16 Nov. Unpub. Record Group 156. National Archives.

1855d   Maj. W.H. Bell to Col. H.K. Craig, 17 Nov. 1855. Unpub. Record Group 156. National Archives.

1855e   Robert Hale to Messrs. Dupont de Nemours, 8 Dec. and other letters in this series. Unpub. Dupont Archives, Wilmington, Del.

1858   Robert Hale to H.K. Craig, 16 Feb. Unpub. Record Group 156. National Archives.

1861a   J. Walsh Crane, Jr. to Simon Cameron, 30 Aug. Unpub. Record Group 156. National Archives.

1861b   Thomas William Lion to Sec. of War, 1 Oct. Unpub. Letters Received by Sec. of War, Microcopy No. 492, Roll 8, Frames 1061–1062. National Archives.

1861c   William Hale, Jr., to George Schuyler, 18 Oct., with testamonial from Capt. R. Twopenny. Unpub. Record Group 156. National Archives.

1861d   Charles Lattimer to George L. Schuyler, 4 Nov. Record Group 156. National Archives.

1863a   H. Freeman Morse to Edward M. Stanton, 14 May. Record Group 156. National Archives.

1863b   H. Freeman Morse to Edward M. Stanton, 3 July. Unpub. Record Group 156. National Archives.

1865a   Robert Hale to Gen. A.B. Dyer, 2 Dec. Unpub. Record Group 156. National Archives.

1865b   Robert Hale to U.S. Ordnance Dept., 29 Dec. Record Group 156. National Archives.

1962a   P.A.H.J. van Aarsen to author, 23 May. In "Rockets, Holland, 19th Cent." file, National Air and Space Museum.

1962b   Associazione Nazionale Granatieri di Sardegna to author, 28 Nov. In "Italy, Rockets, 19th Cent." file, National Air and Space Museum.

1963a   Sächsische Landesbibliothek to author, 29 Oct. In "Germany, 1800–1899 Rockets" file, National Air and Space Museum.

1963b   Tulane University to author, 3 Oct. In "Torpedoes, Rocket" file, National Air and Space Museum.

1963c   Sächsisches Landeshauptarchiv to author, 9 Nov. In "Germany, 1800–1899 Rockets" file, National Air and Space Museum.

1964   Genikon Epiteleion Stratoy, Athens, to author, 18 Jan. In "Greece, Rockets, 19th Cent." file, National Air and Space Museum.

1968a   Botelho Machado to Mitchell R. Sharpe, 26 Jan. In "Latin America, Rockets, 19th Cent." file, National Air and Space Museum.

1968b   Archivdirektion Stuttgart to author, 9 Sept. In "Germany, 1800–1900, Rockets" file, National Air and Space Museum.

1968c   P.R. Gifford to author, Borough of Colchester Public Library, Colchester, England, 17 Nov. and 22 Nov. In "Hale, William" file, National Air and Space Museum.

1968d   French Patent Office to author, 19 Nov. In "Hale, William" file, National Air and Space Museum.

1968e   Ministry of Public Building and Works, Brompton Cemetery, London, to author, 16 Dec. In "Hale, William" file, National Air and Space Museum.

1968f   University of Chicago to Mitchell R. Sharpe, 11 June. [Includes letters from Thomas Cooper to James Madison, 18 Feb 1813, and from Thomas Williamson to James Madison, 15 Apr. 1816] In "Rocketry, U.S., 19th Cent." File, National Air and Space Museum.

1969a   John Bensusan Butt, Colchester, England, to author, 14 March. In "Hale, William" file, National Air and Space Museum.

1969b   Österreichische Stadtsarchiv—Kriegsarchiv to author, Vienna, 6 June. In "Hale, William" file, National Air and Space Museum.

1973a   Mrs. L.T. Callahan to author, 8 Mar. In "Lion, Thomas William" file, National Air and Space Museum.

1973b   Jeremy Norman, San Francisco, to author, 3 Apr. In "France, Rockets, 19th Cent." file, National Air and Space Museum.

1974a   Nederlandsch Historisch Scheepvaart Museum, The Hague, to author, 17 Jan. In "Holland, Rockets, 19th Cent." file, National Air and Space Museum.

1974b   Col. John S. Weeks to F.C. Durant, III, 13 May. Copy in "Hale Rockets" file, National Air and Space Museum.

1974c   F.C. Durant, III to Col. John S. Weeks, 21 May. Copy in "Hale Rockets" file, National Air and Space Museum.

1984   Society of the Middle Temple, London, to author, 8 Nov. Copy in "William Congreve" file, National Air and Space Museum.

Lettow-Vorbek, Oscar
1869   *Geschichte des Kriegs von 1866 in Deutschland* (Berlin), 1.

Lewis, Richard
1874   *History of the Life-Boat, and its Work* (London).

Ley, Willy
1958   *Rockets, Missiles and Space Travel* (New York).
1964   *Missiles, Moonprobes and Megaparsecs* (New York).

Life Saving and War Rocket Co., Ltd., Board of Trade
1877   papers, B.T. 31/11562, Public Records Office, London.

Lion, Thomas William
1865   U.S. Civil Pension. Unpub. No. 1,014,603. National Archives.

Lloyd, Bvt. Col. F.T.
1895   Report of the Operations of the Royal Artillery in the Soudan in Febru-

ary and March, 1884. *Minutes of Proceedings of the Royal Artillery Institution* (Woolwich). 13: 38.

Lloyd, Christopher, and Hardin Craig, Jr., eds.
1952   Congreve's Rockets 1805–1806. in *The Naval Miscellany, Vol. 4* (London). Publications of the Naval Records Society. 92: 424–468.

Log of the *Erebus* rocket ship
1814   Unpub. ADM 51/2401, v. 8. Public Record Office, London.

London, International Exhibition, 1862
1862   *Official Catalogue of the Industrial Department.* (London).
1863   *Reports by the Jurists* (London).

London, Post Office
1848   *London Post Office Directory* (London).
1859   *London Post Office Directory* (London).
1860   *London Post Office Directory* (London).

Llave y Garcia, Joaquin de la
1896   *Lecciones de Artillería* (Madrid).

Los, Roman
1969   *Artyleria Krolestwa Polskiego 1815–1831* (Warsaw).

Lyle, D.A.
1880   *Annual Report of the . . . U.S. Life-Saving Service* (Washington, D.C.).

Lunsmann, F.
1936   Kriegsraketen zu Beginn des 19. Jahrhunderts. *Zeitschrift für Heeres-und Uniformkunde* (Berlin). 12: 91–93.

Maceroni [Francis]
1838   *Memoirs of the Life and Adventures of Colonel Francis Maceroni* (London), 2.

Madol, Hans Roger
1930   *The Shadow King—The Life of Louis XVII of France* (New York and Boston).

Mahon, John K.
1967   *History of the Second Seminole War, 1835–1842* (Gainesville, Fla.)

Malleson, Colone, ed.
1889   *Kaye's & Malleson's History of the Indian Mutiny of 1857–8* (London), 4.

Manarin, Louis H., ed.
1966   *Richmond at War—The Minutes of the City Council* (Chapel Hill, North Carolina).

Mandryka, A.
1962   Fizycne Podstawy Odrzutu Dziala I Ruchu Rakiety w Ujeciu Uczonych

XVII i XVIII Wieku. *Kwartalnik Historii Nauki I Technniki* (Warsaw). 7: 447–460.

Mansell, Lt. A.
1881   Mountain Guns in the Naga Hills. *Minutes of Proceedings of the Royal Artillery* 11: 263–270.

Marchand, Leslie A.
1957   *Byron: A Biography* (New York), 3.
Marine, William M.
1913   *The British Invasion of Maryland 1812–1815* (Baltimore).

Mariotte, Edmé
1686   *Traité du Mouvement des Eaux et des Autres Corps Fluids* (Paris).

Marmont, Marshal, Duke of Ragusa
1862   *The Spirit of Military Institutions* (Philadelphia).

Marshall, A.
1915   *Explosives, Their Manufacture, Properties, Tests and History* (London).

Marshall-Cornwall, Gen. Sir James
1972   Early Rockets. *Proceedings of the Royal Artillery Historical Society* (Woolwich). 3: Jan.: 36–61.

Marvin, Charles
1880   *The Eye-Witnesses' Account of the Disastrous Russian Campaign Against the Akhal Tekke Turcomans* (London).

[Marx, Karl]
1853   Europe . . . The Rocket Affair. *New York Herald Tribune* (New York). 14 May: 5.

Mater, Jean
1944   American Rocket Pioneers—Patrick Cunningham. *Astronautics* (New York) 58: June: 14.

Matignon, J.
1900   Le Tube Lance-Fusée. *La Nature* (Paris). 29: 22 Dec.: 49–50.

Mauncy, Albert
1962   *Artillery Through the Ages* (Washington, D.C.).

[Maurice, Sir John Frederick]
1874   *The Ashantee War* (London).

McCabe, James D., Jr.
1871   *History of the War Between Germany and France* (New York).

McNeil, William H. and Jean W. Sedlar
1970   *Classical China* (New York).

Meade, Robert Douthat
1956   *Judah P. Benjamin: Confederate Statesman* (New York).

Meijer, J.H.
  1880   De vuurpijltoestellen van Maijer. *De Zee* (Amsterdam) 2: 8: 291–293.
  1881   Meyer's draagbaar vuurpijlwerptoestel. *De Zee* (Amsterdam). 2: 2: 49–53.

Memorandum
  1977   Alfred J. Bachmeier, 24 Mar. Copy in "Hale Rockets" file, National Air
             and Space Museum.

Merrill, J.W.
  1870   *Records of the 24th Independent Battery, N.Y. . . . Artillery* (Perry, New
             York).

Methley, Noel T.
  1912   *The Life-Boat and its Story* (Philadelphia).

Meyer, Moritz
  1819   Ueber die Theorie des Steigens der Raketen. *Militär-Wochenblatt* (Ber-
             lin). 162: 31 July: 1077–1079.
  1837   *Historique de la Technologie des Armes a Feu* (Paris).

Miller, John
  1829   *Memoirs of General Miller in the Service of . . . Peru* (London), 1.

Mitra, Haridas
  1963   *Fireworks and Fire Festivals in Ancient India* (Calcutta).

de Moges, Marquis
  1860   *Recollections of Baron Gros's Embassy to China and Japan* (London).

de Montgéry [Jacques-Phillipe Merigon]
  1825   Traité des Fusées de Guerre. *Annales Maritimes et Coloniales* (Paris). 1825:
             2: 2: 565–741.

Montù, Gen. Carlo
  1934   *Storia della Artiglieria Italiana* (Rome), 5.

Moor, Edward
  1794   *A Narrative of the Operations Against . . . Tippoo Sultan* (London).

Moore, William
  1813   *A Treatise on the Motion of Rockets* (London).

Moore Smith, G.C.
  1903   *The Life of John Colborne* (London).

Mordecai, Maj. Alfred
  1860   *Military Commission to Europe in 1855 and 1856* (Washington, D.C.).

Morris, Donald R.
  1965   *The Washing of the Spears* (N.Y.).

Munier [Dominique-Nicolas]
  1830   Théorie du Mouvement et du Tir des Fusées. *Mémoires de l'Académie
             Royale de Metz* (Metz). 11: 114–129.

Murray, Sir James A.H.
  1908   *A New English Dictionary on Historical Principles* (Oxford).

Museum of Artillery, Woolwich
  1963   *Catalog of the Museum of Artillery in the Rotunda at Woolwich* (Woolwich).

Myers, William Starr, ed.
  1917   *The Mexican War Diary of George B. McClellan* (Princeton, N.J.).

N.B.
  1853   Aerial Travelling. *The Mechanics Magazine* (London). 59: 167–168.

Nagy, István G.
  1974   Some Contributions to the History of Early Spin-Stabilized Rockets. Preprint A 74–29. Paper presented at the 25th Congress, International Astronautical Federation, 30 Sept.–5 Oct.
  1977   Hungarian Rocketry in the 19th Century. In R. Cargill Hall, ed., *Essays on the History of Rocketry and Astronautics: Proceedings of the Third Through the Sixth History Symposia of the International Academy of Astronautics*, 1: 42–50. NASA Conference Publication 2014 (Washington, D.C.).

Napier, H.D.
  1927   *Field Marshal Lord Napier of Magdala* (London).

Nascimento, Alfredo Ferreira do
  1955   Uma 'Nova Arma' Inventada, em 1796, por un Artilheiro Português. *Revista de Artilharia* (Lisbon). 52: Sept.–Oct.: 91–100.

National Air and Space Museum, P.E. Garber Facility
  1980   Preservation Report—Hale Rockets NASM No. 6301 Catalogue No. 1979–727 through 732. Unpub. Copy in "Hale Rockets" file, National Air and Space Museum.

Needham, Joseph
  1986   *Science and Civilisation in China* (Oxford), 7:5

Nemetz, Walter
  1957   Die Kriegsraketen im Österreichischen Heere. *Mitteilungen des Österr. Staatsarchivs* (Vienna). 10: 257–274.

Nicaise, Lt. Alexandre
  1859   *Considérations sur les Fusées de Guerre* (Brussels).

Noer, Friedrich Augustus, Graf von
  1890   *The Emperor Akbar* (Calcutta), 2.

Nobel, Alfred
  1896   French patent No. 258,781 for "Telemetre Photographique," 10 Aug.

Nolan, E.H.
  1857   *The Illustrated History of the War Against Russia* (London). 1–2.

Nye, James
    1852   *Thoughts on Aerial Travelling* (London).

Olejar, Maj. Paul D.
    1946   Rockets in Early American Wars. *Military Affairs* (Baltimore). 10: Winter: 16–34.

Oman, Carola
    1953   *Sir John Moore* (London).

Osten, J.B.
    1849   Iets over de Congrevische Brandpijlen. *De Militaire Spectator* (Breda, Holland). 2: 64–68.

Owen, C.H.
    1871   *The Practice and Principles of Modern Artillery* (London).

Paixhans, Henri-Joseph
    1822   *Nouvelle Force Maritime* (Paris).

Parry, William
    1825   *The Last Days of Lord Byron* (London).

Partington, J.R.
    1960   *A History of Greek Fire and Gunpowder* (Cambridge, England).

Peru, Ministry of War and Marine
    1851   *Memoria presentada al Congreso Estraordinario* (Lima).
    1858   *Memoria presentada al Congreso Estraordinario* (Lima).
    1860   *Memoria presentada al Congreso Estraordinario* (Lima).

Pezuela, Juan, Marques de Viluma de la
    1833   *Sobre el Origen, Progreso . . . de los Cohetes de Guerra* (Madrid).

Phisterer, Frederick
    1912   *New York in the War of the Rebellion 1861 to 1865* (Albany, N.Y.), 2.

Pictet, Adolphe
    1848   *Essai sur les Propriétés et la Tactique des Fusées* (Turin).

Ponticny, Victor de
    1845   Des Fusées de Guerre sans Baguette . . . par William Hale. *Journal des Armes Spéciales* (Paris). 6: 320–324.
    1846   Fusées de Guerre sans Baguette. *Journal des Armes Spéciales* (Paris). 7: 433–435.

Pralon, Auguste
    1883   *Un Page de l'Histoire de l'Artillerie—Les Fusées de Guerre* (Paris).

Preuss, Charles
    1958   *Exploring with Frémont* (Norman, Okla.).

The Proprietors, Congreve Rocket Factory
  1829–33   The Proprietors of . . . Congreve Rocket Factory Offer to Sell to the
             [British] Government the Exclusive Right to Manufacture the Congreve
             Rockets. Unpub. letters. W.O. 327 44/643, Public Record Office,
             London.

Prothero, Rowland E.
  1966   *The Works of Lord Byron* (New York).

Quenell, Peter
  1938   *The Private Letters of Princess Lieven to Prince Metternich 1820–1826* (New
             York).

R.G.P.
  1852   War Rockets as a Substitute for Artillery. *Colburne's United Service Maga-
             zine* (London). 68: Jan.: 161–168; Mar.: 403–409.

Raikes, Henry, ed.
  1846   *Memoir of the Life and Services of Vice-Admiral Sir Jaheel Brenton* (London).

Rees, Abraham
  1819   Rocket. *The Cyclopaedia: or, Universal Dictionary of Arts, Sciences, and
             Literature* (Philadelphia), 31.

Reisner, Maj. H.
  1860   Über die Verwendung der Raketenwaffe in dem Feldzuge 1848 in Italien.
             Österreichische Militärische Zeitschrift (Vienna). 2: 361–368.

Richards, George H.
  1841   Biography of the Late Major General Alexander Macomb. *New York
             Military Magazine* (New York). 1: 4 Sept.: 193–194.

Richardson, Maj. [John]
  1837   *Movements of the British Legion* (London).

Robinson, Ralph
  1945   The Use of Rockets by the British in the War of 1812. *Maryland Historical
             Magazine* (Baltimore). 40: Mar.: 1–6.

Robson, J.O., ed.
  1948   Rockets in the Napoleonic Wars: The Diary of William Laycock. *Journal
             of the Society for Army Historical Research* (London). 26: Winter: 147–150.

Rogers, H.C.B.
  1971   *Artillery Through the Ages* (London).

Rogier, Charles
  1818   *A Word for My King and Country. A Treatise on the Utility of a Rocket
             Armament* (Knutsford, Cheshire, England).

Rohrmann, Ludwig
  1891   British patent No. 12,669 for "A New or Improved Apparatus for Obtain-
             ing Birds'-Eye Photographic Views," 25 Apr.

Roman, Alfred
1884   *The Military Operations of General Beauregard* (New York), 1.

Röpnack, Maj. Gen. Adolf
1961   Erste Raketen-Artilleristen waren Bayerns. unkn. German newspaper, 18 Feb.: n.p.

Royle, Charles
1900   *The Egyptian Campaigns 1882 to 1885* (London).

Rowbotham, Cmdr. W.B., ed.
1967   *The Naval Brigades in the Indian Mutiny 1857–8* (London), Publications of Naval Records Society, 87.

Ruffini, Paulo
1833   Osservazioni intorno al moto dei Razzi alla Congrève. *Memorie della Reale Accademia di Scienze . . . di Modena* (Modena). 1: 56–78.

Ruggieri, Claude-Fortuné
1802   *Élémens de Pyrotechnie* (Paris).

Russell, W.H.
1855   *The War* (London), 1–2.

Rzikowsky Dobrzisch, Leopold von
1860   Fragments aus Geschichte der Belagerung von Venedig im Jahre 1849. *Österreichische Militärische Zeitschrift* (Vienna). 2: 177–181.

Sandemann, Hugh David, ed.
1869   *Selections from Calcutta Gazettes of the Years 1816 to 1823 Inclusive* (Calcutta), 5.

Sarkar, Jadunath
1960   *Military History of India* (Calcutta).

Schmidt, Capt. Leopold Friedrich
1838   Ueber Kriegsraketen also Ersatz für die . . . Kanonen. *Öesterreichische Militärische Zeitschift* (Vienna). 1: 204–212.

Schmitt, Frederick P., Cornelis de Jong, and Frank H. Winter
1980   *Thomas Welcome Roys—America's Pioneer of Modern Whaling* (Newport News, Va.).

Schmoelzl, Joseph
1857   *Erganzungs-Waffenlehre* (Munich).

Schneiter, T.D.
1870   French patent No. 9116 for "Fusées-Postes," 31 Dec.

Scoffern, John
1852   *Projectile Weapons of War and Explosive Compounds* (London).

Secretary, Royal Artillery Institution, et al.
1900–1901 The Rocket Troop. A Controversy. *Minutes of Proceedings of the Royal Artillery Institution* (Woolwich). 27: 297–300.

Sharpe, Mitchell R.
n.d. *Development of the Lifesaving Rocket—A Study in 19th Century Technological Fallout* (Huntsville, Ala.).
1970 Robert Emmet's Rockets. *The Irish Sword* (Dublin). 9 (Summer): 161–164.

Shaw, Maj. J.F. de F.
1929–30 The Services of the Royal Artillery in the First Boer War (1880–81). *Journal of the Royal Artillery* (Woolwich). 56: Oct.: 327–357.

Simienowicz, Casimir
1729 *The Great Art of Artillery* (London).

Simpson, Capt. H.C.C.D.
1891 Notes on the Equipment and Services of Our Mountain Artillery . . . *Minutes of Proceedings of the Royal Artillery Institution* (Woolwich). 18:187–204.

Skoog, Dr. A. Ingemar
1974 Wilhelm Theodore Unge: An Evaluation of His Contributions. In Frederick C. Durant III and George S. James, eds. *First Steps Towards Space (Smithsonian Annals of Flight No. 10)* (Washington, D.C.): 259–267.
1977 The Swedish Rocket Corps, 1833–1845. In R. Cargill Hall, ed. *Essays on the History of Rocketry and Astronautics: Proceedings of the Third Through the Sixth History Symposia of the International Academy of Astronautics.* NASA Conference Publication 2014 (Washington, D.C.). 2: 9–22.

Smith, D. Bonner, ed.
1954 *Russian War, 1855 Baltic Official Correspondence* (London), Navy Records Society Publications, 84.

Smith, Capt. F.M.
1870 *A Handbook of the Manufacture and Proof of Gunpowder . . . at the Royal Gunpowder Factory, Waltham Abbey* (London).

Sohlman, Ragnar
1950 *Ett Testament* (Stockholm).

Sokol'skii, V.N.
1967 *Russian Solid-Fuel Rockets* (Jerusalem). NASA Technical Translation (TT 66–51152).

Sonkin, M.
1952 *Rooskaya Raketnaya Artilleriya* (Moscow).

Sonnenfeld, Anton Fuhrer von
1850 *Ballistik der Kriegs Rakete.* Unpub. Copy in National Air and Space Museum Library, Washington, D.C.

Souza, Maj. Augusto Fausto de
1874   *Manual das Muniçoes e Artificios de Guerra* (Rio de Janeiro).

Splingard, Capt. [Jean-Baptiste]
1858   Notice sur une Nouvelle Fusée de Guerre. *Journal de l'Armée Belge* (Brussels). 15: 12–15.

Stephens, Edward Bell
1837   *The Basque Provinces* (London), 1.

Strandh, Dr. Sigvard
1964   Wilhelm Teodore Unge, A Swedish Pioneeer in Rocketry. In *Daedalus. Tekniska Museets Arsbok 1964* (Stockholm): 87–108.

Strangl, Raimond
1944   *Raketen in der Kriegstechnik* (Dorfen, Germany).

Susane [Louis Auguste Victor]
1863   *Les Fusées de Guerre* (Metz).

Switzerland, Army
1862a   *Anleitung zur Bedienung der Raketengeschutze* (Aarau, Switzerland).
1862b   *Ordonnanz über das Raketengestell und den Raketenwagen* (Aarau, Switzerland).

Switzerland, Federal Council
1853   *Verordnung Betreffend Die Organization Der Raketenbatterien* (Bern).

Tavares, Francisco Antonio
1869   *Notice sur les Fusées de Guerre Inventée . . . par . . . Tavares* (Lisbon).

Teisen, J.
1962   Fortidens Raketskyts. *Tidsskrift for Sovoessen* (Copenhagen). 133: Apr.: 143–150.

Teng, S.Y.
1961   *The Nien Army and their Guerilla Warfare 1851–1868* (Paris).

Tennant, William
1804   *Indian Recreations* (London).

Thiroux, Charles Victor
1849   *Observations et Vues Nouvelles sur les Fusées de Guerre* (Paris).

Thompson, David Whittet
1944   The Catamaran Expeditions. *United States Naval Institute Proceedings* (Annapolis, Md.). 12: Feb.: 143–155.

Thornton, Lt. Col. L.H.
1930   *The Congreves: Father and Son* (London).

Tojhusmuseets
1948   *Bog om Treaaskrigen 1848, 1849, 1850* (Copenhagen).

[Trant, Thomas Abercromby]
    1827   *Two Years in Ava From May 1824 to May 1826* (London).

Trench, Capt. F. Chenevix
    1874   The Russian Campaign Against Khiva, in 1873. *Journal of the Royal United Service Institution* (London). 18: 212–226.

Trengrouse, Henry
    1821   *Apparatus for Saving Lives in Case of Shipwreck. Transactions of the Society . . . for the Encouragement of Arts* (London). 38: 20–21.

Tvede, Capt.
    1868   Den Amerikanske Hvalfanger-Virksomhed under Island. *Tidsskrift for Fiskeri* (Copenhagen). 2: 50–69.

Tylden, Maj. G.
    1948   The Use of War Rockets in the British Army in the Nineteenth Century. *Journal of the Society for Army Historical Research* (London). 26: Winter: 168–170.

Tyrell, Henry
    1855   *The History of the War with Russia* (London), 1–3.

U.S. Army, Ordnance Dept.
    1839   Terms of Agreement with A.C. Goell for Making War Rockets at Washington Arsenal, 31 May. Unpub. Record Group 156, Ordnance Office Special File, 1812–1912. National Archives.
    1840   Report of Board of Officers Appointed to Inquire into, Examine and Report the Condition of the Rocket Manufactory of the Washington Arsenal under Charge of Mr. Goell, 12 Dec. Unpub. Record Group 156. National Archives.
    1880   *A Collection of Annual Reports . . . Relating to the Ordnance Department* (Washington, D.C.), 2.

U.S. Congress
    1814   *Report of the Committee of the Invasion of the City of Washington* (Washington, D.C.).

V.E.
    1878   Heerwesen Persiens. *Jahresberichte über Beranderungen und Fortschritte und Militärwesen* (Berlin). 5: 173–176.

Vasconcellos, Capt. Genserico de
    1922   *Historia Militar do Brasil* (Rio de Janeiro).

Vaupell, Otto
    1876   *Den Danske Haers Historie* (Copenhagen), 2.

Vergnaud, A.D., and P. Vergnaud
    1865   *Manuels-Roret Nouveau Manuel Complet l'Artificier* (Paris).

Verlohren, Heinrich August

    1910   *Stammregister und Chronik der Kur-u. Königl. Sachs. Armee von 1670 bis zum Beginn d. 20. Jh.* (Leipzig).

Walton, John

    1973   Where Danger Lurks Beneath the Sands. *Soldier* (Aldershot, England). 29: 12: 24–26.

Wattenwyl, Brig. Gen. R. von

    1945   Der Schweizerische Raketenfrühling 1850–1867. *Schweizerische Militärzeitung* (Zofingen, Switzerland). 91: Oct.: 497–505.

Welsh, Col. James

    1830   *Military Reminiscences* (London), 1.

Weygand, Gen. [Maxime]

    1936   *Histoire Militaire de Mohammed Aly et de ses Fils* (Paris), 1.

Whinyates, Col. F.A.

    1897   Captain Bogue and the Rocket Brigade. *Minutes of Proceedings of the Royal Artillery Institution* (Woolwich). 24: 131–136.

    1900–1901 The Rocket Troop. A Controversy. *Minutes of the Proceedings of the Royal Artillery Institution* (Woolwich). 27: 435–436.

Wilhelmi, Otto

    1897   U.S. patent No. 585,805 for "Rocket," 6 July.

Williams, Beryl, and Samuel Epstein

    1955   *Rocket Pioneers on the Road to Space* (N.Y.).

Winter, Frank H.

    1965   Landmarks on the Road to Space Travel—Danish Rocketry. *Militaert Tidsskrift* (Copenhagen). 94: Feb.: 55–66.

    1969   Man, Rockets and Space Travel. *Mankind* (Los Angeles). 2: Dec.: 9–23.

    1972   Sir William Congreve: A Bi-Centennial Memorial. *Spaceflight* (London). 14: Sept.: 333–334.

    1973a   William Hale—A Forgotten British Rocket Pioneer. *Spaceflight* (London). 15: Jan: 31–33.

    1973b   Camera Rockets and Space Photography Concepts Before World War II. Unpub. paper presented at the 24th International Astronautical Federation Congress, Baku, USSR, Oct.

    1974   TransPlanted Torpedoman. *United States Naval Institute Proceedings* (Annapolis, Maryland). 100: 80–82.

    1977   Vincenz von Augustin and His Raketenbatterien. In R. Cargill Hall, ed. *Essays on the History of Rocketry and Astronautics: Proceedings of the Third Through the Sixth History Symposia of the International Academy of Astronautics.* NASA Conference Publication 2014 (Washington, D.C.). 1: 23–41.

    1978   Raketterne ved Københavns Belejring 1807. *Marineshistorisk Tidsskrift* (Copenhagen). 11: 75–96.

1979a   The Earliest Space Photography Concepts. In *[Proceedings of the] VIII Semana Astronautica Barcelona, 5–9 Febrero 1979* (Barcelona): 251–263.

1979b   The Rocket in India from 'Ancient Times' to the 19th Century. *Journal of the British Interplanetary Society—Astronautics History* (London). 32: Dec.: 467–471.

1982   A New Look at Early Chinese Rocketry, 1200's–1900. *Journal of the British Interplanetary Society—History* (London). 35: Dec.: 522–529.

Winter, Frank H., and Mitchell R. Sharpe

1971   The California Whaling Rocket and the Men Behind It. *California Historical Quarterly* (San Francisco). 50: 4: Dec.: 349–361.

1974   Edward Mourrier Boxer and His Rockets in Peace and War. *Spaceflight* (London). 16: Nov.: 427–429.

Wittemore, Maj. James M., and Lt. F. Heath

1878   *Ordnance Memoranda No. 21. Ammunition . . . Pyrotechny, etc.* (Washington, D.C.).

Wojskowa, Bronislaw

1933   *Wojsko Polski 1815–1830* (Warsaw).

Wolseley, Lt. Gen. Sir Garnet J.

1882   *The Soldier's Pocket-Book for Field Service* (London).

Wood, William, ed.

1923   *Select British Documents of the Canadian War of 1812* (Toronto), 2.

Wrede, Alphons Freiherr von

1905   *Geschichte der K. und K. Wehrmacht* (Vienna), 4.

Yuan, Wei

1888   *Chinese Account of the Opium War* (Shanghai).

Zulavsky, Sigismund

1861–65   In Records of Confederate General and Staff Officers, Unpub. Microcopy 324, Roll 72. National Archives.

Index

Boldface page references indicate that the subject matter is illustrated on that page; *italics* refer to captions.